FIGHTS, GAMES, and DEBATES

A publication from the
Center for Research on Conflict Resolution,
The University of Michigan

FIGHTS, GAMES, and DEBATES

ANATOL RAPOPORT

Ann Arbor: The University of Michigan Press

Fourth printing 1970

Copyright © by The University of Michigan 1960

SBN 472-75604-4

Library of Congress Catalog Card No. 60-9971

Published in the United States of America by
The University of Michigan Press and simultaneously
in Don Mills, Canada, by Longmans Canada Limited
Manufactured in the United States of America
by Vail-Ballou Press, Inc., Binghamton, N.Y.

TO NICOLAS RASHEVSKY

FOREWORD

THIS BOOK is addressed to any serious student of human conflict on the intrapersonal, interpersonal, organizational, social, or international level.

In an earlier book (86),* I presented the scientific outlook as a model of orientation of supreme value to men, an outlook to be nurtured as a natural, internalized view of the world and to be extended to matters beyond the traditional domain of natural science, that is, to viewing ourselves, our aspirations, compulsions, and goals. The hope was expressed that if this comes about, many kinds of human conflicts, which now seem unresolvable, will either not arise or can be resolved or, at least, will not lead to destructive struggles.

Thus, I thought, a link existed between science and ethics, or, as expressed in the title of that earlier book, between science and the goals of man. The whole argument rested on a notion that human conflicts were predominantly manifestations of *debates,* and that violent conflicts, including wars, were, to paraphrase Clausewitz's grim comment, continuations of debates by other means.

This view is open to two objections. First, it seems improbable that science can alleviate conflicts by settling debates in areas outside its specific jurisdiction. Second, it appears that not all conflicts are results of clashes between incompatible assertions.

Numbers in parentheses refer to entries in the bibliography at the end of this volume.

The first objection is not as crushing as it appears, if the role of science is properly understood. The objection stems from a view, widespread in the United States, that science is purely instrumental, and that the scientist is a technician, whose job is to find means for attaining prescribed goals. In this view, science is confused with technology. Technology is indeed instrumental, and the goals of technology must be prescribed. But science is autonomous; it has its own goals, and the *practice* of science inevitably modifies the outlook and therefore the goals of its practitioners and of societies in which science is practiced. Since science itself has a unified outlook, it tends to unify outlooks and to harmonize goals among people of most diverse cultural backgrounds and so to resolve many "debates" outside of the specific areas of scientific investigation. In short, even outside of science, outlooks and goals are not chosen arbitrarily. Their choice depends vitally on what one believes to be the case. Or, more accurately, beliefs and desires are much more tightly interlocked than is generally imagined.

The second objection is a serious one, and I have no recourse but to admit its force. The view that all conflicts arise from "debates," that is, from clashes of convictions about "what is" or even about "what ought to be," does seem too limited. At least two types of struggle do not stem from anything resembling a debate. In one type it is irrelevant or altogether impossible to express the "positions" of the opponents in words. This is the type of struggle which I will call a "fight." In the other type, the starting point is not disagreement, but on the contrary an agreement, namely an agreement of the opponents to strive for incompatible goals within the constraint of certain rules. This type of struggle is now technically called a "game."

If the essence of a debate is the pitting against each other of opponents, each of whom wishes to *convince* the other, or at least to convince uncommitted bystanders, then certainly neither the fight nor the game fall into the category of debates. Concepts can always be stretched, and definitions can be twisted. So if one were intent on fitting all struggles into a single category, one could argue that in fights and in games, too, each opponent tries to "convince" the other or the on-lookers of his prowess or cunning. But such interpretations detract from the central notions involved in each type of conflict. Our task here will be to emphasize specific characteristics of each type. In each of the three main parts of this book, following our classification of conflicts, a different framework of thought will underlie the development of the argument.

Of most direct relevance to fight-like conflicts are the various theories of aggression. These comprise a large section of current psychological literature. The interested reader may consult the review paper of E. D. McNeil (71), in which a bibliography of over four hundred titles is included. This field is outside the scope of my competence, and I have not touched on those theories. Instead I have devoted Part I to some mathematical models of mass conflict and their ramifications. These approaches are still comparatively unknown to the student of social science, probably because not many are able to read mathematics and largely because the "yield" of these theories is still meager. Formal mathematical conclusions still seem of little relevance to the way individuals or masses in conflict actually behave. The student of such events tries rather to describe them in all their vividness and to "explain" them in terms of relations which can be intuitively grasped. I believe, however, that the formal mathematical approach has a bright future in all areas of knowledge, including behavioral science. I offer what there is of this method, as it has been used to deal with mass behavior, for what it is worth. With the ever-increasing spread of mathematical literacy among the social scientists, these first crude attempts may serve to stimulate better ones.

I believe, moreover, that the theories of mass behavior have a special relevance to the kind of struggles which I have lumped with "fights," because in these theories the rational components of behavior are deliberately ignored. The mathematical sociologist describes the operation of "blind forces." Possibly when more is known about the way the nervous system operates, theories of a similar kind will develop to describe the dynamics of aggressive behavior in individuals.

My acknowledgments for the ideas dominant in Part I are primarily to Lewis F. Richardson (8) and to Nicolas Rashevsky (88, 90). The work of these men is representative of an approach to social behavior which I have called "social physics."

To avoid misunderstanding, it might be advisable to differentiate the sense in which I have used this term from several other senses in which it has been used.

Over a hundred years ago, some excerpts from the writings of A. Comte were published in the United States under the title *Social Physics* (19) with a curious subtitle, "A Book to Exterminate Political Vermin and Moral Quacks." A perusal of that volume fails to reveal any proposals more drastic than the well-known "positivist" program of Comte—to apply criteria of knowledge accepted in the physical sciences to social sciences.

More recently, "social physics" has been used specifically to designate another approach, exemplified in the work of J. Q. Stewart (115) and could properly be applied to still another approach, taken fifty years ago by S. Haret (40) and recently by R. Fürth (32). There are important differences among the methods. Stewart's investigations are largely attempts to establish regular quantitative "laws" in large-scale social behavior by empirical means. He collects data and tries to express what he finds in formulas. A portion (but not all) of Richardson's work is also of this nature (95); but that is not the work we will examine here. Haret tried to draw direct analogies between physical laws and social behavior. This attempt has now only historical interest. The recent attempt of Fürth of somewhat similar nature is much more sophisticated and deserves serious attention.

However, the methods exemplified in the work of Rashevsky and specifically of Richardson, which dominate Part I of this book, are of a different sort. No attempt is made to seek analogies of physical laws in social behavior. Nor are the conclusions derived from masses of data. The method is autonomous and theoretical. An investigation starts with more or less plausible *assumptions* related to some basic quantitative relations which *may* underlie social behavior. *Consequences* of these relations are the end products of the investigation. They may or may not be compared with observations. This is also the method of mathematical physics, and this is why I refer to it as social physics.

The philosophical base of the ideas immanent in social physics (of all types) has been advanced by the exponents of the deterministic view of history and sociology, such as Malthus, Marx, Tolstoy, and to some extent Spengler and Toynbee. Essentially, the same ideas appear in the works of the grand-scale theoretical biologists, those who deal with whole bio-systems, often from quite abstract points of view. The work of many of these men depends heavily on mathematical development. Such are the investigations of Volterra (124), Lotka (58), Rashevsky (89, Chapter LIV), Gause (33, 34), Fisher (29), S. Wright (135, 136, 137), Beverton and Holt (7), Neyman, Park, and Scott (75), Slobodkin (111), and many others. One also finds some insightful formulations of a more general nature in the work of the exponents of an "organismic general system theory," where certain aggregates of organisms are treated as living systems of higher order, as, for example, in the writings of Emerson and Gerard (25, 35, 36, 38). This approach is already found in cruder form in the social philosophy of Herbert Spencer, who relied heavily on analogies drawn between biological and social evolution (112, Vol. 1, Part II). To me all these ideas appear to be cut from the same ideological cloth: freedom or indeterminacy of the particles composing a large aggregate is irrelevant to the fate of the aggregate, which is subject to its own laws. How this outlook is related to the "fight-like" conflict will appear in the exposition of Part I.

Part II is derived entirely from the ideas of game theory and related areas (mathematical theories of the decision process), and so my acknowledgments go to all the workers of that vast and fertile field. My particular indebtedness is to the profoundly insightful critical survey of Luce and Raiffa (61). It is primarily their book which convinced me that game theory is more important because of its failures than because of its mathematical successes. For it is the shortcomings of game theory (as originally formulated) which force the consideration of the role of ethics, of the dynamics of social structure, and of individual psychology in situations of conflict.

It may be argued that this last insight is anything but a discovery. Any humanist would castigate game theory for neglecting "ethics"; any sociologist would criticize it for omitting social structure from its treatment of coalition formation; any psychologist would dismiss the assumption of "complete rationality" as unrealistic. There is, however, an important difference between seeing shortcomings on a priori grounds and arriving at these shortcomings by way of rigorous reasoning. The former leads to the conclusion that a theory is unrelated to its subject matter; the latter may show the way of bringing the theory closer to its subject matter.

The theory of games has made a sharp impact on my own thinking about conflict. As I said, I thought a decade ago that conflicts were chiefly outgrowths of clashes of outlooks. I was aware, of course, that a game is not a conflict of this sort. But if it were pointed out to me then that a war could also be viewed as a "game," I would have dismissed this notion as gruesome. I was aware also that at the nerve center of American economy, the stock market, a gigantic game was being played, and this too I dismissed as a travesty on human values. In other words, I felt that games ought not be played in certain contexts, for example, where human lives and human welfare are at stake. I also felt that the primary payoffs in those games, that is, power or symbols of power, were perversions or denigrations of human goals.

But a preoccupation with game theory has opened up for me a vista of whose existence I had no idea. I found that if one forgets "ethics" altogether and approaches game theory on its own terms, that is, if one accepts as given the existence of irreconcilable (especially *partly* irreconcilable) conflicts of interests and follows through the *logic* of the situations examined, one gets an entirely new slant on conflict and on the requirement of any discipline which proposes to deal with conflict and with values scientifically.

The ethical implications of game-theoretical conclusions, as applied to situations of conflict, have been especially clearly brought out in two essays, Braithwaite's (12) and Schelling's (105). The former author brings out the positive contributions of game theory to ethics, while the latter launches a spirited attack. These two essays have served me well in starting a train of thought on this subject.

In Part III, I shall be dealing with struggles deriving from clashes of outlooks. The principal ideas there will center about the nature of an "outlook" and about the peculiar resistance that well-integrated outlooks offer to attempts to change them. My indebtedness for these ideas goes largely to Carl R. Rogers (98, 99) and to Kenneth Boulding (11). Here I can acknowledge only the source of the direct impacts. The origin of these ideas is much more diffuse than that of the ideas in Parts I and II. Nevertheless, the two authors mentioned deserve the credit for bringing the notion of "empathetic understanding" especially sharply into focus, specifically in the light of large-scale problems which confront the people of our century.

I should also mention my close association with students of communication on the level of education, literature, and human relations: my associates in the International Society for General Semantics, particularly my old friends, S. I. Hayakawa, Wendell Johnson, and the late Irving J. Lee. Much of what I have to say in Part III is so intimately interwoven with ideas to which they had given eloquent expression that it is impossible to say how much of that discussion is simply a restatement of what all of us fervently believe. Needless to say, any errors of interpretation or other shortcomings are entirely my own.

CONTENTS

Introduction: Three Modes of Conflict   1

PART I: THE BLINDNESS OF THE MASS

CHAPTER I   A Theoretical Arms Race   15
II   A Real Arms Race   31
III   Psychological Epidemics   47
IV   Co-operation and Exploitation   60
V   Critique of Social Physics   85

PART II: THE LOGIC OF STRATEGY

VI   Game Theory and Its Forerunner, Gambling Theory   107
VII   Enter the Foe   130
VIII   The Meaning of Strategy   140
IX   The Strategy Mixture   151
X   What If the Opponent Is Both Friend and Foe?   166
XI   Games with Collusion   180
XII   Coalitions   195
XIII   Experiments in Strategic Conflict   213
XIV   Critiques of Game Theory   226

PART III: THE ETHICS OF DEBATE

An Apology   245
XV   To Learn Is To Select; To See Is To Select   248
XVI   The Blindness of Involvement   259
XVII   Ways of Persuasion   273
XVIII   The Assurance of Understanding   289

xvi | *Contents*

xix The Region of Validity   292
xx   The Assumption of Similarity   306

THE DEBATE

The Case for Collectivism   313
The Case for Individualism   335

Concluding Remarks   359
Notes   361
References   381
Index   390

THREE MODES OF CONFLICT

1.

TOM SAWYER, having just discovered a new way to whistle, strolls down the street on a sunlit June evening at peace with himself and the world. Suddenly a stranger stands before him. Recognition is instantaneous: here is a city dandy.

Tom is only thirteen, but already his world is divided into rigid categories. His week, for example, consists of five days of school (part-time prison); glorious Saturday, when he can do or pretend to do all the things he considers worth while doing; and Sunday, another day of compulsion, on which he must act out the role of Protestant respectability.

The stranger before him wears Sunday clothes on a week day, and these clothes are newer and handsomer than Tom's "other clothes." Therefore, for this stranger Sunday must be not simply a concession to the powers which demand a tribute (parents and God), but a way of life. The stranger acts out respectability not because it is demanded but because *he* is respectable; he has identified himself with the enemy; he is the enemy, an affront to Tom's self-respect. Tom, therefore, instantly hates the stranger.

The stranger's psyche is not revealed, because the unity of the narrative demands that the world be pictured through Tom's eyes; but we can imagine a similar "semantic reaction" in the other boy, based on quite another set of identifications, convictions, and stereotypes.

It took many words to say this, but the mutual identification happened instantaneously in both boys, who, of course, could not even begin to describe the process. It simply happened, just as our recognition of the smell of hydrogen sulphide suddenly happens and defies analysis. Somehow a multitude of cues and impressions fall into place, and out comes an identification and a readiness to act as the situation "demands."

The two enemies stand poised for combat. What follows is a series of maneuvers, verbal jabs, and feints, in which invitation to join the combat is mixed with caution (the enemy's strength is being gauged). Each jab, however, calls for a counterjab, and so must be followed by another, somewhat bolder one. Actually, the combat has already begun. The exchange of words is necessary to put each combatant into the proper emotional state for the exchange of blows to follow. The thrusts follow one another to the inevitable outburst of physical violence. The physical combat, too, must run its course. It is terminated only when the proper stimulus for its termination occurs: when the defeated boy "hollers 'nuff."

2.

ONE NIGHT in 1908 Frank Marshall sat facing a chess board. No one sat opposite him; Marshall was playing against himself. Call it practicing. Or call it research. Until about fifteen years ago it did not occur to many people to associate research with games. Yet the thoughts of the mathematician and of the chess player are of the same sort. Both move in mazes of deduction. Stripped to essentials, the "skeleton" of these thoughts is of this nature: "If so, then so, unless so, in which case so . . . But on the other hand, if so or so, then this, which leads to that . . ." Put different kinds of "flesh" on these bones, and you have mathematics or logic or chess or bridge or the "elementary" reasoning of Sherlock Holmes, or the scheming of a diplomat.

Marshall was investigating a particular class of situations known in chess as the Ruy Lopez game. The Ruy Lopez game starts after both players have played their King's Pawns and after White has played his King's Knight to attack the Black Pawn, and Black has played his Queen's Knight to defend it. The move which characterizes the game as Ruy Lopez is White's King's Bishop attacking the Black Queen's Knight on the third move. It is a powerful game for White, and Frank Marshall, the United States champion, hated to take Black's part in it.

But on this night in 1908 Marshall made a discovery. He found that as Black in Ruy Lopez he could, following the eighth move, steer the game into channels which would offer several opportunities for setting subtle traps for White. He consulted the literature, studied all the Ruy Lopez games he could find, and did not come across this variation. It was new!

But now Frank Marshall was faced with a problem. Who should be his victim? That there would be no more than one victim seemed likely. Once Marshall's variation became known (and, of course, it would immediately become known to all the chess players who mattered), the traps would be avoided, or, perhaps, the Ruy Lopez game would be abandoned altogether, or, still worse, perhaps further analysis would show that Marshall's stratagem was unsound, that is, could be countered to Black's disadvantage.

"That one time has to count," Marshall may have mused.

Resolved to make it count, he waited ten years for the worthy opportunity. All these years, whenever he played Black, Marshall studiously avoided the Ruy Lopez game. Instead, he played Petroff's Defense (counterattacking the center pawn on the second move with his King's Knight). This went on until the New York Tournament in 1918. There he singled out his big quarry—Capablanca. The Cuban habitually played the Ruy Lopez game, and as Marshall, playing Black, sat opposite him in the big tournament, he gave Capablanca the opportunity to develop this line of play.

We can only surmise what went on in Capablanca's mind when he saw Marshall play the Queen's Knight instead of his usual King's Knight on the second move. (Capablanca had, of course, studied all of Marshall's published games and knew that for ten years Marshall as Black had never allowed the Ruy Lopez game to develop.)

The game went on in its accustomed channel. On the ninth move, Marshall, following Capablanca's capture of the Black Queen's Pawn, recaptured the pawn with the Knight. Capablanca sensed what was coming. His choice was to give Black the opportunity to develop his ferocious attack (in the hope that he could withstand it and launch an even more deadly counterattack); or to avoid the challenge with some cautious defensive move. Here is what Capablanca himself writes about it:

I thought for a while . . . knowing that I would be subjected to a terrific attack, all the lines of which would of necessity be familiar to my adversary.[1] *

How did he know this? He probably concluded this from the fact that Marshall, for the first time in ten years, submitted to a Ruy Lopez opening. Capablanca could guess that Marshall was playing one of the most important games in his career and that he must have investigated as much of the maze of deduction bearing on this variation as was humanly possible.

"The lust of battle, however," Capablanca continues, "had been aroused within me. I felt that my judgment and skill were being challenged by a player who had every reason to fear both (as shown by the records of our previous encounters), but who wanted to take advantage of the element of surprise and of the fact of my being unfamiliar with a thing to which he had devoted many nights of

---

* *The superscripts refer to the Notes at the end of the text.*

toil . . . I considered the position then and decided that I was in honor bound, so to speak, to take the pawn and accept the challenge, as my knowledge and judgment told me that my position would be defendable."

And so the battle was joined. On the thirteenth move, Black made a brilliant attacking thrust with a knight which apparently could be captured but whose capture would have led to immediate disaster for White. White, of course, avoided the trap. On the fifteenth move, another more subtle trap was set in which one false move could have cost White the game. This trap was also avoided. On the twenty-ninth move, White's Queen's pieces suddenly came into play, and the tables were turned. The defender became the attacker. On the thirty-sixth move, it became clear that White could force a checkmate in five moves, and Marshall resigned, his ten-year dream dissolved in defeat.

How does one reduce this drama to logical analysis? What are its essentials, and are they worth a serious investigation? The game theorists have undertaken this task and in their researches have gone as far beyond what had been known about the logic of strategy as modern logicians have gone beyond the simple syllogisms of Aristotle.

3.

A GOOD EXAMPLE of a debate is the second part of Thomas Mann's novel, *The Magic Mountain*—a struggle for the simple soul of a "modest young man." The struggle is carried on by two composite personalities: Settembrini, the protagonist of scientific humanism, individual freedom, secularism, and liberalism; and Naphtha, who combines within himself the ideals of both the Catholic Church and of Communism.

Settembrini praises the pagan joy of life. He abhors the medieval spirit, its scholasticism, its mysticism, its emphasis on the misery of the human condition, as reflected both in its verbal expression and in its art. Settembrini loathes the emasculated human body of Gothic sculpture. For him the Renaissance was indeed an awakening from a bad dream.

Naphtha, on the contrary, scorns classical, rational, humanistic thought. The Middle Ages represent to him the height of triumph of the spiritual over the carnal, man's closest approach to salvation, the one chance he had to realize the City of God. Naphtha feels that man threw away that chance in a wild pursuit of sensual pleasure, trivial factual knowledge, and corrupting power. But let the adversaries speak for themselves (65, pp. 501-11):

Settembrini: . . . you know, too what inhuman atrocities, what murderous intolerance were displayed by the century to which the production behind me owes its birth. [They are talking about a fourteenth-century sculpture.] Look at that monstrous type the inquisitor for instance, the sanguinary figure of Conrad von Marburg —and his infamous zeal in the persecution of everything that stood in the way of supernatural domination. You are in danger of acclaiming the sword and the stake as instruments of human benevolence.

Naphtha: Yet in its service labored the whole machinery by means of which the Holy Office freed the world of undesirable citizens. All the pains of the Church—even the stake, even excommunication, were inflicted to save the soul from everlasting damnation—which cannot be said of the mania of destruction displayed by the Jacobins.

He scores a point, you see. The Jacobins with their guillotine were on the side of rationality, secularism, and progress.

"As for the degradation of humanity," Naphtha goes on, "the history of its course is precisely synchronous with the growth of the bourgeois spirit. Renaissance, age of enlightenment, the natural sciences, and economics of the nineteenth century have left nothing undone or untaught which could forward this degradation."

He goes on to attack modern astronomy and declares that eventually mankind will return to the Ptolemaic system, in which the Earth was the center of the universe, as it could not be otherwise, for the greatest drama of being, man's fall and salvation, has displayed itself there.

This is too much for Settembrini. "What about science?" he shouts. "What about the unfettered quest for truth?" Ironically, it is he, the representative of cool-headed science, who is upset as one would expect a devout believer to be in the presence of blasphemy. Naphtha, the religious fanatic, on the contrary, remains cool and collected. To him faith is a vehicle for knowledge. The intellect is secondary. So-called evidence is worthless if it contradicts philosophically established truth. (Who made up the rules of evidence anyway?)

Before we in our enlightenment dismiss Naphtha as entirely befuddled, let us recall that hardly any of us would believe his senses if in adding up a column of figures he got different sums when adding up and down. No matter how many times we saw this happen, we could not believe the result. It *must* add up the same, whether we add up or down. The laws of arithmetic demand it, and the "evidence of the senses" is entirely irrelevant in this case. To Naphtha, as to St. Thomas Aquinas, the structure of the universe was a compelling consequence of certain articles of faith, which the devout could no more discard than the user of arithmetic can discard the commutative law of addition $(A + B = B + A)$. So-called "evidence" is declared to be simply in error. This is also the way Christian Scientists view disease.

Let us return to our debate. The chips are now down:

Settembrini: Answer me this: answer me in the presence of these two young listeners. [They are fighting for the soul of Hans Castorp, the hero of the novel; his cousin Joachim is also present.] Do you believe in truth, in objective scientific truth, to strive after the attainment of which is the highest law of all morality, and whose triumphs over authority form the most glorious page in the history of the human spirit?

Naphtha: There can be no such triumphs as those you speak of, for the authority is man himself—his interests, his worth, his salvation—and thus between it and truth no conflict is possible. They coincide.

Settembrini: The truth, according to you—
Naphtha: Whatever profits man, that is truth.

If we substitute The Working Class, or The Party, for Man, we see the position often defended by the Communists of our day. Naphtha too is a Communist. True, no real Communist would pay homage to the medieval hegemony of the Catholic Church and prophesy its rebirth. But Naphtha is not a real person (no one is in that novel, except possibly the hero). Naphtha is the embodiment of a certain view in which there is no contradiction between the authoritarianism of the Catholic Church and that of a world proletarian state. He points out that the Fathers of the Church abhorred commerce, money, and interest.

Naphtha: . . . For they were in favor of making production dependent on necessity and held mass production in abhorrence. Now then: after centuries of disfavor, these principles and standards are being resurrected by the modern movement of Communism. The similarity is complete, even to the claim for world domination made by international labor as against international industry and finance: the world proletariat, which today is asserting the ideals of the *Civitas Dei* in opposition to the discredited and decadent standards of the capitalistic bourgeoisie.

The year is 1908. Naphtha does not know (nor does his creator, who is writing this novel in the nineteen-twenties) that the Communists too would soon come to worship mass production, natural science, home appliances, and classical art. But he did capture the spirit common both to the ideology of the Middle Ages and to Communism, as it was originally inspired, the ideal of the Anonymous and the Communal.

WE HAVE before us a prototype of each of three kinds of conflict: a fight, a game, and a debate. We wish to identify the essential differences among these types of struggle.

Let us begin by examining the meaning of "opponent" in each of these struggles. It seems that in a fight, the opponent is mainly a nuisance. He should not be there, but somehow he is. He must be eliminated, made to disappear, or cut down in size or importance. The object of a fight is to harm, destroy, subdue, or drive away the opponent.

Not so in a game. In a game, the opponent is essential. Indeed, for someone who plays the game with seriousness and devotion, a strong opponent is valued more than a weak one. In a way, therefore, the opponents in the game co-operate. First, they co-operate in the sense of following absolutely and without reservation the rules of the game. Second, they co-operate in "doing their best," that is, in presenting to each other the greatest possible challenge. The challenge is what makes the game worth while. We shall see in our analysis that even when there is no question of actual co-operation, as for example in game-like life-and-death struggles, the *assumption* that the opponent will try to do "his best" contributes to the validity of rational analysis, which both must accept. So in a way, at least, there is a "community" between the opponents. The opponent speaks the same language; he is seen not as a nuisance but as a mirror image of self, whose interests may be diametrically opposed, but who nevertheless exists as a rational being. His inner thought processes must be taken into account.

"I wish what my brother wishes," Charles V is said to have remarked with grim humor, "namely the City of Milan."

This assumption (that the opponent is like self) reveals the other sense in which the adversaries in a game "co-operate," even if their interests are opposed. Sometimes a situation is reached in a game when the outcome becomes perfectly clear. For example, in a chess game it may appear evident that White can force a checkmate in five moves, as in the game we have described. At this point, the game is broken off. *Both* players recognize the situation, and it is pointless to continue the struggle. In a very simple game like tick-tack-toe it is evident to anyone who has played the game a few times that *every* game is bound to be a draw, because to every move aimed at a winning position, there is a countermove, which effectively blocks it. Therefore, there is no point in playing tick-tack-toe, and this game is not played by people who thoroughly understand it. In a sense, this agreement *not to engage in a struggle whose outcome is known in advance* is a form of co-operation.

In summary, then, the essential difference between a fight and a game from our point of view is that while in a fight the object (if any) is to harm the opponent, in a game it is to outwit the opponent. A fight, in our idealized sense, involves no calculations, no strategic considerations. Each adversary simply reacts to the other's and to his own actions. In principle, if we knew how these reactions occur, we could predict the whole progress of the fight from the way it started without reference to the goals of the opponents or to the *potentialities* of the outcomes. Even the one discernible goal—to harm the opponent— is sometimes absent. Such is the much-quoted and much-misunderstood "struggle for existence" in the universe of competing species.

In a game, the potentialities and evaluations of *alternative* outcomes must be taken into account, if the reactions of the opponents to each other's moves are to be understood or described systematically. In short, the essential difference, as we see it, is that a fight can be idealized as devoid of the rationality of the opponents, while a game, on the contrary, is idealized as a struggle in which complete "rationality" of the opponents is assumed. In consequence, the analyses of fights and of games will involve very different intellectual tools, as will appear in Parts I and II.

Let us now look at the essential features of a debate. Let us disregard for the moment the situation in which the objectives are to convince some bystander, although we suspect that this situation is the most common. Let us take a debate at face value: the opponents direct their arguments *at each other*. It is clear that here neither the harming of the opponent nor the "outwitting" of the opponent is relevant to the objective. The objective is to *convince* your opponent, to make him see things as you see them. "Techniques" appropriate in fights (e.g., thrusts and threats) or in games (e.g., stratagems) may be used, but their value is determined only by the final result: is the opponent convinced, *really* convinced? If this objective is kept constantly in mind, the debate appears to be a process very different from either the fight or the game, and different concepts must enter the analysis of this process.

Conflict, as has been pointed out (61, p. 1), is a theme that has occupied the thinking of man more than any other, save only God and love. In the vast output of discourse on the subject, conflict has been treated in every conceivable way. It has been treated descriptively, as in history and fiction; it has been treated in an aura of moral approval, as in epos; with implicit resignation, as in tragedy; with moral disapproval, as in pacifistic religions. There is a body of knowledge called military science, presumably concerned with strategies of armed conflict. There are innumerable handbooks, which teach how to play specific games of strategy. Psychoanalysts are investigating the genesis of "fight-like" situations within the individual, and social psychologists are doing the same on the level of groups and social classes.

In matters pertaining to debate, we have fancy-sounding "forensics," and chatty monosyllabic manuals of salesmanship. (In the outlook of American business enterprise, to sell means to convince.) We have criticism, which is sometimes an analysis of debated issues. We have arbitration boards and courts, bodies set up to mediate debates. We have legal systems and philosophies of law.

All these various approaches to conflict and to its resolution cannot even be meaningfully compared with each other, so different are the points of view and assumptions representative of them. Some deal exclusively with the etiology of conflict and remain morally noncommittal. Others also deal with etiology but with a view of developing preventive measures, therefore on the basis of a moral commitment with regard to conflict. Still others take conflicts for granted and examine means of winning or settling them.

The task here will be to examine not conflicts for their own interest but rather *different kinds of intellectual tools for the analysis of conflict situations*. Ideas rather than situations will be central, although, of course, real situations will often serve as illustrative examples. To be specific, although we shall be talking about some aspects of mass behavior, nothing in what we say can be reasonably expected to be of use to, say, an advertising man, who understandably is also interested in mass behavior for reasons of his own. Although much will be said about strategies as they pertain to intellectual games, nothing in this book will help anyone to become a better bridge player or to design a better military campaign or to make money in stocks. Although much of what we say about conflict has been inspired by certain notions arising in psychotherapy, nothing can be construed about the actual usefulness of these notions in the treatment of mental or emotional disturbances. Nor (perish the thought) should Part III be searched for indications of how to win a debate.

The aim is to examine and analyze three widely different modes of thought about conflict and to provoke thought in the reader, as my own thoughts have been provoked by the ideas reflected here. This book is mainly a vehicle for sharing intellectual experience.

PART I
THE BLINDNESS OF THE MASS

The equations are merely a description of what people
would do if they did not stop to think.—*RICHARDSON*

A THEORETICAL ARMS RACE

INSTEAD OF TOM SAWYER and his adversary Alfred Temple, imagine now, as Lewis F. Richardson suggested (94), two sovereign states, Jedesland and Andersland, each wanting peace but each apprehensive of the intentions of the other. Listen to the defense minister of Jedesland, as Richardson quotes him, speaking to the inhabitants of this planet in A.D. 1937.

> The intentions of our country are entirely pacific. We have given ample evidence of this in the treaties which we have recently concluded with our neighbors. Yet when we consider the state of unrest in the world at large and the menaces by which we are surrounded, we should be failing in our duty as a government if we did not take adequate steps to increase the defenses of our beloved land.

We have all heard this speech in many languages. Let us not doubt the sincerity of the defense minister. Let us grant that he personally fervently desires peace, and moreover that his government would by all means prefer peace to war. But neither the defense minister nor the members of his government are pacifists. Also the vast majority of the rank and file citizens of Jedesland are "normal." They will not go out of their way to attack others, but if attacked, they will counter with "natural" responses of self-defense and revenge. They will fight for what is theirs and for the way of life they cherish. It behooves them, therefore, to be ready to fight if the necessity arises.

Necessity, to their way of thinking, can arise only from an outside source: an attack on Jedesland. Therefore, the accumulation of armaments, etc., cannot, as they see it, belie their essentially peaceful intentions. If every nation were concerned only with self-defense, there would by definition be no occasion for war, since war could arise only from an aggressive act, which self-defense is not.

All this is sensible and consistent. There is, however, another country, the neighbor of Jedesland, namely Andersland. The defense minister of Andersland pronounces a speech, which is a literal translation into the language of Andersland of the speech pronounced by the defense minister of Jedesland. Moreover, the ideas, ethical prescripts, and intentions of the people of Andersland are likewise exact replicas of those of Jedesland. They have no hostile designs any more than their neighbors. But they are also willing to fight, to die, if necessary, in defense of *their* way of life, which they fear is threatened by Jedesland.

We have drastically simplified a well-known international situation. Perhaps we have simplified it beyond recognition. Let us nevertheless pursue the consequences of this "model" to the bitter end, not to draw conclusions about what must have happened or what will happen in a given historical setting but only to see what *would* have happened if the situation were as it is here depicted.

We are about to make some deductions. Such deductions are usually made with the help of a special language (a mental tool) known as mathematics. But many people who cannot read this language shrink away from its symbols. So we will postpone the use of mathematical symbols whenever possible, and, wherever we can, we will avoid them altogether. This will not be possible in all cases. At any rate, we will try to do as much as we can without mathematical symbolism and will succumb to it only when words fail us.

In plain language, the situation between Jedesland and Andersland is as follows: the more armaments Jedesland accumulates, the more incentive is provided for Andersland to accumulate armaments, and the more armaments are accumulated by Andersland, the more Jedesland is stimulated to arm. If neither side had *any* armaments to start with, it is conceivable that the armament race would not start *if* the incentives to arm came entirely from the armaments of the other. But then the slightest move on the part of one would start the whole process. The process is self-perpetuating. The theoretical "equilibrium" at the mutually disarmed state is "unstable," as the physicist would say. To argue that the disarmed state could persist is to argue that an egg could be balanced on an unbroken end. This is possible in theory (if the center of gravity of the egg is *exactly* above the point of support) but not in practice, because minute disturbances are unavoidable and self-perpetuating. Once an egg starts to topple, it will topple all the way.

By the reasoning just given, the armaments of both countries would continue to increase indefinitely. Certainly, one could argue, this could not happen in real life. There are limits to everything. In particular, there are limits to how much of its national product a state can allot to armaments, not to speak of the limit to the national product at a given level of resources and technology.

We must therefore consider limiting factors. Intuitively, we feel that because of the limits, the levels of armaments must stabilize themselves. And this is as far as the "verbal" analysis can go. If we turn to mathematical analysis, we can say more. We can derive consequences not drawn from verbal analysis. These consequences frequently give us ideas on how to proceed with the construction of a theory. Let us see how this is done.

THE MODEL

The construction of a mathematical model usually involves four steps:

1. Some variables are defined: quantities which during the process examined will assume different values. In our case, armament expenditures, their rates of change, and time will be the variables.

2. Some relations among the variables are assumed and formulated as equations. In our case, the rates of change of armament expenditures of one country will depend on the armament expenditures of the other.

3. The equations are solved. Here we derive other relations among the variables which are consequences of the relations assumed.

4. The results are interpreted.

Let us at once give our variables mathematical names. Let x and y stand for the armament expenditures of our two countries in some standardized money units per year, and let t stand for time in years. The rates of change of x and y respectively will be denoted by dx/dt (i.e., the ratio of a small change of x to the change in t during which it occurs) and dy/dt.

The first task is done: we have identified the variables. Obviously, there are many more relevant variables, but we are keeping our model as simple-minded as possible. Recall that the purpose of this model is not to draw conclusions about how armament races actually develop but only to get ideas, which, perhaps, otherwise might not have occurred to us. So let us stick to just the variables defined.

The next step is to set up the equations. The equations should say precisely what has been said vaguely in words. For example, we assumed that "the more one arms, the more the other is spurred on to arm." But such an assumption may mean different things. It may mean that each country adjusts the level of its armaments to the level of its neighbors; or it may mean that each adjusts the *rate of increase* of its armaments. Also the adjustments may take place in many different ways, hopelessly many, if each particular way is counted. But the whole *class* of such adjustments can be described in a single equation—therein lies the power of mathematical notation.

For example, we can assume that each country is spurred on to increase its expenditures at a rate which is proportional to the existing expenditures of the other. The word "proportional" is both precise and noncommittal. It says that if we divide the rate of growth of expenditures of one country by the actual expenditures of the other *at any time,* the ratio will be the same. It does not say *what* that ratio will be (hence the noncommitment); but it gives a definite relation between the rate of growth of one and the existing level of the other, namely, that of a constant ratio. The degree of specificity in any mathematical formulation can be tightened or loosened at will, and that is what makes the mathematical method flexible: the model can reflect any degree of our knowledge *or of our ignorance* of a situation. In any case, the model serves as a starting point of deduction. Now we are ready to put the equations down. They look like this:

$$dx/dt = ay \qquad (1)$$
$$dy/dt = bx \qquad (2)$$

Here the rates of growth of the expenditure levels (on the left) are set equal to the expenditure levels of the respective rivals (on the right), multiplied by appropriate constants, *a* and *b,* the constants of proportionality. We do not know what these constants are. But we need not know them to continue our analysis. These "parameters," as they are called, will be carried along in our reasoning. What we will deduce is how the conclusions will *depend* on the values of these parameters.

We have not yet included all of our assumptions in the equations. Let us now put in the "limiting factors." Suppose excessive armament loads become a burden, so that the actual level of the armament load tends to depress the *rate of increase* of the expenditures, again proportionately. We should then subtract from each term on the right side of equations (1) and (2) other terms represented by the armament expenditures multiplied by other appropriate constants. But now an *x* term should be subtracted from Jedesland's equation, and a *y* term from Andersland's. That is to say, although it is the rival's expenditures which spur you on to increase yours, it is your own expenditures that hurt and so put a brake on their rate of increase. Now the equations will look like this:

$$dx/dt = ay - mx \qquad (3)$$
$$dy/dt = bx - ny \qquad (4)$$

Here *m* and *n*, like *a* and *b*, are parameters, that is, unknown constants. They too will be "carried along" in our reasoning and will appear in our conclusions.

Now that we have gotten so far, let us throw in another pair of terms for good measure, to satisfy those who argue that not mutual stimulation but permanent underlying grievances are behind the armament expenditures.

The alert reader may ask at this point how we can expect within the framework of our model (which has been constructed on the assumptions of mutual stimulation) to satisfy those who deny the validity of these assumptions. This will become apparent as soon as we put the equations down. The final form of our mathematical model of the idealized armament race is now as follows:

$$dx/dt = ay - mx + g \qquad (5)$$
$$dy/dt = bx - ny + h \qquad (6)$$

These equations say that the rates of armament expenditure increases will depend positively on the expenditure level of the rival (the first term), negatively on one's own expenditure (the second term), and positively on the "permanent grievances" (the last term). The extent of the dependence is given by the respective constants of proportionality (the parameters); that is, *a* and *b* measure the extent of (positive) dependence on mutual stimulation; *m* and *n* measure the extent of (negative) dependence on the home expenditures; *g* and *h* are the magnitudes of the "grievances." The equations can now satisfy a great variety of conditions.

Recall that we have not specified the magnitudes of the parameters, *a, b, m, n, g,* and *h*. To be sure, we cannot without violating the basic assumptions of our model assign negative values to the first four of them. If we did, the model would go in reverse, that is, the armaments of the rival would act as a brake, and one's own armaments as a spur. Actually, there is no reason why consequences of such a model should not also be investigated. Indeed, something of this sort is implied in the theory of "deterrence." But we have committed ourselves to one picture, and we will stay with it. Thus, the coefficients of *x* and *y* on the right sides of equations (5) and (6) will be allowed to assume any values which are not negative. The "grievance" terms, *g* and *h,* however, will be free to vary over the entire range of real numbers, positive or negative. Negative values of these constants can be interpreted as reservoirs of "good will" instead of "grievances." We shall want to consider such cases since they are important in the so-called unstable situations to be treated below.

To set any constant equal to zero means to ignore the effect with which it is associated. For example, if *m* or *n* is zero, there is no "brake" on the armament race; if *g* or *h* is zero, the corresponding "grievance" is not taken into account. If all the constants except *g* and *h* are zero, then *only* the grievances are considered as contributing to armaments. Thus, whether one holds with Thucydides[2] that an armament race is a self-stimulating process, or with Lord Amery[3] that self-stimulation has nothing to do with armament races, that armaments are motivated only by underlying national grievances or ambitions, one can use the same mathematical model. One needs only to adjust the appropriate constants to get the one or the other theory.

In the general formulation just given, the relative magnitudes of the constants reflect the "weights" assigned to the various factors. Actually, this mathematical model is extremely limited; it takes into account only three factors supposedly influencing rates of growth of armaments, and moreover all the influences are supposed to be additive.[4] These are very special assumptions out of innumerable ones that can be made. But note that even this extremely limited "theory" contains within it several of the verbal arguments: armaments accumulate because of mutual fear; there are limitations on the accumulation of armaments; there are factors independent of armament levels which contribute to the accumulation of armaments.

Even though the mathematical precision of equations is often not justified by the kind of observations we are in position to make, there is an advantage of translating theoretical assertions into mathematical equations. It allows us to draw *compelling* consequences from our assumptions. Frequently, these consequences can be compared with observations more directly than the original assumptions. Whether the derived consequences agree with the observations or not, this comparison will suggest further specific investigations. Thus, the mathematical model serves a *heuristic* purpose rather than an explanatory one. Properly viewed, it leads not to conclusions about the dynamics of actual armament races but rather to conclusions about what *would* occur if the dynamics of armament races were of the kind assumed. These "would-be" conclusions, results of mental experiments, as it were, serve as links in a chain of reasoning. If they can be coupled with observations suggested by the reasoning and modified in accordance with the results of the observations, they can become the building blocks of a future realistic theory.

Let us return to our model. One may proceed to solve the pair of differential equations [5] (5) and (6). This is step 3 in our scheme (see p. 18). The solution will give us the dependence of x and y, that is, the armament expenditures, on t (time), on the unknown constants, a, b, m, n, g, and h, and on the initial conditions, that is, the armament expenditures at time zero. The initial conditions of some armament race, say that of the European Powers during 1909–13, are known. If we can make some estimates about the values of the constants, we shall have an explicit formula for the arms race to be compared with what actually happened. This, following Richardson's investigations, will be done in Chapter II. But even if we do not know the values of the parameters, and even if we do not solve the differential equations, we can draw some instructive conclusions from equations (5) and (6).

THE QUESTION OF STABILITY

Let us ask the following question. Under the conditions described, will armament expenditures become "stabilized," that is, reach a constant level, which can be interpreted as a "balance of power," or, to use the currently appropriate term, a "balance of terror"? We see at once that if there is no "braking," that is, if m and n are zero, no such stabilization can occur if g and h (the grievance terms) are positive. But suppose there is braking. Will stabilization always occur? If not, what are the conditions of stability?

"Stability," as we use the term, requires that the levels of expenditures ultimately remain constant. Mathematically, this means that the rates of change of expenditures become zero. These rates are given by equations (5) and (6). Therefore, if we set these expressions equal to zero, we will have the condition of balance—a necessary condition, that is, one which *must* be fulfilled if balance is to continue. But whether this condition is sufficient, that is, whether it will *guarantee* a continued balance, is another question to be answered in the analysis to follow. We put down the condition of balance:

$$ay - mx + g = 0 \tag{7}$$

$$bx - ny + h = 0 \tag{8}$$

If the constants, *a, b, m, n, g,* and *h* were known, these would be two equations in two unknowns to be solved for *x* and *y.* But our constants are no more known than our "unknowns," that is, the variables *x* and *y.* So we cannot solve our equations numerically. We could, of course, solve them in terms of our constants. But we are not now interested in an explicit solution. We only want to know under which conditions the balance is *stable,* that is, will persist once reached. This question can be answered with the aid of the graphical method.

Recall that a pair of first-degree equations in two unknowns can be represented by two straight lines, whose intersection (if any) is the solution. To draw the actual lines on graph paper, we must know the constants. But we do not need to know the constants to draw two *typical* lines of this sort. Besides, we do know *something* about the constants, namely, that *a, b, m,* and *n* are not negative. Moreover, if *x* and *y* represent armament expenditures, no evident meaning can, for the time being, be ascribed to these variables if they are negative; and so we need to consider for the present, only the portion of the graph which falls in the first quadrant, where both *x* and *y* are positive.[6]

Both lines represented by equations (7) and (8) will have positive slopes, that is, they will run from "southwest" to "northeast." The fact that *a, b, m,* and *n* are all positive guarantees this. We shall here consider only the case where these straight lines intersect in the first quadrant, so that the "balance of power" (the intersection) is interpreted in terms of the corresponding levels of armament expenditure; Consider first the situation pictured in Figure 1.

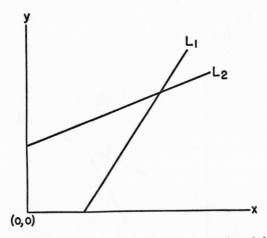

Figure 1. Graphical representation of the "balance of power." The intersection of the two lines represents the pair of expenditure levels, at which the rates of change of these levels is zero.

The line L_1, whose equation is (7), contains all the points (x, y), at which dx/dt is zero; that is to say, if the respective armament expenditures x and y are such that the point (x, y) lies on L_1, the armament expenditures of Jedesland are stabilized. Similarly, if the point (x, y) lies on L_2, dy/dt is zero, and the armament expenditures of Andersland are stabilized. Call L_1 and L_2 the optimal lines of Jedesland and Andersland, respectively. It follows that if a point (x, y) lies on *both* of the optimal lines, then both armament expenditures will remain constant, since the rates of change of both will be zero. The intersection of L_1 and L_2 represents the balance of power point. Note that L_1 intersects the X-axis at a positive value of x, and L_2 intersects the Y-axis at a positive value of y. This means that the grievance terms g and h are positive; in other words, even if both countries were suddenly disarmed (that is, if x and y were placed at the origin of co-ordinates), they would start arming, motivated by the grievances.

Let us now see whether our system is stable. To see this, suppose the level of armament expenditures is not the balance of power point, but some other point, say (x_0, y_0), as shown in Figure 2.

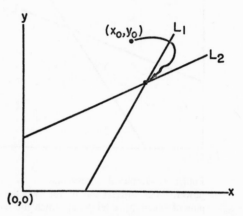

Figure 2. The approach of armament expenditures toward the balance of power point in the stable case.

It will not stay there, because the rates of change of x and y are not zero at that point. The point (x, y) will therefore move away from the initial point (x_0, y_0). The direction of its motion will be determined by the values of dx/dt and dy/dt. In general, however, the horizontal motion will be such as to bring it toward L_1, since this motion is controlled by Jedesland, and the vertical motion will tend to bring it toward L_2, since this is the direction controlled by Andersland. For convenience we may consider these two motions separately. We can now verify from the diagram (see Figure 2), and it can be proved mathematically that wherever the initial point of armament expenditures may be, it will move toward the balance of power point in the case pictured in Figure 2. This is the case of the stable balance: a deviation from the balance point in whatever direction will tend to be "corrected."

Now look at a different situation, pictured in Figure 3.

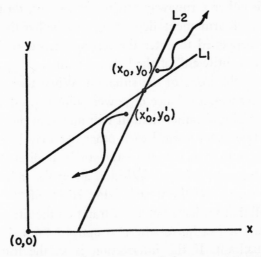

Figure 3. The movement of the armament expenditures away from the balance of power point in the unstable case.

Here the positions of L_1 and L_2 are reversed. If the intersection is to be in the first quadrant, this can happen only if at least one of the grievance terms is negative, that is, only if at least one of the countries has a reservoir of "good will" for the other.

Suppose now the initial point is (x_0, y_0) in Figure 3. The attempts of both countries to bring the expenditure levels to their respective optimal lines now results in the motion of the point not toward the balance of power point but away from it. In this case, both levels increase indefinitely. The "braking power" of m and n is not sufficient to stop the armament race. But suppose the initial point is (x_0', y_0') in Figure 3. Again the expenditure levels move away from the balance of power point, but this time in the opposite direction, toward complete disarmament at the origin (0, 0). If the initial point is outside the scissors-shaped region enclosed by the lines L_1 and L_2, the analysis is more complicated. The gist of it, however, is the same. The situation pictured in Figure 3 is unstable. The end result is either a runaway armament race or, on the contrary, complete disarmament, depending on whether the initial point (x, y) happened to enter the scissors-shaped region ("northeast" or "southwest" of the balance point).

Note the irony of the situation. When there are underlying grievances, a balance of power point is possible. However, when good will rather than ill will underlies the basic attitude of the two states toward each other, we may have a runaway armament race as an alternative to total disarmament. Still, before we jump to any conclusion about the stabilizing effects of grievances and the unstabilizing effects of "friendship," let us recall that we have put a constraint on the situation, namely, that the intersection of the two optimal lines shall be in the first quadrant. If the intersection is in the third quadrant, and the grievance terms are negative, then wherever the initial point (x, y) may be in the first quadrant, it will end up at (0, 0), that is, at complete disarmament. In other cases, unilateral disarmament may result. The determinants of the process are the relative magnitudes of the parameters, a, b, m, n, g, and h. In summary, the following typical cases tell the story.

Case 1. If $mn > ab$, $g > 0$, h > 0, there will be a stable balance of power.

Case 2. If $mn > ab$, $g < 0$, $h < 0$, there will be total disarmament.

Case 3. If $mn < ab$, $g > 0$, $h > 0$, there will be a runaway armament race.

Case 4. If $mn < ab$, $g < 0$, $h < 0$, the situation will be ambiguous. There will be either a runaway race or disarmament, depending on the initial levels of armament expenditures.

In all of these cases, only positive values of x and y were assumed to be meaningful. In Chapter II, we shall extend meaning also to negative values of x and y.[7]

INTERPRETATION

What can we learn from this analysis? Let us review what we have done. We have contrived an extremely artificial situation, a model, which bears *some* resemblance to what we can abstract from the dynamics of armament races; that is, we have put into the simplest type of mathematical equations the usual arguments given about the causes of armament races, namely, underlying grievances and mutual fear, and the limiting factors, such as the constraints of excessive armament burdens. So long as these factors were discussed in conventional language, not much could be concluded as to what would happen, for example, whether the armament expenditure levels could be stabilized, whether a runaway race would result, or whether total disarmament was thinkable. Once a translation was made into quantitative relations, at least theoretical conclusions about the "fate of the system" could be made. The truth of these conclusions depends, of course, entirely on the accuracy of the model. It goes without saying that the model here depicted is grossly inaccurate and oversimplified. Note, however, that the "would-be" conclusions are in accordance with common sense, to a degree. The presence of grievances would prevent total disarmament. Balance of power is possible if the degree of mutual suspicion is sufficiently tempered by constraints on the sizes of the armament burdens to be tolerated. Underlying good will can insure disarmament, provided mutual suspicion is not too great or provided the armaments had already been brought down below a certain critical level or had not risen above it, etc.

What the model gives us that common sense conclusions do not is a neat quantitative way of expressing these results. So far, these results are little more than shorthand notation for the common sense conclusions (although it can be argued that being rigorously deduced, they deserve more confidence as conclusions). Not much more can be done with them, because so far we lack any measuring devices or even proper units to determine the magnitudes of the parameters on which the results depend.

It would seem that the unit of armament expenditure should be some sort of money unit. But what is a unit of mutual suspicion? What is a grievance unit? And how do you measure the magnitudes associated with these units? Only when these questions are answered can any progress be made to put the model to any sort of test. Until then it remains an empty mathematical exercise. We see, however, by implication the heuristic value of the exercise: it raises questions. Now that "mutual suspicion" (or stimulation), "grievance levels," etc., have been brought into focus as the components from which the model is built, we must try to make operational sense of these concepts if the model is to have meaning. This is precisely the work undertaken by Lewis F. Richardson in his thirty-year study of war (8), in which he used mathematical models such as those described. The results of his investigations will be described next.

CHAPTER II

A REAL ARMS RACE

IN THE FIRST DECADE of our century, it was clear that soon there would be a war among nations who were at that time called the Great Powers. It was also clear that France and Germany would be the principals and that each would be supported by a Great Power ally, France by Russia and Germany by Austria-Hungary. Moreover, it was known that Great Britain would in all likelihood take the side of France. The role of Italy was not clear. Although the other nations of Europe were not "Great Powers," their participation on one side or the other of the conflict was actively solicited by the principals. Thus, in the Balkans, a conglomeration of little states, all potentially hostile to each other, Russia counted on Serbia as an ally. (Ethnically Slavic territory, claimed by Serbia, had been incorporated into the Austrian empire.) Germany counted on Turkey, because of the long-standing enmity between Turkey and Russia (who had supported the Slavic nations in their wars of independence against Turkey).

The role of Bulgaria, like that of Italy, was also ambiguous. On the one hand, Bulgaria owed its independence from Turkey to Russian pressure; on the other hand, Bulgaria was Serbia's rival and had dynastic ties with Germany.

Quite aside from this network of alliances and counter-alliances, the rivalry of the Great Powers in the building of their colonial empires was reaching its climax. During the nineteenth century, almost all of Africa and much of Asia was incorporated into the colonial systems of Great Britain, France, Germany, Belgium, The Netherlands, Portugal, and Italy. Some had started building their empires early and had gotten the biggest and the choicest pieces of the "backward" world. Others, notably Germany and Italy, felt that they had not gotten their just shares. All of these circumstances are conventionally held to be the "causes" of World War I.

Let us see what the word "cause" can mean in this case. A "cause" is a circumstance offered as an explanation of some other circumstance, and an "explanation" must be viewed as a statement which makes something unexpected appear expected. Therefore, whether an explanation is felt to be needed and whether an explanation which is offered is accepted depends on what is expected and what is not.

In everyday affairs, we do not ask for explanations of usual events, only of unusual ones. For instance, we do not often ask why a man, who has been working regularly, goes to work on some particular day. But if he does *not* go to work one day, we may well ask why he did not. Similarly, if we toss a penny 100 times and it falls heads nearly 50 times, we do not ordinarily look for a cause.[8] But if it should fall heads 90 times out of the 100, a search for a "cause" would seem justified.

As we have said, an explanation is commonly accepted as satisfactory if circumstances are uncovered which make the event to be explained an *expected* event. If we learn that a man took sick, his absence from work seems explained, because sick people often stay home. If we learn that a coin is "biased," the predominance of heads is not surprising, etc. To accept the explanation of World War I on the basis of the patchwork of alliances and rivalries for markets and colonial possessions means to assume that *given* the rivalries etc., war *usually* occurs.

But note that this criterion for accepting an explanation,

which we have just described, depends on impressions and attitudes. Nothing was said about any *actual* connection between events purported to be causes and those viewed as effects. That such actual connection is often irrelevant for accepting an explanation is seen clearly in the predominance of so-called superstitions. Many people readily accept explanations without inquiring into actual connections between events. "Bad air" had been accepted as the cause of malaria for centuries (not unreasonably, in view of the marshy breeding places of the carriers of this disease). Violations of taboos can be readily supported as explanations of floods and earthquakes, because such violations can always be recalled as having occurred shortly before the disasters.

A scientific ("scientific" is a matter of degree, not a description of a fixed category) explanation differs from a "common sense" explanation in that it attempts to eliminate fortuitously connected events from its list of causal relations. The controlled experiment is directed toward this end. In its simplest setting, the controlled experiment tests a presumed "cause" of an event by noting whether the event consistently occurs in the presence of the presumed cause and consistently fails to occur in its absence, if the presence or absence of the presumed cause can be imposed at will.

There are, however, situations where controlled experiment is impossible to apply. If, for example, we wished to ascertain whether the alliances and the rivalries among the European states were indeed the causes of World War I, then to invoke the method of controlled experiment to decide this question would mean to turn the clock of history back to some moment before that war, remove all the alliances and the rivalries, and see whether in their absence the world war would have occurred or not—an impossible task.

There is a prevalent notion that the possibility or the impossibility of controlled experiment determines the essential difference in method between the natural and the social sciences. But this is not quite so. Controlled experiment is obviously impossible in astronomy; the most fundamental conception of biological science, that of organic evolution, has not been corroborated by controlled experiment, at least not on the grand scale on which it was conceived. Important as controlled experiment is for a critical evaluation of an explanation, it is not the only method developed in science. Another is a mathematical description of some process derived from a set of simple, plausible postulates. Indeed, it is this sort of explanation which can be said to differ qualitatively (instead of only in degree) from the common sense explanation, of which controlled experiment can be viewed as a refinement.

MATHEMATICAL DESCRIPTION AS EXPLANATION

Typically, in a mathematical description each of a set of values of one variable is linked with a corresponding value of another. If the range of values is continuous, the mathematical expression amounts to stating an unlimited number of assertions in the form "If so, . . . then so," the prototype of the assertion of causal relation. Even in the absence of controlled experiment, this sort of description can sometimes be considerably convincing as an explanation. True, it may not be possible to assign arbitrary values in arbitrary order to the independent variable (the presumed "cause") as in the controlled experiment, but the explanation is strengthened by the great number of linked observations. In fact, every pair of values linked in the mathematical expression can be viewed as a separate observation testing the causal relation.

Strictly speaking, the notion of causality is de-emphasized in the explanation based on a mathematical description. Understanding is imparted in a somewhat different sense. To begin with, the process becomes understandable because the mathematical description makes it predictable. Second, it becomes more understandable, because it has been *deduced* from the assumptions. In this respect the mathematical explanation is an extension of the familiar kind: the process explained is seen as a *consequence* of something that had been assumed, just as in the case of the man who had failed to show up on his job. It is assumed that sick people are likely to stay home; it is discovered that the man is sick; therefore his absence becomes an instance of a deduced consequence and so is interpreted as a usual occurrence.[9]

Faced with the problem of seeking scientific explanations of war, we obviously cannot take recourse in controlled experiment. But the other way, the mathematical description of events deduced from plausible assumptions and leading to testable conclusions, is open to us, *provided* some quantifiable variables can be singled out for study.

THE AMOUNT OF HOSTILITY

In Chapter I we assumed with Richardson that "hostility" as reflected in armaments is such a quantifiable variable. Accordingly, certain assumptions were made concerning the way the mutual hostilities of nations are interrelated, and certain consequences were derived from the assumptions, for example, conditions under which the "hostility" would become stabilized or, on the contrary, would tend to increase without limit or to disappear. Other consequences involving the time course of the growth of hostility can also be deduced from the same assumptions. To compare these consequences with observations, one must know what to observe. Manifestations of hostilities among nations are often apparent in the invectives that appear in speeches and in the press. The difficulty of incorporating hostility as a variable in a mathematical description is in finding a suitable *index,* an objectively measurable quantity to represent the "amount" of hostility. It is in terms of such quantities that the variables x and y in the equations of Chapter I must be interpreted.

We have already said that armament expenditures in

money units could serve as an index of hostility. Negative amounts of this quantity would also be interpreted in a similar fashion. Richardson proposes indices of international trade as measures of the amount of *co-operation* between states. Accordingly, the *net* amount of hostility should be taken as the difference (with the proper sign) between armament expenditures and international trade of the nations concerned. If this quantity turned out to be negative, that is, if trade exceeded armament expenditures, then the magnitude of the difference would be interpreted as net co-operation.

Since the theory described in Chapter I involves only two nations, it can be applied to pre-World-War Europe only if the powers are coalesced into two opposing camps. Accordingly, Richardson lets France-Russia be one of the opponents, and Germany-Austria-Hungary the other. From equations (5) and (6) of Chapter I he deduces the mathematical relations to be put to the test, namely the relation between *the rate of change of the total hostility in the system* and the *total hostility level* itself, measured, as we have said, in terms of the difference between armament expenditures and trade.

The combined equation becomes

$$dz/dt = (a - m)(z - W) \qquad (9)$$

Here z is the combined total armament expenditure per year of France, Russia, Germany, and Austria-Hungary and dz/dt is its rate of change. The parameters a and m have the same meaning as in Chapter I. The parameters b and n of the second nation have been set equal, respectively, to those of the first, so that a now represents both coefficients of mutual stimulation, and m both coefficients of restraint. The parameter W combines within itself terms which depend on the volume of mutual trade between pairs of hostile powers and also the ratio of the grievance terms g and h to $(a - m)$.

We shall examine the significance of W later. First note

what the equation says with regard to the ratio of the *rate of growth* of armaments to the existing levels of armaments. It says, first of all, that if the rate of growth of armaments is plotted against the level of armaments for each year of the armament race, the resulting plot will be a straight line. Here, then, is the first testable proposition, deduced as a consequence of the theory.[10] It is testable, because the armament expenditures of the countries concerned are available.

Table 1 shows the defense budgets of the powers concerned.

Table 1

The armament budgets in millions pounds sterling of the four powers in the years immediately before World War I (after Richardson).

	1909	1910	1911	1912	1913
France	48.6	50.9	57.1	63.2	74.7
Russia	66.7	68.5	70.7	81.8	92.9
Germany	63.1	62.0	62.0	68.2	95.4
Austria-Hungary	20.8	23.4	23.4	25.5	26.9
Totals	199.2	204.8	214.9	238.7	289.0
Increases		5.6	10.1	23.8	50.3

Figure 4 shows the plot of the rate of growth vs. the levels.

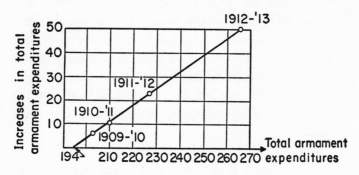

Figure 4

The plot is indeed a straight line. Since the prediction checks out, we can say that the conjecture that an arms race is a self-stimulating "mechanistic" process is *to a certain degree* corroborated. Richardson remarks: "The mere regularity of these phenomena shows that foreign politics had then a rather machine-like quality intermediate between the predictability of the moon and the freedom of an unmarried young man" (94).

INTERPRETATION AND CRITIQUE

If the process were "machine-like" subject to the laws postulated in the assumptions, the plot of the rates of growth of armaments vs. the levels would necessarily have to be a straight line. Is the converse true? If we observe the plot to be a straight line, can we conclude that the process is necessarily governed by the laws inherent in the assumption? No.

To begin with, only four points have been plotted. Note that if there are only two points, we can *always* connect them by a straight line. So for two points no matter how the arms race process were governed (if it were governed at all), we would have a straight line plot. In that case, nothing whatever could be deduced from the plot: if every theory leads to the same kind of plot, then no theory is preferable to any other. We have not two points, but four. But it is not too unlikely for two additional points to fall merely by chance on the straight line already determined by the first two. If there were more points to plot, the chance of their falling on the same straight line would be smaller, and the theory would then receive stronger confirmation if they did fall on the same straight line. Unfortunately, no further points have been plotted.

Another weak spot in the argument for the two-nation arms race theory is the wide prevalence of the sort of time-course deduced for the armament levels. The level of armaments of the Great Powers was shown to be exponentially increasing, that is, increasing in geometric progression. But this sort of increase is typical of many processes. Almost every population at its inception goes through a period of exponential growth. The number of scientific papers published in any rapidly developing field follows an exponential growth, sometimes for many years. Many industrial indices grow in the same way. Certainly mutual stimulation based on mutual fear is not a necessary component in many of these processes. Why should it be specifically assumed for the growth of armaments?

In view of the meagerness of the data supporting the equation deduced from Richardson's theory, the justification of the conclusion is clearly not sufficient at this point. Richardson recognizes this. He proceeds, therefore, to ask further questions in search of further corroboration. In particular, he examines the theoretical meaning of the parameters a and m, to see if such theoretical meaning can be further supported by data.

THE PARAMETERS AS RATES OF ARMAMENT AND DISARMAMENT

Let us return to one nation's armament equation:

$$dx/dt = ay - mx + g \qquad (10)$$

Suppose now the opposing nation were to disarm and suppose all the grievances were settled, that is, suppose y and g both became zero. Then the equation would become

$$dx/dt = -mx \qquad (11)$$

Solved for x as a function of time, this gives

$$x = x_0 e^{-mt} \qquad (12)$$

Here x_0 is the armament level when the disarmament begins, and m is the rate of disarmament.[11]

This is a well-known equation, sometimes called the equation of radioactive decay. It represents the amount of radioactive material left after an initial quantity x_0 has been disintegrating for time t; also the number of organisms left alive under the condition of a constant excess of death rate over birth rate, and many other mathematically analogous situations. In words, the armament level of a disarming state should decrease, according to our model, by a constant factor over constant intervals of time. Specifically, when $mt = 1$, the remaining armament expenditure will have sunk to $1/e$ or about 37 per cent of its original value.

What is a reasonable value of m? Richardson guesses that $mt = 1$ when $t = 5$ years ("the life time of a British parliament"); hence his estimate of m is 0.2 per year. The disarmament rate of Great Britain following World War I suggests a larger value, but Richardson argues that "linear equations are valid only for moderate disturbances from equilibrium . . . we can hardly expect them to apply to so violent a disturbance as the war."

Turning now to the other parameter, a, Richardson notes that it is related to the "catching up time" in an armament race. Instead of imagining the utopian situation of a nation without enemies or grievances, he now imagines the equally unlikely situation where one of the participants in an arms race stops and waits for the opponent to catch up.

Assuming that the armament level of the opponent, that is, y, is frozen at some fixed value y_1, equation (10) becomes (without the grievance term)

$$dx/dt = ay_1 - mx \qquad (13)$$

Now if the nation which is to catch up starts from scratch (i.e., $x = 0$), a will have the value

$$a = \frac{dx/dt}{y_1} \qquad \text{or} \qquad 1/a = \frac{y_1}{dx/dt} \qquad (14)$$

But y_1 is the amount to be caught up with, and dx/dt is the initial speed of getting there. Therefore $1/a$ can be interpreted as the "apparent catching up time"—apparent because the situation depicted is usually only in the minds of those who are trying to catch up.

There was, to be sure, one situation when catching up was accomplished, namely, the German rearmament of the 1930's under Hitler. Germany did catch up with Great Britain in about three years. Therefore, Richardson can estimate $1/a$ to be about three years or $a = 0.3$ per year approximately (for Germany). This value would, of course, depend on a country's industrial potential. We are now considering coalitions, each about twice the size of Germany alone. Therefore, a bigger value of a should be taken but of the same order of magnitude. The difference $(a - m)$ represents the slope of the straight line plotted in Figure 4. This slope has the value 0.73 per year. If now the reasonable values of 0.9 and 0.2 be taken for a and m respectively, their difference just about corresponds to the value it should have to represent the slope.

Because of the roughness of the estimates, this argument cannot be taken as a strong corroboration of the theory, any more than the straight line fit of four points. But at least the estimated values do not contradict the values deduced from the findings.

Let us now see what the constant W can suggest about the character of the arms race. From the derivation of equation (9), it appears in Richardson's treatment that

$$W = Q - \frac{g + h}{a - m} \qquad (15)$$

Here Q is the total value of trade between all the pairs of the potential belligerents; g and h are the grievance terms, as before. Therefore, W is the excess of the total co-operation over total grievances, the latter appropriately measured relative to the coefficients of mutual stimulation and restraint. The measure of good will (as of hostility) is in money units.

Note now where the straight line of Figure 4 intersects the horizontal axis—at the point between 190 million and 200 million pounds sterling, actually at £194 million. At that point, the rate of growth of armaments would have been zero. That is to say, the net amount of good will existing between the potential belligerents would have just covered £194 million of defense expenditures to keep the rate of growth of armaments at zero. Noting the defense expenditures for the year 1909 we see the figure £199 million—just a little too much to be covered by good will.

". . . and so began an arms race which led to the Great War," Richardson concludes.

FURTHER CRITIQUE

Does this excess of £5 million of war expenditures over the theoretically tolerable level constitute another corroboration of the arms race theory? In other words, can we suppose that if £5 million more were expended in 1909 on interrival trade or £5 million less were expended on armaments, the armament race would not have started? If we follow Richardson's reasoning, we must conclude no less. Recall that he takes for a the value 0.9 and for m the value 0.2. The condition for instability deduced earlier, namely $mn < ab$ (p. 27) becomes in the case of the European powers $a^2 > m^2$, since a was taken equal to b and m to n. The values chosen by Richardson insure this inequality by a large margin. Therefore, the European system was definitely unstable. It was bound to go into a spin, either toward ever-increasing armaments or toward increasing co-operation, depending on where it started from. It appears from the data that the unstable balance point was at the total armament expenditure of £194 million. This can only mean that exceeding this critical level by a minute amount was bound to lead to the explosive arms race (in Richardson's interpretation, war), while keeping the armament expenditures below this critical level by an equally minute amount would have not only prevented the arms race but would have led Europe to the opposite "explosion" of unlimited co-operation! [12]

Now analogous situations do exist in chemistry: the difference between stability and explosion may be a very minute difference in temperature or the presence or absence of an extremely minute quantity of a catalyst. As we shall see in Chapter IV, similar situations are suspected in some conditions of precarious biological balance. But somehow we shrink away from the conclusions that a similar delicate disequilibrium could have determined the history of Europe (and thus largely of the world) in the twentieth century. Such a conjecture seems to us almost as bizarre as the arguments that the course of history was irretrievably set by the fact that Napoleon suffered from a cold in some critical battle. Still, the strangeness of an argument is not sufficient reason for its categorical dismissal.

Richardson's choice of the participants in the arms race is likewise subject to criticism. He had a choice of including or excluding nations which became members of the coalitions. For example, Great Britain and Italy were not included. Their exclusion can, of course, be defended. Great Britain, although a member of the Entente, was not a full-fledged ally of France and Russia; Italy oscillated between her allegiance to the Triple Alliance (with the Central Powers) and pressures to join the Allies. Suppose, however, the exclusion of these powers resulted in a poor fit of theory to observation and their inclusion resulted in a better fit. Could it not then be argued with equal justification that they *should* have been included?

Now consider Richardson's estimate of the parameter *a*. He takes it from the fact that Germany caught up with Great Britain in armaments in about three years. Now $1/a$ would be the actual catching up time only if the constraint governed by the parameter *m* were not operating. With this constraint operating, the catching up time should be longer, and it should also depend on the level of armaments to catch up with. But aside from this complication, which probably would make little difference in the time it took to catch up with Great Britain, we must look at the situation during the years 1933–36 (when Germany was presumably catching up) more closely. It seems that Germany was stimulated to rearmament not so much by the existing level of armaments of Great Britain but rather by other more powerful influences. Even dismissing the possibility that Nazi Germany might have been stimulating *itself* into accelerated armament, we find an important disturbing element quite in accord with Richardson's two-nation theory, namely the rapidly accelerating armament of the Soviet Union. Data, given by Richardson in the same monograph, show that both German and Soviet armaments increase sharply from 1933 on, while the armaments of the other powers remain relatively constant. In view of the political situation of the period, is it not reasonable to view this increase as symptomatic of an arms race between Germany and the U.S.S.R.? If so, then dx/dt of Germany was not determined by the relatively constant British level of armaments but by the start of an arms race with Russia, and so does not warrant an estimate of the parameter *a* on the basis of catching up time with Great Britain.

To pursue our critique, Richardson's equations demand that W, the excess of trade over grievances (translated into money), remain a constant over the period of the race and moreover that this constant should not exceed the total armament expenditures; otherwise the arms race would go into reverse. Comparing the trade figures (94, Table II, p. 19) with armament expenditures (Table 1), we see that the latter kept just ahead of the former, except for the year 1911, when the two were nearly equal. Therefore, when we take grievances into account (which we feel did exist between the two camps) we find that the arms race was indeed destined to have taken place. But was W indeed a constant, as demanded by the theory? Trade was not a constant during that period, as the figures show. Therefore, to consider W constant the grievances must be supposed to go up and down *with* the volume of trade by just the right amounts—a farfetched supposition.

All these matters make the acceptance of the arms race theory at face value difficult. Too many uncomfortable questions concerning the psychology of theoretical investigations arise willy-nilly when the path of deduction leads over too many qualifications. We feel that a scientist of even the greatest integrity may see the evidence which supports his theory in sharper focus than other evidence. He will therefore be impressed, as Richardson apparently was, by the "astonishingly good agreement," as he puts it, between predicted and observed relations. Here the scientist stands in gravest danger of self-delusion. When Pierre Besuhoff, the hero of Tolstoy's *War and Peace* becomes an addict of cabalistic calculations (the numerology of names), he plays with various spellings and arrangements of his own name, title, nationality, etc., and with those of Napoleon, until he finds the right combinations to make both yield the number 666, the mystical number of the Beast in the Apocalypse. Pierre is thus led to the conclusion that he is destined to save Europe from Napoleon (120, Vol. 4, p. 109 ff). Is this sort of preoccupation, tainted with paranoid obsessions, simply an exaggeration of what the dedicated scientist does when he puts selected pieces of evidence together in support of a theory?

This need not be always so, of course. The scientist may well be aware of the inevitable biases concomitant to strong involvement in the search for regularity and of simplicity in nature. He may then counter these biases by deliberately seeking to *upset* his theories by putting them to severe tests. But aside from such self-imposed discipline, not unusual in science (to which we must add, of course, the severe attitudes of the scientist's colleagues, who will usually be not far behind with attempts to demolish his theory), there are positive aspects even to such far from satisfactory investigations as Richardson's. We will take these up in Chapter V.

In the meantime, we shall examine one more sample of his often naïve but always interesting approaches to the theory of human conflict.

CHAPTER III

PSYCHOLOGICAL EPIDEMICS

IN SPITE OF THE FACT that our per capita murder rate is thought to be among the highest in the world; in spite of the fact that lynching has been traditionally associated with the United States; in spite of the saturation with violence of our popular fiction entertainment, the actual incidence of overt violence in our society is comparatively low. At any rate, it would appear low to someone concerned only with countable instances of deadly violence.

The greatest outbreak of internal violence in the United States was, of course, the Civil War. The sociologist or the political scientist, who is concerned with other criteria than simply the volume of bloodshed, may feel that the Civil War with its vast political and social underpinnings, should not be put in the same class with riots, murders, and lynchings; and he may be right by his standards. However, all classifications are arbitrary, or rather different purposes are served by different classifications. Our purpose, for the time being, following Richardson's example (95), is to evaluate the amount of violence in a given society or in a given period only in terms of the number of victims involved. A victim of violence is one who dies in consequence of someone's intent. Wars, therefore, are the most intense manifestations of violence. From this point of view, wars are distinguished from smaller outbreaks (murders, feuds, etc.) only by their magnitude.[13]

Beside the colossal internal outbreak of violence which

was the Civil War, all other internal outbreaks will appear puny, but in their totality will add up to respectable proportions. Still, even counting executions (because we are counting without regard for justification or motives), the total for the United States will appear smaller than for many other societies. Our murder rate is relatively high, but this form of violence is amply matched elsewhere by the greater incidence of riots, political terror, and communal strife. For instance, at the height of the purges in the U.S.S.R. in 1938, executions reached a rate of 3000 per day according to Soviet sources. It is estimated that six million persons were put to death in German occupied territory in the period 1940–45. The postwar outbreaks in India claimed as many victims as some good-sized wars.

All these figures are confined to "internal" strife. If we include "regular" wars between sovereign states, the most organized form of extermination, we see that mankind, at least throughout its recorded history, has been subjected to constant outbreaks of this sort. Sometimes they come in large, engulfing waves, as major wars, sometimes in smaller disturbances as local wars and social explosions. For the rest, violence is "endemic," that is, appears in isolated, seemingly nonpropagated instances such as murders and executions.

INFECTIOUS VIOLENCE

If we keep our attention fixed simply on the size of the outbreaks (as a man from Mars might, who is ignorant of "causes" and rationalizations of violence), fatalities of this sort appear no different from other fatalities, which we attribute to "diseases," to "old age," or to accidents. The man from Mars would, perhaps, distinguish two general types of fatalities: some seem to be bunched; others isolated. According to this classification, deaths from wars, typhus, and cholera would fall into the first category; while those from cancer, heart diseases, traffic accidents, and isolated murders would fall into the second. Lynchings would appear as a borderline case. On the one hand, since the victims of lynchings are for the most part single individuals, lynchings might seem "non-infectious." But in another sense they have some aspects of an infectious disease. As our man from Mars watched a lynching, it would appear to him that at first there was a growing crowd of people around a "nucleus." As the crowd grew, the behavior of the individuals in it would grow more and more agitated and uniform. The process would culminate in someone's death, after which the crowd would disperse. Thus, the man from Mars might think that he is dealing with an outburst of an epidemic, in which, however, mortality was limited to only one or a very few individuals in each outburst. He would be reinforced in this conclusion as he watched riots, which he might then classify with lynchings in the same class of limited "epidemics." And certainly wars, both internal and external, would appear to the man from Mars, who studied violence in this way, as instances of vast pandemics with high mortality.

Outbursts of infectious internal violence have been declining in the United States. Sixty years ago violent industrial strife and lynchings were fairly common occurrences. I still remember the Detroit race riots of twenty years ago, and my father's generation remembers the Chicago race riots of forty years ago. Today such outbreaks are rare. This is not to say that all violence of epidemic proportions has disappeared from American life. It may have taken other guises. But it has practically disappeared in its overt physical form.

Forever? We don't know. Outbreaks of the bubonic plague in Europe have been separated by centuries, but the conditions for such outbreaks always existed as long as people were crowded in cities with inadequate sanitary facilities and as long as the primary agents of the disease and its carriers remained unrecognized. If outbreaks of mass violence depend on underlying causes similar to those underlying other epidemics, it is possible that the ebb and flow of these phenomena will remain uncontrolled until those underlying causes are discovered and countered. We do not know whether the analogy is a fruitful one, but it has so appeared to some, enough to inspire theoretical investigations of the subject.

Typical hotbeds of mob violence seem to be societies in which the "mob" is a physical reality. Such a mob is no longer familiar to us, Americans. Its occasional appearance (e.g., in Little Rock in September 1957) is sufficiently rare so as to occasion nationwide concern. Our crowds, by and large, are not mobs. For example, the business sections of our cities are teeming with people during working hours. But this milling humanity on the sidewalks, in the subways, and in lobbies of public buildings differs markedly from the crowds which make real mobs. Nothing seems to connect these people in the American city crowd to each other. Each goes about his business. The typical crowdedness is only a consequence of the fact that the "businesses" are in geographical proximity. The closest thing to a mob in the United States is the Times Square crowd on New Year's Eve and on presidential election nights. That crowd does behave like a (good-natured) mob. Mass spectacle audiences are also near-examples, and possibly the small crowds in some intimate night clubs are others. In all these gatherings, it is possible, for example, to *address* the crowd, to capture attention. The real mob always has an "ear." It *was* possible to address the crowd in the Roman Forum or in the oriental bazaar. Those were real urban mobs. They were subject to "moods." They were united by some common activity, either as spectators or as participants in the innumerable processions, parades, ceremonies, public proclamations, public executions, outdoor theatrical performances, etc. The mob is a population which lives publicly outdoors.

This mob has disappeared from the American scene and has carried with it into seeming oblivion the phenomenon of overt mob violence. But in the Old World cities, this open-air population still exists and within our memories has given awesome exhibitions of violent action. Communist, Fascist, and many Latin American regimes came to power on the crests of waves of mob action: demonstrations, rallies, riots, pogroms, etc. Both in the Old World and in Latin America it still seems possible to gauge and to control the "mood" of an entire city.

We might, however, ponder on the question whether the events characteristic of mob action are not still operating in the United States in another sense. We have no more St. Bartholomew nights and no more storming of Bastilles, but we do have epidemics involving often trivial and ephemeral behavior patterns: the passing adoration of a singer, the ups and downs of brand names, fads, and fashions. There are more serious instances, too, as in the outbreak of witch hunts in the early fifties. The conditions which bring about a mob *mentality* have not disappeared. Psychological epidemics of various sorts have a fertile soil in our society.

Before the advent of mass media, the primary channel of infection of the psychological epidemic was direct contact with a carrier. Therefore, in its old setting, the psychological epidemic can be taken as formally analogous to the organic kind. In an organic epidemic, the infected and infectious individual transmits the disease to a number of others, who, in turn, transmit it. The transmission is "nonconservative," that is, the giver of the disease is not thereby deprived of it. Ordinarily, if there were no limiting factors, every such epidemic would ultimately involve every individual alive, because in all likelihood a chain of links exists (through which contact is possible) from any individual to any other. But there are in the case of organic epidemics, among others, the following:

1. *Natural immunity.* Not everyone who is exposed will contract the disease.

2. *Limitations of infectiousness.* An infected individual is infectious only during a limited period. For one thing, he usually either recovers or dies after a certain time and in either case ceases to be infectious. Thus, carriers are not only added to the population during the course of an epidemic but also are removed from it.

3. *Immunity conferred by the disease itself.* This is true of many infectious diseases. The accumulation of immune persons reduces the number of potential carriers.

4. *Decrease of virulence in the pathogenic organism.*

5. *Organized measures limiting contact among the members of the exposed population.* These are quarantine, the closing of public places, etc.

If what is spread is not an organic disease but an attitude, a behavior pattern, or a piece of news, quite similar limiting factors can be listed. People vary in their susceptibility. "Infectiousness," for example, the tendency to pass on a piece of news, may wear off with the passing of the novelty of the news. Security measures against leaks of information are analogous to quarantine precautions, etc. If the quantitative effects of all these factors and the factors making for spread are known, the course of psychological epidemics (fads, rumors, etc.) is in principle predictable, like the course of organic epidemics. In particular, in many instances the following theoretical result is obtained by mathematical deduction: for a given type of epidemic there may be a "critical" number of initial infections. If this critical number is exceeded, the epidemic will "explode," otherwise the incidence will decrease and the incipient epidemic will die out.[14]

Such "critical threshold" effects are, of course, quite common in physical and chemical events. If you strike a match lightly, it will not light. The friction has generated some heat, but not enough to trigger a chain reaction in the head of the match. If pressure is increased, so that the heat generated brings the temperature to the ignition point, the rest of the process becomes self-perpetuating. Nerves, too, have their thresholds. Within certain limits an electric current can be passed through a nerve without inciting a propagated impulse in the nerve, but once the threshold of stimulation is passed, the impulse starts and proceeds of its own accord, "riding" on the electrochemical reaction within the nerve. All such chain reactions partake of the nature of epidemics. In combustion, for example, the associated chemical change (oxidation) in some molecules is accompanied by the release of sufficient heat to initiate this reaction in neighboring molecules, which in turn release heat, etc. The explosion of a uranium bomb operates on the same principle. The penetration of "slow neutrons" into an atom of the uranium isotope U-235 results in the release of neutrons by the atoms hit, which neutrons in turn penetrate other atoms. The existence of the "critical mass" has the same meaning here as the existence of a "critical infection density" in an epidemic. These analogies are not mere metaphors. They are based on an underlying similarity of the *mathematical structure* of the events, which affords the possibility of describing the various processes by similar types of mathematical equations. Phenomena of widely disparate content are conceptually unified by similar mathematical form.[15]

If now certain aspects of mass behavior can be shown to have similar properties, of which the most important is non-conservative propagation by transmission, the general theory of contagion can be extended to treat those aspects of mass behavior. That people imitate each other is commonly observed. In imitation, then, a behavior pattern is transmitted from one individual to others. Moreover, the thing transmitted is not "conserved," that is, the person receiving it gains it, but the person giving it does not necessarily lose it. Propagation with multiplication then becomes possible, and we have the necessary ingredients of a generalized epidemic.[16]

This is the starting point of Richardson's description of war moods, their outbursts, and changes (96).

THE MOOD EPIDEMICS

Richardson pictures the "mood" of an individual as a state to which and out of which the individual can be converted. There are, of course, gradations of moods, as there are different severities of a disease. But it is possible to describe a mood epidemic (as it is to describe a disease epidemic) by enumerating a number of sharply distinguished "states." In the case of a disease, for example, we might distinguish the incubation state, the infected and infectious state, the infected but noninfectious state, the recovered state, the deceased state, etc. The larger the number of states assumed, the more complex we can expect the theory to be. However, to get a theory started at all, we must make a commitment to some definite description, and the choice of the description is often determined by the possibility of handling its implications.

For his theory of war moods, Richardson chooses the following "states," related to the attitudes of one population toward another: friendly, hostile, and war-weary. He assumes, moreover, that the psychological state of any given individual always involves a *pair* of these, an "overt" one and a "covert" one. Sometimes the two moods are the same, but more often they are different. The idea is a drastic schematization of the Freudian theory of the "unconscious." Overtly, a man may be aware only of friendly feelings toward another, but underlying these friendly feelings may be a covert hostility, of which even the carrier of the hostility may be unaware.

Such situations are so widely known in so many fields that one cannot but admit the plausibility of this idea. We know that certain diseases are dormant until some set of conditions makes for their sudden emergence. We know also that many inheritable traits are carried for several generations without being overtly observed until a certain combination of genes in some particular individual gives these traits overt ("phenotypic") expression. We are aware of the eruption of a volcano but not of the gradual building up of pressures which produces it.

And so, Richardson supposes, there is always a pair of such moods in an individual. There is no reason why there could not be more, but, as we said, a commitment must be made to some definite picture.

As in his treatment of the theoretical arms race, Richardson goes on to consider two nations, but this time he is outspoken: he is examining Great Britain and Germany on the eve of World War I. He supposes that before the outbreak of the "war fever" the majority of the inhabitants of these countries harbored the "friendly" mood toward the population of the other state both overtly and covertly. However, there was also a pool of covert hostility (stemming perhaps, from British-German rivalry). Occasionally, hostility comes to the surface. A sector of public opinion in Germany entertains the idea that inevitably Germany is to wage war for a "place in the sun" and moreover that it is necessary for a nation to wage war in order to maintain its vitality.[17] There are, perhaps, similar manifestations in Britain, although to a lesser degree.

The problem of gauging the "amount of hostility" prevailing in one nation against another at a given moment is indeed a difficult one but not necessarily a totally insoluble one. In principle, one could design "indices" of hostility as well-defined quantitative measures. The existence of mass communications (mainly newspapers at that time) makes this possible through a content analysis of newspaper material, of public utterances, etc. There is no way of knowing what the "real" index of hostility is, nor indeed whether "amount of hostility" is a meaningful idea.[18] But once this concept has been chosen as an object of investigation, one must try to do one's best with it.

At any rate, Richardson argues that the amount of overt hostility in Britain and in Germany in the few weeks preceding the outbreak of World War I could be reasonably estimated in terms of the fraction of adult population in the hostile mood and in terms of the frequency and intensity of hostile expression in public life. The estimate, according to Richardson, shows a very sudden, explosive rise from the moment when the assassination of Grand Duke Ferdinand of Austria became known. His indices are newspaper utterances, speeches, collapse of resistance in Britain against the declaration of war, especially when Belgium was invaded, the pro-British declarations of Irish nationalists, who until then were largely preoccupied with their own affairs, etc. The events in Germany, of course, followed a similar course with even greater intensity. It is reasonable to suppose that at the outbreak of the war, the population of Germany was almost unanimous in its support of the war. Thus the rise of overt hostility in both nations went from a low value (measured as per cent of overtly hostile individuals) to nearly 100 per cent.

This state of affairs persisted until the lines were stabilized in September 1914 on the Western Front. From that time on, Richardson observes, another effect set in, characteristic of wars of attrition: "war weariness." It may not have been conscious at first, but it grew as the expected quick victory failed to materialize, as casualties mounted, as amputees became common in the streets, as shortages began to pinch. In a year or so, war weariness became overt here and there. Editorials and public statements began to appear in favor of a negotiated peace. In 1917 in a British by-election, an antiwar candidate got 23 per cent of the vote. In the summer of 1918, the German High

Command announced that further offensives were futile; the stalemate character of trench warfare was at last openly recognized. Deterioration of war morale picked up momentum during the fall of 1918, and overt war-mindedness all but disappeared at the time of the armistice.

As one Nazi leader later put it, "Peace broke out."

Some overt hostility lingered in the British "Hang the Kaiser" movement and smoldered among the German military caste and among isolated fanatics, who soon were to band together to form the nucleus of a new crystallization of overt hostility twenty years later.

This course of events resembles the well-known courses of many epidemics with their sudden outbursts, gradual declines, and equally sudden disappearances and with their endemic reservoirs of infection, which eventually nurture new epidemics.

The mathematical model proposed by Richardson to treat the phenomenon of war fever depends essentially on a contagion process. The assumptions have to do with the probabilities of passing from one state to another as a result of contact. The "states" are mood pairs, an overt mood and a covert one. The simplest mathematical models of organic epidemics usually involve two states: the uninfected and the infected. An uninfected individual has a certain probability of passing to the infected state upon contact with an infected individual. The rate of increase of the infected, therefore, in this simplest model is proportional to the product of the infected and the uninfected fractions of the population. If this is so, then the fraction of the infected should follow a well-known sigmoid-shaped curve (the "logistic") and should eventually approach 100 per cent.

No known epidemic in a human population has ever been observed to fit this model. In order to fit observed epidemic curves, modifying assumptions have to be introduced. The simplest such assumptions involve immunity, limited periods of infectiousness, etc. Essentially, this amounts to considering more than two states. In Richardson's model of war-mood contagion, there are six states (actually state pairs, each with an overt and a covert component): (friendly, friendly); (friendly, hostile); (hostile, friendly); (hostile, war weary); (war weary, hostile); and (dead). The equations are generalizations of the logistic equations. The contributions of the rate of increase (or decrease) of each of the states is taken as a sum of terms, each proportional to a product of a pair of fractions, representing the proportions of a pair of states in the population.

In chemistry, such equations describe the dynamics of bimolecular reactions, that is, those in which new molecules are formed when a pair of molecules collide. In the mood epidemic similar collisions can be imagined, except that collisions need not be physical. The probability that an individual passes from one mood to another may depend on the proportion of individuals in a certain state in the *hostile* population, with whom the individual does not necessarily come in direct contact but of whose mood he may be somehow aware.[19]

The six-state contagion model (represented by six simultaneous differential equations of the second degree) is quite complex, and Richardson does not undertake to solve the equations. Instead, he depends on plausible semiquantitative arguments to show that the rise and fall of war moods derived from this contagion model should follow approximately that which is actually observed.

The mathematical details of Richardson's treatment are of little interest here. Moreover, even the drastically simplified mathematics which he actually uses is too involved to be justified by the extremely meager and ambiguous data. The theory collapses of its own weight, as it were. What is important is not the theory (which is a bad one) but the very idea of treating war moods by methods identical with those based on the mathematical theory of epidemics. It is highly instructive to examine the validity of such methods in principle, and especially to examine their limitations. In other words, it is useful to ask what conditions must be met in order that such methods should be applicable to real situations. It may turn out that such conditions are all but impossible to fulfil. On the other hand, it may turn out that such conditions could be approximately met in certain situations. It is those situations that the mathematically inclined sociologist or historian should examine. It is as legitimate to look for areas of inquiry in which an available tool is useful as to look for tools useful in a given situation.[20]

In Chapter V, we shall have more to say about the value of mathematical models of the sort examined. For the present, we will look at just one more model conceived in a similar spirit, because it provides a conceptual bridge between the approach inspired by physical science, which we have been discussing, and an entirely different approach, which will be our concern in Part II.

CHAPTER IV

CO-OPERATION
AND EXPLOITATION

A MATHEMATICAL MODEL very similar to Richardson's model of the armament race leads to a deduction of relations which can be interpreted as co-operative and exploitative patterns of behavior. It is of interest for two reasons; first as an illustration of how practically identical mathematical methods can be applied to theories of widely different content; second, because the theme of co-operation and exploitation is an important adjunct in the discussion of conflicts. For the notion of "co-operation" may be said to have two opposites. One is conflict; the other exploitation. The mathematical relations between conflict and co-operation, as they are treated in Richardson's theory, were discussed in Chapter II. Here we shall be concerned with a similar mathematical treatment of co-operation and exploitation.

The theme of co-operation and exploitation is, of course, a common one in the discussions of social relations. These are emotionally charged words, and the labeling of some social relation as co-operative or exploitative usually exposes the point of view of the labeler. The relation between the owners (or managers) and the workers of an industrial enterprise has been passionately described in one way or another, depending on the describer's conception of economic and political systems. The epithet "parasite" has been flung at a wide variety of social roles—at the entrepreneur and at the unemployed worker; at the soldier and at the bureaucrat; at the artist, the racketeer, the union official, the jurist, the physician, the king, and the king's jester. In fact, anyone whose presence is resented in the social order is termed a "parasite."

In the living world, parasites are numerous and diverse. There are internal parasites, like tapeworms and liver flukes. There are external ones like body lice and fleas. There are fungi, like mushrooms and molds. In popular conception, a parasite is pictured as a highly simplified, "degenerate" organism (e.g., a tapeworm, which is almost exclusively a digestive apparatus). Yet some parasites have developed exquisitely complex patterns of existence. It is largely true, however, that a parasite harms his host, since part of the host's nourishment is diverted to the parasite, but the latter's biological processes are not geared to respond to the host's needs.

Since the host can live without the parasite, but the parasite cannot live without the host, the host must have been around longer. There are indications that the ancestors of present-day parasites have not always been parasitic. They once led an honest life, but have somehow become "adapted" to the parasitic way of life.

The question of how this came about is interesting not only from the biological point of view but also from the social. For it can certainly be argued that some social roles may properly be called parasitic, say that of the professional criminal. Could one, then, trace the evolution of such roles, and could this evolution show analogies to the evolution of biological parasites?

Karl Marx, who implicitly defined the role of the entrepreneur in the productive process as a parasitic one (his whole theory of surplus value is built on this idea), did attempt to trace the social evolution of this role from the independent artisan to the master, who employed at first apprentices, then journeymen; and who later emerged as the organizer of the shop and finally abandoned all participation in the actual productive process. According to Marx, the capitalist returned nothing of social value for the profit accruing to him from ownership (68, Vol. I, Parts III–V).

Besides the evolutionary outlook, which characteristically colored nineteenth-century social thought, there was another, a sort of "Platonic" one, best exemplified by Ricardo in his development of a model of the "economic man." This way of thinking tries to get at the "essence" of an aspect of human activity by stripping the activity to what seems to be its most elementary form. Thus, Ricardo begins his exposition of political economy by asking the reader to imagine man's economic activities as they might have gone on in a primitive state—as if a hunter, that is, a primitive individual producer, and a farmer, another individual producer, came in contact to initiate the first socio-economic act, the exchange of commodities (93).

There is no point now in belaboring the artificiality and the simple-mindedness of such schemes. Ricardo's probably stems from the thinking of Rousseau and reveals that author's naïve implicit assumption of a unique "natural" state from which complex social arrangements later developed (100). However, simple-minded as such ways of thinking are, they are sometimes eminently successful in some areas of science. They have served as steppingstones to further investigations.

A MATHEMATICAL MODEL OF ELEMENTARY PRODUCTION AND EXCHANGE

In this spirit, as a springboard of reasoning, let us consider a Ricardian socio-economic model of two individuals producing and exchanging goods. We shall depart in two respects from Ricardo. First, we shall not expect the model to be taken seriously as representative of any real situation. The model is only a heuristic prop. Second, we shall be using mathematical rather than verbal reasoning, so that at least our conclusions will be rigorous consequences of our assumptions, even if the model may not fit any real situation. When we do look for situations, of which our model may be an idealization, we shall not insist on a socio-economic context. If no socio-economic situation fits even remotely, perhaps a biological one will, or perhaps some other hitherto unexpected interpretation will turn up. The greatest advantage of mathematical models is that they are contentless, so that if the situation for which a model has been designed does not fit, one can abandon the situation and look for another.

Think, then, of two isolated men, X and Y. Each produces goods, and they exchange parts of their produce. Ordinarily, exchange is motivated by each individual's desire to have some of the goods which he himself has not produced. The farmer needs shoes; the cobbler wants bread. Accordingly, each gives to the other a fraction of what he produces. For simplicity, suppose that the two fractions are always equal. Call this fraction of exchanged goods q. Each therefore keeps the remaining fraction $p = 1 - q$.

Now we must introduce utility, another conceptual prop that has dominated economic thinking for a long time. Utility is supposed to be a measure of "satisfaction" accruing to an individual from a certain state of affairs, and the assumption made about the "economic man" is that he will choose the arrangement from which the greatest amount of utility accrues to him under the constraints of the situation. For example, if a farmer comes to market to trade a goat for a pair of shoes, the trade is made possible if after the redistribution of goods, both the farmer and the cobbler have enjoyed increases of utility (or, at least, if both anticipate an increase of utility from the exchange).

Assume, then, that to each of our two men a certain measure of utility accrues from each situation. A positive contribution to utility is made by the total amount of work product which the man receives, but the amount of work he has put in to produce his output contributes a negative amount—a utility cost.

In economics the concept of utility is sometimes invoked to determine the ratios of exchange. But in our hypothetical situation, the rules of exchange are fixed, say by law, custom, or some other constraint. However, the men are still able to adjust to the situation so as to maximize their respective utilities: they can do so *by controlling their productive output.* This is presumably what the individual would do if he were alone. The more he worked, the more he would get and so the more utility would accrue to him on that account. The more he worked, however, the more tired he would get and the more *negative* utility would accrue to him on that account. If at some point the net utility were maximized, this would be the point at which he would fix his output. We wish to investigate a similar situation where an exchange of outputs between two individuals is involved.

Again, as in the case of the arms race, we must make some assumptions. We must assume something about *how* utility depends on the reward and on the effort. For the effort we take the simplest possible assumption, namely that the negative utility depends proportionately on the effort. For the reward, however, we assume a sort of "diminishing returns" effect. As the reward increases, the utility also increases, but at a decreasing rate. It is as if to say that a ten-dollar raise means much more to the man who is making twenty dollars a week than to one who is making two hundred dollars. If the increase of utility is to be inversely proportional to reward already accrued, the proper mathematical function to express utility in terms of the product received is the logarithmic function.[21] Combining the logarithm of the reward with a negative term proportional directly to the effort, we write for the utilities (satisfactions) of the two men the two equations[22]

$$S_x = \log (1 + px + qy) - \beta x \qquad (16)$$
$$S_y = \log (1 + qx + py) - \beta y \qquad (17)$$

We are interested in a balance point, if any. At this balance point the rates of change of the respective utilities with respect to the variables under the control of each man must be zero. Therefore, we must differentiate S_x with respect to x, the variable controlled by X, and S_y with respect to y, the variable controlled by Y, and set both results equal to zero simultaneously. The procedure yields the following two equations.

$$px + qy = p/\beta - 1 \qquad (18)$$
$$qx + py = p/\beta - 1 \qquad (19)$$

Again, as in the armament race, we have two straight lines, the "optimal lines," which represent all the points of balance for each of the men respectively—that is, each has a balance point for each value of the other's output. Therefore, each will try to adjust his output so as to bring the common point upon *his* optimal line. Recall, however, that each individual controls a separate co-ordinate: X can move only horizontally on our diagram; Y only vertically (cf. Figures 5 and 6).

Equations (18) and (19) tell us a number of things. First, the balance point can be in the positive quadrant only if $p/\beta > 1$. This means either that p is not too small or that β is not too large. Recalling the meaning of these constants, we see that there will be a meaningful point of balance only if (a) the fraction *kept* by each individual is not too small, or (b) if their reluctance to work is not too large.

It is, perhaps, not surprising that in a "society" upon which sharing has been imposed, production is possible only if the shared fraction is not too great and work is not too distasteful. Of course, we have deliberately omitted from our model the rewards which accrue from co-operation. We have also neglected the possible positive contributions to utility accruing from the process of work itself. We have neglected all considerations of solidarity, conscience, etc. We have made a "society" of two nonsocial individuals, and our somewhat disappointing result (that the members of the society will work

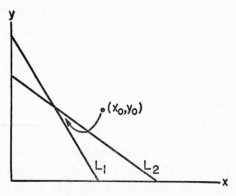

Figure 5. The optimal lines in the miniature production and exchange system (the stable case).

at all only if they are made not to share too much, even though sharing is perfectly symmetric) reflects the drab "psychology" with which we have endowed our puppets.

Let us, nevertheless, look further. Suppose a balance point

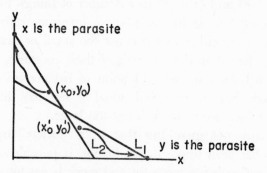

Figure 6. The optimal lines in the miniature production and exchange system (the unstable case).

exists. Here, as in the arms race, the situation may be stable or unstable. We note that in contrast to the armament race, the slopes of the optimal lines are now negative, instead of positive (they go from "northwest" to "southeast"). If now X's optimal line is steeper than Y's, as in Figure 5, the balance is stable: if any disturbance occurs, say due to a temporary laxity of one or the other, the balance will be re-established at the same point. But if Y's optimal line is steeper, as in Figure 6, the balance is unstable. Any disturbance will be self-perpetuating. But the point which determines the production outputs of the two will not fly off to infinity, as it tended to do in the arms race. In the unstable case, the production point will end up either on the horizontal or on the vertical axis. Translating this result into what will happen in our "society," we see at once its sinister implication. If the end state is on the horizontal axis, Y does no work; he becomes a parasite on X; if the end state is on the vertical axis, X is the parasite. Either result is bound to happen in the unstable case, because the slightest disturbance of equilibrium will precipitate it. Which one will be the parasite depends on the direction of the initial disturbance. Whoever relaxes his effort a trifle will become the parasite. This is so because in the unstable case of our model any such relaxation on the part of one will be immediately *compensated* by the other and consequently will instigate another lapse of the same kind.

The roles of X and Y are completely interchangeable. The only reason that stability is associated with the greater slope of X's optimal line is in the way the axes of Figures 5 and 6 have been labeled. Let us now see under what conditions X's optimal line will be steeper, that is, when will the situation be stable.

From analytic geometry we know that this will be the case if $p > q$.[23] Contrariwise, instability, leading to parasitism, will occur if $q > p$. In terms of our model these conditions have a "social significance." Stability will occur when each individual relies on his own efforts more than on the other's, that is, keeps the greater proportion of his own product and exchanges the smaller portion.

Although it may be tempting for some people to see in our toy a vindication of "economic individualism" as promoting efficiency, morality, or social equity, we must once more insist that absolutely no conclusions are warranted at this point concerning the nature of co-operation and conflict in the social sphere. Presently we will obtain results which will suggest directly the opposite, but which will be equally hazardous to interpret.

Suppose now a stable balance exists. Let us see how much utility accrues to X and Y when they have attained the point of balance. First we calculate the co-ordinates of that point, that is, the point of intersection of lines L_1 and L_2 in Figure 5. The co-ordinates are $x = p/\beta - 1$; $y = p/\beta - 1$, and these are the amounts produced by X and Y respectively when balance is achieved. Next we calculate the utilities by substituting these values of x and y into equations (18) and (19). The results are

$$S_x = \log (p/\beta) - p + \beta \qquad (20)$$
$$S_y = \log (p/\beta) - p + \beta \qquad (21)$$

Now is this the best our puppets can do? An individual who works alone adjusts his output so as to maximize his utility, and so does the best for himself that the situation allows. Have our individuals done the best for themselves? Let us check.

Suppose each produced $1/\beta - 1$, which is greater than $p/\beta - 1$, since 1 is greater than the fraction p. Then the utility accruing to each would be $\log (1/\beta) - 1 + \beta$. Is this more or less than what they get at the balance point? Let us calculate the difference. Subtracting $\log (p/\beta) - p + \beta$ from $\log (1/\beta) - 1 + \beta$, we get

$$\log (1/\beta) - 1 - \log (p/\beta) + p \qquad (22)$$

(the β's have canceled out).

Recall that the difference of the logarithms of two numbers is the logarithm of their quotient. We can therefore write (22) as

$$\log (1/p) - 1 + p = \log (1/p) - (1 - p) \qquad (23)$$

This will be positive or negative, depending on whether $\log (1/p)$ or $(1 - p)$ is the greater. Our p, being a fraction, may be anything from 0 to 1. If we plot $\log (1/p)$ and $(1 - p)$ on the same graph against p, we see that for all values of p (except $p = 1$, where both are zero) the logarithm is the greater. Therefore both parties do better if they produce $1/\beta - 1$ than if they produce $p/\beta - 1$, except when $p = 1$, in which case they do equally well. But $p = 1$ only if there is no sharing at all (since each, remember, keeps the p-th fraction); so this case does not even come under consideration.

It appears, therefore, that the "balance point," if it exists, even if it is stable, is *not* the "best" point from the standpoint of either party, although each party does best at the balance point if the other party is there too! Our dynamics always leads our puppets to the balance point, if it is a stable one. Something, then, must be "wrong" with our economic dynamics: it does not provide enough "incentive" for the participants to do well for themselves. We begin to suspect that what is wrong is that it is a dynamics of purely selfish interests. Each adjusts only his own utility without regard for the other's.

However, we should also investigate the case of the parasite, who, we recall, emerges in the case of the unstable balance. Let us see how well the parasite does.

Let X be the parasite. Then he produces nothing, and Y (the "host") must adjust accordingly. Y's optimal line is given by the equation $qx + py = p/\beta - 1$. But now $x = 0$. So Y must produce so as to satisfy the equation $py = p/\beta - 1$, that is, $y = 1/\beta - 1/p$. We assume throughout that $\beta < p$, so that $1/\beta - 1/p$ is positive (otherwise nobody works). We now compute the resulting utilities and get

$$S_x = \log (1 + q/\beta - q/p) \qquad (24)$$
$$S_y = \log (p/\beta) - 1 + \beta/p \qquad (25)$$

Again we wish to compare these with $\log (1/\beta) - 1 + \beta$, the utility accruing to each if each produces the "social optimum," that is, $1/\beta - 1$. (We shall soon explain why we call this particular level of production the "social optimum.") First, let us compare the two utilities accruing to the host, Y. Taking the difference, we have

$$\log (1/p) + \beta (1 - 1/p) \qquad (26)$$

It can be shown [24] that this expression is always positive as long as $p > \beta$. But this condition is always assumed (otherwise there is no production); and so the host Y is always better off at the "social optimum" than in his role as "host." This is hardly surprising, and so we have not learned much. But let us look at the parasite. Is he better off as a parasite or as a full co-operator? The difference in X's utilities between what he gets at the social optimum and as a parasite is now

$$\log p - \log (\beta p + qp - q\beta) - 1 + \beta \qquad (27)$$

Whether this quantity is positive or negative depends on β/p, which can range between 0 and 1. When $\beta = p$, expression (27) reduces to $\log (1/p) - 1 + p$, which, we have seen, is always positive. At the other end, when β is near zero, the expression approaches $-\log q - 1$. Since we are dealing with the unstable case, where $p < q$, we must have $q > \frac{1}{2}$ (recall that $p + q = 1$). Then $-\log q - 1$ is negative,[25] and X is better off as a parasite. As β passes from its maximum permissible value (p) to its minimum value (o), the difference (27) changes at some value of β from positive to negative. We could compute this value in terms of p and q, if we needed it, but we do not need it for our qualitative conclusion, which is this:

1. In the stable case, both parties are better off at the social optimum than they are at the (stable) point of balance.

2. In the unstable case, the host is always better off at the social optimum.

3. The parasite would be better off at the social optimum if β were greater than a certain critical value, but he is better off as a parasite if β is smaller than this critical value.

The last conclusion, put into plain language, means that it pays to be a parasite if your host is not too lazy. This sounds like a common-sense conclusion, but note that an equally reasonable conclusion might have been, "It pays to be a parasite if *you* are sufficiently lazy." This conclusion, however, is *not* borne out by our model: the parameter of "laziness," β, is the same for both, and we have seen that parasitism begins to pay off (compared with co-operation, which, as we shall see, leads to the social optimum) when this parameter is sufficiently *small*, not sufficiently large.[26] Of the two common-sense conclusions, which contradict one another, as common-sense conclusions frequently do, one is vindicated by mathematical analysis, and the other is refuted.

THE SOCIAL OPTIMUM

Let us now see the reason for calling the point where $x = y = 1/\beta - 1$ the "social optimum." It has also been called by mathematical economists the Pareto point, after the Italian economist and sociologist V. Pareto, who called attention to its properties.[27] The point represents the optimum output of the *pair* in the sense that their *joint* utility (the sum of the two) will be greatest at that point.

We have seen that in the stable case, the two do better *individually* as well as collectively if they adjust their production at the Pareto point, and even in the unstable case, the parasite sometimes would do better by co-operating with his host instead of exploiting him. But how can this ethically gratifying point be reached? We have seen that it cannot be reached if each party adjusts his individual utility: this process yields either the balance point (if it is stable) or leads to parasitism. One way of driving this miniature production system to the Pareto point is by linking the production of the two parties. If, for example, they made a "contract" in which each obliged himself to produce as much as the other, then it can be shown that the Pareto point will be the point of balance (84).

Another way is to link the utilities. Let us see how this can be done.

Suppose that our puppets have developed a "social conscience," that is to say, the utility of one is to some extent dependent on the utility of the other. Let us take the simplest form of dependence, a "linear" one, that is, the new utilities will be the "weighted sums" of the old utilities. Thus,

$$S_x^* = AS_x + BS_y \tag{28}$$
$$S_y^* = CS_x + DS_y \tag{29}$$

Here A, B, C, and D are weighting factors. We see that this situation subsumes the preceding as a special case: if $A = 1$; $D = 1$; $B = 0$; $C = 0$, each S* becomes identical with the old S. Our present model is therefore an extension of the old one. From it we can derive all the old results, if the above values are assigned to A, B, C, and D, and some new results if other values are assigned.

Since S_x and S_y are given in terms of the output variables, *x* and *y*, the sharing fractions *p* and *q*, and the reluctance co-efficient β, it follows that the new utility functions S_x^* and S_y^* can also be so expressed. In addition, they will depend on four new parameters, A, B, C, and D, the measures of the relative concern for self and for the other ("ego" and "alter," as psychologists say) of X and Y. Having put down our new (and more complicated) expressions for the utilities, we can repeat the entire procedure of calculating points of balance, stability, etc., pertinent to the new situation (87). Some of the results are as follows.

If and only if A = B and C = D, the balance point will coincide with the Pareto point, and moreover the equilibrium at this point will be stable regardless of the values of *p* and *q*. Translating, this means: "The only 'ethics' which leads to the attainment of maximum joint utility in the model of society we have considered is the 'egalitarian ethic,' in which the concern for self and for other are of equal weight."[28]

It is instructive to see what happens if we push concern for the other to the extreme at the expense of concern for self. In this case, let A = D = 0; C = B = 1. We have a situation similar to the "completely selfish" case, but now S_x and S_y are reversed. Each individual, however, still controls only his own output. The equations are now

$$S_x^* = \log (1 + qx + py) - \beta y \qquad (30)$$
$$S_y^* = \log (1 + px + qy) - \beta x \qquad (31)$$

Obviously, the only thing X can do to increase his (socially determined) utility is to increase output, since the negative term in S_x^* is not affected by *x*. The same holds for Y. But when both do it, they contribute to each other's negative terms, $-\beta y$ and $-\beta x$, respectively, thus pushing utilities down. And there is no way for them to get out of this trap. They think they are doing each other "good," but in reality they are contributing to each other's misery. (Think of a married couple, each of whom is trying to please the other in ignorance of the other's real likes and dislikes.)

Our 100 per cent altruistic X and Y will never become parasites, it is true, but in the absence of communication (which might have established an agreement) they will work themselves to death.

THE STRUGGLE FOR EXISTENCE

Many ideas prevalent in Europe in the second half of the last century about the nature of social process can be traced to an analogy drawn between biological and social evolution. Indeed, the fundamental idea in the theory of natural selection, credited largely to Darwin and Wallace, stems from an idea posed by Malthus (64) in a social context: more are born than can survive. From this principle came the notion of struggle for existence and survival of the fittest.

Herbert Spencer based a social philosophy on this idea, a philosophy which furnished the rationale for competition as a basis of social life and an impetus to progress. In its extreme form the struggle for existence is pictured in grim vividness with overtones of emotion which one usually associates with the fightlike conflict.

Biologists, whose business it is to examine the actual working of natural selection, find little evidence to justify the inclusion of anthropomorphic notions in the description of the process. There is little drama in the biological struggle for existence. The "struggle" is not necessarily typified by big fish eating little fish, nor by individual beasts fighting for prey or for territory or for mates—events which easily lend themselves to translation into situations rationalized or glorified by the champions of competition. The competing organisms may not even be aware of each other's presence. The whole process is dominated first and foremost by differential survival rates. There need be no contact between the "competitors," let alone any emotional reaction to the process.

Again, as has been done with other situations, the struggle for existence can be pictured as a system of equations. In some respects, the equations will resemble those representing the arms race, those describing mood epidemics, and the co-operation-exploitation equations examined in this chapter. As in the other cases, certain insights can be gained by eliminating the *content* of the equations, that is, the characteristically biological situation, and by concentrating on their purely mathematical properties. Later, the biological content may be reintroduced, and we may ask whether the mathematical insight has helped us to understand better the struggle for existence.

First consider the growth of a population in an environment which places no limitations on the size of the population it can support. Here both birth rate and death rate can be considered constant. The case where death rate exceeds birth rate is not interesting, since that population is doomed. Suppose, therefore, that birth rate exceeds death rate. The equation of growth will be

$$dN/dt = bN \qquad (32)$$

Here b is the excess of birth rate over death rate. The solution, which gives the population N as a function of time t, is

$$N = N_0 e^{bt} \qquad (33)$$

Here N_0 is the initial population. This is the famous Malthusian population curve, an unlimited growth in geometric progression. This situation can never occur in real life. There are always limitations to population growth, the obvious ones being availability of food and space. These limitations can be well represented by adding a negative term to equation (32), proportional to the square of the population:

$$dN/dt = bN - qN^2 \qquad (34)$$

The square term represents the degree of "crowding," as reflected in the frequency of contacts between pairs of individuals, say collisions in the competition for food or for space. (It can be shown that in a freely mixing population, the frequency of such contacts is proportional to the square of the population density.)

The solution of equation (34) yields a sigmoid-shaped curve,[29] one that starts to grow slowly, then increasingly faster, then more slowly again, finally flattening out to a constant level. Such curves are actually observed, for example in the growth of bacterial cultures in a medium kept constant by the addition of nutrients and removal of wastes.

The saturation level determined by equation (34) is obtained by setting $d\mathrm{N}/dt$ equal to zero. In our case, this turns out to be b/q.

The form of equation (34) suggests the form for a system of two such equations, representing the population curves of two competing species. Here the simplest assumption will be made, namely, that in addition to the inhibiting effect on unlimited growth provided by *intra*-species crowding, there is also an inhibiting effect provided by *inter*-species crowding. We do not know the relative magnitude of these effects. So we introduce parameters w_1 and w_2 to represent them. The two equations become

$$d\mathrm{N}_1/dt = b_1\mathrm{N}_1 - q_1\mathrm{N}_1^2 - w_1\mathrm{N}_1\mathrm{N}_2 \qquad (35)$$

$$d\mathrm{N}_2/dt = b_2\mathrm{N}_2 - q_2\mathrm{N}_2^2 - w_2\mathrm{N}_1\mathrm{N}_2 \qquad (36)$$

Here the last terms of each equation represent the interspecies inhibitions to population growth. Note that if there were only one species present, for example, if N_2 in equation (35) were zero, or if N_1 of equation (36) were zero, each of these equations would be formally identical with equation (34), which yields the growth curve of one species.

As they stand, the equations are not quite the same as the arms race equations of Chapter 1, nor the co-operation-exploitation equations (16, 17). But all of these equations have one feature in common. If we look for a balance point, that is, if we set the rates of increase (or decrease) equal to zero, we obtain the equations of two generally intersecting straight lines. Moreover, in all of the situations the intersection of these straight lines represents a stable balance under certain conditions and an unstable one under other conditions.

Setting dN_1/dt and dN_2/dt in equations (35) and (36) equal to zero, we obtain

$$b_1N_1 - q_1N_1^2 - w_1N_1N_2 = 0 \qquad (37)$$

$$b_2N_2 - q_2N_2^2 - w_2N_1N_2 = 0 \qquad (38)$$

Now an obvious pair of solutions is $N_1 = 0$ and $N_2 = 0$, which states that in the absence of *both* populations, the system remains in equilibrium. This is, of course, quite true, but totally uninteresting.[30] We therefore suppose that neither N_1 nor N_2 is zero and look for another balance point. If neither N_1 nor N_2 is zero, we can divide both sides of equations (37) and (38) by these quantities respectively and obtain these equations for the two "Cournot lines" (cf. note 7) L_1 and L_2:

$$L_1: b_1 - q_1N_1 - w_1N_2 = 0 \qquad (39)$$

$$L_2: b_2 - q_2N_2 - w_2N_1 = 0 \qquad (40)$$

We get the balance point by solving these equations simultaneously:

$$N_1 = (q_2b_1 - w_1b_2)/(q_2q_1 - w_1w_2) \qquad (41)$$

$$N_2 = (q_1b_2 - w_2b_1)/(q_2q_1 - w_1w_2) \qquad (42)$$

Now this balance point can have biological meaning only if N_1 and N_2 are both positive. (There is no such thing as a negative population.) This will be the case if

either: $q_2q_1 > w_1w_2$ and $q_2b_1 > w_1b_2$ and $q_1b_2 > w_2b_1$

$$(43)$$

or: $q_2q_1 < w_1w_2$ and $q_2b_1 < w_1b_2$ and $q_1b_2 < w_2b_1$

$$(44)$$

Another way of writing the same equations is

$$\text{either: } q_2/w_1 > b_2/b_1 > w_2/q_1 \tag{45}$$
$$\text{or: } w_2/q_1 > b_2/b_1 > q_2/w_1 \tag{46}$$

These inequalities say that a balance point will exist if the magnitude of b_2/b_1 (the ratio of the net rates of increase) is bracketed between the magnitudes of the "cross-ratios" q_2/w_1 and w_2/q_1.

We next consider under what conditions this balance point (if it exists at all) will be stable. Following exactly the same reasoning as in the analogous cases treated above, we find the condition to be

$$q_1 q_2 > w_1 w_2 \tag{47}$$

In words, the product of the self-restraint coefficients is greater than the product of the other's restraint coefficients. This reminds us of the condition for the stability of the arms race: the product of the self-restraint coefficients is greater than the product of the mutual stimulation coefficients.

What happens if there is no balance point? This is the case if the two straight lines (39) and (40) do not intersect in the first quadrant. In that case, one of the lines will always lie above the other. The species, whose line is farthest from the origin of the co-ordinates is bound to be the sole survival in the struggle for existence. The conditions for the survival of N_1 are

$$b_1/w_2 > b_2/q_2 \text{ and } b_1/q_1 > b_2/w_2 \tag{48}$$

and the conditions for the survival of N_2 are just the reverse:

$$b_2/q_2 > b_1/w_2 \text{ and } b_2/w_2 > b_1/q_1 \tag{49}$$

Figure 7 represents the entire situation graphically.

An important consequence of inequality (47) is the following. The net increase rate of neither population makes any difference for the *stability* of the system. The stability is determined entirely by the relative magnitudes of the inter-species and the intraspecies restraint coefficients. If, however, the system *is* stable, then the relative rates of increase do in-

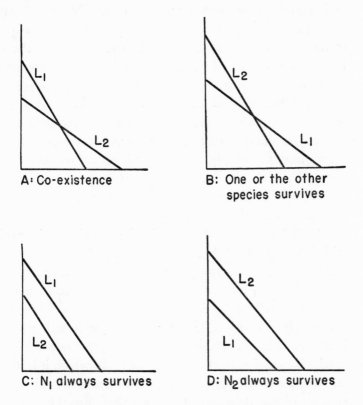

Figure 7. The four situations in the struggle for existence of two species after Gause (34). See also (111).

fluence the point of balance. But an unstable system will remain unstable, no matter what the net rates of increase are.

Several biomathematicians, primarily Lotka (58), Volterra (124), and Kostitzin (50) have investigated the formal properties of several systems of equations, of which ours are examples. Each system is a simulation of some interesting biological situation. For example, if the sign of the last term in equation (36) were reversed, the system might be interpreted as a predator-prey (exploitative) system. This is so, because each encounter between a member of the N_1 species (prey) and of the N_2 species (predator) contributes to the depletion of the former (minus sign) and to the increase of the latter (plus sign). If both of the last terms are positive, the relation between the two species might be interpreted as symbiotic. Nor is it necessary to limit the mathematical system to the relatively simple ones here considered. Nevertheless, it seems prudent to delay further purely formal development of the theory until the simple systems had been put to some observational or experimental tests, so that one may use the discrepancies between observation and theory as a guide for introducing modifications of the theory.

G. F. Gause of the U.S.S.R. has been a pioneer in working with laboratory-bred populations (e.g., paramecia) to test the validity of the mathematical theory described above. Some of his results were quite encouraging (34). In recent years, the theory was refined by introducing chance as a factor in the struggle for existence. The role of chance is well illustrated in the unstable case. Here we can say only that one or the other species is bound to be the sole survivor, but which it is depends on which way the balance happens to tip. If we calculate the chances of the balance tipping in either direction, we ought to predict what percentage of identically bred *populations,* whose parameters make the balance point unstable, will end up at the one or the other extreme. This has actually been done. It has been shown that if a mixed population of two species of a flour beetle is placed in exactly the same environment, in which either population is known to be able to survive *alone,* the end result is always either the survival of one species or of the other, and the chances of each result can be calculated from the biological parameters (75).

It is believed by most biologists that no two species can coexist in the same niche, that is, in exactly the same set of conditions relative to their requirements. Many thousands of species may, of course, coexist in a given portion of space, but this is not the same as saying that they coexist in the same niche. The space may contain many different nutrients, many different opportunities for protection, etc. If many species coexist, this is taken to mean that each utilizes its particular niche, that is, has its own peculiar way of making a living, which may partly compete with what the others are doing but not in every respect. Putting two species of flour beetle in the same box containing only flour is the nearest thing to putting two species into the same niche. Experiments show that when this is done only one species survives, even if there is nothing like "fighting" between the species, as the naïve view pictures the struggle for existence.

A glance at equation (47) indicates the mathematical reason for the survival of only one species. The equation says that the system is unstable if the interspecies coefficients of inhibition (w_1, w_2) are greater than the intraspecies coefficients (q_1, q_2).

Now members of the same species which is sexually reproducing *must* meet if mating is accomplished by personal contact. Therefore, the inhibitory effect of "collisions" is to some extent countered by the enhancing effect of collisions between members of the opposite sex *of the same species*. This effect does not operate when members of different (noninterbreeding) species collide. One would expect, therefore, that the w's would be larger than the q's, which is the condition of instability.

This argument applies to a lesser degree to species which mate without personal contact (like fishes) and not at all to asexual species.

One would expect, therefore, that if exceptions to the law

of single species survival exist, they would be likely to be found among asexually reproducing forms.

On the other hand, a biological system containing predators and prey (what folklore calls "natural enemies") may well exist in a state of balance, if the conditions and the biological parameters are right. Indeed, there are portions of our biosphere that exist in a state of balance for a long time. The balance is maintained by a vastly complex chain of events, including a flow of energy through the various metabolic cycles and subcycles, chains of predation, parasitism, and symbiosis. Viewed as a whole, an ecological system of this sort exhibits many of the properties of an organism. What appear as "struggles" viewed from the point of view of individual organisms or individual species become, then, orderly functions of the "superorganism"—the ecological system. These functions are, of course, often extensively "co-operative," in the sense that they contribute to the continued balanced existence of the "superorganism" (25, 35, 36, 38).

Natural selection favors not only individual organisms in their competition with other organisms but also groups of organisms, often comprising several species, according to the degree of integration through co-operative and symbiotic arrangements within those groups. From this point of view, predation can be viewed as an instance of symbiosis as well as of parasitism. It can be shown that under certain conditions the presence of predators is necessary for the survival of the prey as a species: in the absence of predators, the prey may quickly exhaust their food supply through overpopulation and perish. In recent years, the mathematical theories of the type described have been applied to the calculation of optimum fishery policies (7, 127). It appears that sometimes decrease of yield in a fishery industry calls for an *increase* of fishing rate, if the fish population is to be re-established. Thus, a wise use of biological resources can be guided by policies which are based neither on ruthless exploitation for maximum short-term yields (which usually lead to depletion and are self-defeating) nor on conservation motivated by sentiment alone. Knowledge of biological dynamics can give man power to make good use of the biological world and yet preserve its richness.

Theoretical investigations of the sort described are instructive in that they place large-scale statistically determined processes, which from a certain point of view may look like struggles, into the neutral setting of scientific theory. Equations are devoid of emotional content, and their conclusions are inescapable. To the extent that a process is governed by the forces (or probabilities) from which the equations are derived, the process will go on independently of the way it appears to the individual participants. I think this point of view is instructive, because it calls attention to the limitations on the participant's ability to influence large-scale events. Certainly, if the events are taken on a large enough scale, this conclusion must be true. The conclusion does not justify falling into a totally fatalistic attitude; but the sober question that suggests itself is of crucial importance to understanding the processes around us: to what extent can what sort of events be influenced by whom?

This question may serve to put history into proper perspective and perhaps to instill a measure of humility into the participants of the historical process. One might venture to hope that with humility insight too may come. The analysis of large-scale processes, devoid of extraneous partisan prejudices may yet open man's eyes to the "laws of motion" of historical development, of social struggles, of disastrous explosions of violence. I realize that in even mentioning such "laws of motion" I am inviting outbursts of derision from those who hold "historicism" in contempt.[31] The feelings of those critics of social determinism are somewhat justified by the sorry fate of this approach in the hands of the Marxists. Both Hegel, the "ancestor" of Marx, and his "heir," Lenin, are intellectually repugnant to many for their colossal arrogance, the one wallowing in metaphysical fantasy, the other in demagogy, both pontificating with unbearably dogmatic finality about the fate of human society.

But the fact that the "laws" which Marx supposedly "discovered" were pompously stated and naïvely interpreted does not prove that no discernible regularities in large-scale human affairs can exist. And the very possibility of their existence places on man the responsibility of searching them out. The dispassionate examination of such regularities offers the best hope of escaping a relentless fate.

CHAPTER V

CRITIQUE OF SOCIAL PHYSICS

MOST OF THE STUDIES so far examined have been inspired by the challenge of constructing a logical framework for dealing with the phenomenon of conflict. Some of the studies were attempts to account for selected data. Others held aloof from any data, presumably in order to gain insight into the essential character of certain relations quite apart from the way these relations manifest themselves in real life. In such studies it is not conflict (nor any other content) which is central but rather "dynamic situations" of certain types, whose characteristics (e.g., stability, instability) are thought to be of the same kind as those underlying the genesis and course of certain conflicts.

Dynamic systems as such are most thoroughly studied in physics. This is why we have subsumed all the investigations so far examined under the heading "social physics." The name is more than a metaphor. The method is actually the method of theoretical physics.

Such an approach to the theory of conflict has an underlying philosophy. The best way to examine it is to examine the philosophy underlying physics, particularly those branches where statistical methods are central. This philosophy has had unqualified success in physical science, and for this reason it was hopefully transplanted into theoretical behavioral science. Whether the transplant will "take" in the new habitat is now a subject of much lively controversy. The pros and cons of this question will emerge in the discussion to follow. First, however, we must understand just what this philosophy is and what it is not in its scientific context.

DETERMINISM

We shall call the philosophy determinism. Determinism means many things in many areas of thought. There is some similarity among the meanings, but there are also important differences, which must be brought out, or else argument for or against one type of determinism may be thought to apply or not to apply to another, and this often leads discussions on determinism astray.

There is religious (mystical or mythological) determinism. It views future events as foreordained and inevitable. The plot of some Greek tragedies, for example, is based on the unfolding of events to their predestined conclusion, where it is shown that the efforts of men to forestall this conclusion only insure it. I suppose that the historical determinism of Hegel has a similar flavor, except that its conclusions apply to the general course of human history instead of to the fates of heroes.

Marx borrowed the idea of historical determinism from Hegel and put it on a different basis (turned it right-side-up, the Marxists are fond of saying). Instead of attributing the relentless unfolding of the history of human society to the Absolute or the abstract Idea, as Hegel did, Marx placed the source of his historical determinism in the relations developing among the various groups in society because of the division of labor. How men relate in the process of production (e.g., whether they are owners of the means of production or workers who sell their labor) is supposed to mold the collective world outlooks of men, said Marx. And from the conflicts of these outlooks and the resulting (class) struggles, the evolution of human society is supposed to emerge.

None of the deterministic conclusions mentioned so far is demonstrable. The unfolding of a sequence of events is "explainable" in terms of fate or the will of God or historical determinism of either the idealistic or the materialistic variety; and such explanations are usually accepted or rejected according to how much satisfaction they afford. But they are not explanations according to the "hard-headed" scientific view, which demands a *declaration in advance* as to what will happen under given circumstances. So far, explorations based on mystical and historical determinism have all been supported by hindsight rather than foresight.

There is, however, a type of determinism which meets the "hard-headed" criterion of explanation; that is the determinism based on physical laws. In this sense, the motions of the planets are determined. They are both explainable and predictable on the basis of the equations of celestial mechanics. Since interference with the motions of planets is impossible, this determinism is not only a logical consequence of physical laws (a metaphysician would say of the laws of causality) but also is empirically demonstrable.

Lenin, in his compulsive attempt to establish complete hegemony of Marxist views in philosophy, maintained that Marx discovered the laws of development of human society (57, p. 337). Lenin was convinced that these "laws" were quite as deterministic as the laws of motion discovered by Newton. This striving to place Marx's social science on a par with physical science reveals how deeply the determinism of physical laws impressed those who sought justification of ruthless actions in the determinism of social history.

For about a century, the determinism of mechanics was thought to pervade the entire physical world, and, when it appeared that many of the life processes could be explained in terms of physics and chemistry, some thought that this determinism should be also extended to all events, including the behavior of living and even of intelligent beings. This sort of determinism is incontrovertible on *logical* grounds. If one accepts causality as a principle governing all events, involving matter and energy, then the determinism of all events, *including those events in our brains which we interpret as our own inner conviction of personal freedom,* follows. One can, of course, reject the universality of the causality principle, or else one can insist that there are other events besides the physical. Then one need not accept universal determinism, and one is free to interpret one's inner conviction of "free will" as revealing a reality instead of an illusion.

However, until about 1925 there was no evidence for denying complete determinism of physical events, and to this day there is no way of demonstrating by "hard-headed" criteria the existence of events other than the physical, and so the opposite positions of the argument were really revealed to rest on two incompatible frameworks of thought. The polemic remained sterile.

About 1925 the physicists were forced to modify their strictly deterministic outlook and to admit certain limits to the causality principle. The reasons for this step are technical and are beyond the scope of our discussion. It is important to note, however, that those who were convinced of the reality of free will seized upon the so-called Uncertainty Principle as "proving" their point of view. There is no discernible connection between the Uncertainty Principle and what is thought to underlie "free will," but the principle did make it possible to deny the *universal* operation of causality, and so aided and abetted the antideterminists.

THE DETERMINISM OF LARGE NUMBERS

The determinism which underlies Richardson's mathematical theory of war, which we discussed in Chapters I and II, is unlike any of the forms we have just described. It is not the determinism of fate, nor of the "logic of history," nor of the class struggle, nor of mechanics. It is the determinism of large numbers. To understand the spirit of Richardson's theory (and of others like it) one must carefully distinguish this sort of determinism from the others.

When I was a boy, I used to stop to admire a very large world globe in the lobby of the Chicago Public Library. One thing about that globe struck me as remarkable and kindled thoughts that have smoldered for years. On the southwestern shore of Lake Michigan, where Chicago was supposed to be, there was a round depression gouged out of the globe. New York was also obliterated, but the hole was much shallower. The explanation is obvious and occurred to me immediately. Thousands of people stopped to look at the globe. If they touched it at all, they were most likely to touch Chicago. I pictured them putting a finger on Chicago and saying, "Here is Chicago," or "Here is where we are." A smaller fraction, having found Chicago, would also touch New York. "And here is New York," they would say. That would be about the extent of their "travels" along the globe; none of the other places showed any excessive signs of wear.

Later, it occurred to me to test this "theory" of mass behavior. I examined the city maps posted on the "L" stations. Sure enough, it was always the station where the map was located that was more or less gouged out, more at the busy loop stations, less in the neighborhoods. Still later I verified the same "law" operating in the stations of the Paris *Metro*. In at least one respect, the Parisian *en masse* behaved like the Chicagoan.

The regularity of mass behavior is so commonplace that it is taken for granted. Occasionally, some humorous side of it strikes our attention. It is said that shortly after television became ubiquitous, the water-supply systems were put to severe strain every half hour (exactly on the hour and on the half hour) during the evening: people went to the bathroom when the programs changed. Presumably, this situation is now corrected by proper synchronization of water pressure with the television shows on the basis of quite certain knowledge of what the mass will do, whatever you and I choose to do in our "freedom."

Some years ago a weird story appeared in the *New Yorker*, in which the "law of averages" failed. Civilization was brought to an inglorious chaos, because the streets were empty of traffic at 5 P.M. and jammed at 3 A.M. The story conveys the same jittery feeling as if it described the sudden failure of any of the natural laws that we take for granted (17).

Underlying these "laws of mass behavior" which allow us to predict the diurnal variations of electric power consumption, the ratio of murders to automobile thefts, and the frequency with which the word "of" will occur in almost any collection of a thousand books, is the notion of the "probability" of an event and its connection to the frequency of occurrence of the event among a large number of events.

We are so used to the word "probability" that we do not usually realize that the word has no demonstrable (operational or extensional) meaning when applied to a single event.[32] Anyone will admit that "the probability that a toss of a fair coin will yield tails is one half." Yet this statement has no bearing on the single toss. The single toss will, of course, yield either heads or tails. Believing, as most of us do, in the determinism of mechanics, we admit that once the coin is thrown, the outcome of a single toss is "determined." But it certainly is not determined by a "probability." It is determined by the initial torque exerted on the coin, by the impulse imparted to its center of gravity, and by many other similar factors. If we knew all these, and if we were clever enough at calculation, we could presumably predict the outcome. But what has all this to do with the assertion that the probability of tails is one half? One could say that all those conditions which determine the outcome "heads" are just as likely as all those conditions which determine the outcome "tails." But is this not saying the same thing in other words? What does "likely" mean?

Only when many tosses are made, does "probability one half" acquire demonstrable meaning, namely, that the *frequency* of tails will be approximately one half. This "approximately" can be made more precise but only at the cost of invoking once more the undemonstrable concept "probability." We can calculate the *probability* that the frequency of tails will differ from one half by any stated amount in a given number of tosses, but then we have completed the cycle—we seem to be back where we started. Yet, not quite, really. These probabilities of departure by some stated amount become smaller and smaller as the number of tosses increases. Omitting the mathematical technicalities, we can say that the Law of Large Numbers asserts the following: the probability of any specified departure from the "expected" relative frequency of an event (no matter how small the departure specified) becomes smaller and smaller as the number of tosses becomes larger and larger. Therefore, we can ultimately make a prediction without invoking a probability, namely, "We are practically certain that given a sufficient number of tosses of a fair coin, tails will occur approximately half the time within a very narrow margin of error."

Even here the difficulty has not disappeared. For what is a "fair" coin? The only operational answer (that is, an answer in terms of demonstrable criterion) is this: "A coin which comes up heads half the time in a sufficiently large number of tosses is a fair coin." Again we have completed a cycle. We started out by predicting what a fair coin will do and ended by defining a fair coin as one which does what it has been predicted to do. But these are philosophical difficulties, which have no bearing on the practical usefulness of the Law of Large Numbers. The law obviously works like any law of nature and can be relied upon. It provides a bridge from the (practical) indeterminacy of most single events on the small scale to the (practical) certainty of the total effect of a large conglomeration of such events.

With the advent of statistical mechanics, the method of probability calculation was added to the standard kit of the physicist's mathematical tools. It was shown that many of the laws of physics were really not deterministic laws at all (in the sense that the laws of mechanics or electrodynamics were thought to be deterministic) but only consequences of the Law of Large Numbers.

Thus, the Law of Large Numbers provides a philosophical base for the extension of the determinist view even to situations where a determinism of the fundamental sort cannot be shown to apply, provided one deals with sufficiently large numbers of such events. It seems reasonable, therefore, to extend this kind of determinism to theories of human behavior. This is what Richardson and other builders of mathematical theories of mass behavior essentially do. Theirs need not be the determinism of strict causality. It does not use the argument that free will does not exist, supposedly because all our actions and even our awareness of actions are determined by physical events which are subjected to strict causality. It side-steps the question of whether causality does or does not pertain to individual behavior, because the behavior of the individual in particular instances is irrelevant in determining the behavior of a mass of individuals over a stretch of time, just as the mechanical forces acting on a specific toss of a coin are irrelevant in determining the frequency with which the coin will fall tails. The large-scale determinism has nothing to do with small-scale determinism or indeterminism. Therefore, the "free will" argument is irrelevant to the question of whether large-scale human behavior follows deterministic laws. Such laws are equally compatible with the existence or the nonexistence of "free will" in the individual, however one wishes to define "free will."

So much, I think, is clear. The irrelevancy of the individual's feeling of freedom to the determinism of mass behavior is demonstrable in the case of every "ordinary" individual. Neither you nor I can appreciably change the volume of traffic on Triborough Bridge; so our individual decisions to go there or not to go there play no part in the regular ebb and flow of traffic. The larger the scale of events, the less impact an "ordinary" individual can have on them. Using the language of physics, we might say that the inertia of the mass is too large to be affected by a randomly applied small impact.

But what about sensitive points, where such impacts can be "amplified"? What about the individuals who seem to control decisions which bring the organized apparatus of social coercion into motion? Do the individuals who seem to have the choice of waging war or making peace, do *they* have real power to move large masses of people, or is that power only an illusion? What is the role of the genius in organizing and directing large-scale human events? Carlyle, for one, thought that the man of genius played a decisive role in human history (13).

Tolstoy explicitly denied this role. In the concluding chapter of *War and Peace* he argues that "free will," at least in those matters which determine large-scale events, that is, the free will of leaders to make momentous decisions affecting millions, is an illusion.

Tolstoy argues by analogy. It took a long time to get used to the idea that the earth moves. The idea contradicted not only the doctrines established by the Church but also our immediate sensations. We *felt* that the earth stood still, and we *saw* the heavenly bodies moving around us. To deny the immobility of the earth was to deny the validity of immediate experience, the teachings of religion and of revered philosophers, and common sense itself. Nevertheless, such a denial had to be made if the motions of the heavenly bodies were to *make sense*. Similarly, Tolstoy argues, no matter how convincing inwardly is our sense of personal freedom, including this sense in powerful individuals, who supposedly influence historical events, this too is an egocentric illusion, like the conviction that we stand still while the starry heavens rotate around us. Indeed, Tolstoy concludes, the individuals at the pinnacle of power are the least free among us, being tools of historical forces.

What are the historical forces, then? Hegel believed them to be supernatural. Marx thought he saw them in the interplay of economic relations. Toynbee and Spengler thought of civilizations as organisms which go through definite states of development, growth, maturity, senescence, and death (121, 113). In the mathematical approach to the theory of mass behavior, there is no need to reify these "forces." The laws postulated or derived in a mathematical theory are only relations among quantities. These relations can be viewed as deterministic, in spite of the indeterminism of the minute events which compose the large events described by these quantities.

What role does the leader play in these chaotic interactions of minute events which add up to gross trends, explosive changes, upsurges, and declines of civilizations? The proponents of mathematical theories do not say. The equations are similar to those governing chemical reactions (which are determined by random impacts among the molecules) or those of the population fluctuations studied in ecology, also gross results of seemingly random interactions of organisms with each other and with the environment, or those of mathematical economics.

Is it right to neglect the role of leadership and of power and to treat human affairs as subjected to blind forces? There is only one reasonable answer: we do not know. Any argument on one side or another will reflect only the relative emphasis given to "common sense" (which stems from our inner conviction that we can choose, so that a man in power can choose how to influence large-scale events) or to the supremacy of determinism as reflected in either the organismic development of societies or simply in the operation of the Law of Large Numbers.

The common sense view says:

"Does not the alternative of war or peace and therefore our future history depend on whether the people responsible for decisions are or are not able to make certain agreements and whether they do or do not keep the agreements? Where power is concentrated in few individuals, does not the destiny of a state depend on what the outlook of these leaders happens to be? Suppose Hitler had been admitted to the art academy in Vienna. Might he not have become a painter of pictures instead of houses and, having found satisfaction in this work, might he not have remained historically obscure? Would not the history of Germany and therefore of the world have been different under a different leadership? Suppose Stalin had not succumbed to paranoid delusions. Could not the cold war have been settled or perhaps prevented altogether?"

There are no reliable answers to these questions, because there is no way of verifying "what would have been" on a historical scale. We can never turn the clock back, nor reproduce identical conditions.

The determinist view says:

"The greater the scale of events, the more regular and predictable are the events. Human affairs have no influence on cosmic history. The galaxies will continue their evolution; the sun will run the usual life of a star. When it becomes either somewhat hotter or somewhat cooler, as it must, life on earth will cease, no matter what men will do in their brief history.

So much anyone will grant. Well, let us look at what concerns us somewhat more. Let us look at the history of life on this planet. Certainly, the history of all organisms has run a course quite independent of the trials and tribulations of individual organisms. Certain conditions appear, favoring a certain class of life, and that class flourishes. Conditions change, and that form of life declines and finally vanishes. Why should the course of human history be an exception?

"Oh, yes, *from the inside* it looks to us as if we can influence our history by decisions. But how do we know how things look from the inside of any animal. May it not be that to a hypothetical superhuman intelligence our history appears as an orderly process playing itself out? During the glaciations conditions favored a certain kind of biological adaptation, namely, flexibility of behavior patterns and an accumulation of experience in a 'collective memory.' This adaptation appeared in certain primates who invented speech and symbolic communication, the instruments of collective memory. One species, *Homo sapiens,* profited by the possession of this instrument and began to proliferate. The species is still proliferating, now at an explosive rate. The decision to have or not to have children is presumably everyone's, but whatever you or I decide to do or not to do, the population will probably continue to grow at a tremendously accelerated rate.

"Remember 'from the inside' it does not look like the operation of gross trends acting on the whole species. From the inside, the 'causes of procreation' look like sexual passion or religious conviction or love of children. But how do we know how the world looks from the inside of any animal that seemingly goes about its business and unknowingly contributes in its minute way to the well-charted history of its species?

"Now let us look at conflict. Here are two bucks fighting for a female. This is the way it appears to us, because we are sometimes in a similar situation. We project and are tempted to impute to this fight the same meaning that governs similar conflicts among us. We see such a conflict 'from the inside.' But a biologist views this event as a behavior pattern which has been selected for in the deer, because it has survival value: it insures that the stronger deer will have more progeny.

"It sometimes happens that a behavior pattern originally adaptive becomes maladaptive when conditions change. Exploratory behavior may serve a mink well, until the trappers arrive; then this same inclination 'to explore' may lead to extinction. Let us look at our own large-scale conflicts, wars. How do we know that war is not a built-in adaptation which originally served well in keeping population down or in insuring the propagation of the stronger races but has simply become maladaptive and now threatens the race with extinction? There is no guarantee that species characteristics, which have ceased to be adaptive, can be simply reversed. When sheer bulk became maladaptive for the giant reptiles of the Mesozoic, they could do nothing about it. It was too late. They had to go.

"Or, perhaps, on the contrary, war is still 'adaptive,' like the mass suicide of the lemmings, who periodically swim out from the Norwegian shores in the ocean to drown? It does not look that way from the inside. War looks to some people as an unmitigated evil, to others as a necessary evil, to still others an an opportunity to practice their talents. But is it not conceivable that these subjective attitudes are irrelevant to the nature of war as a biological phenomenon characteristic of a certain species, namely us, just as the subjective conception of sex (with all its sublimations) is irrelevant to its objective meaning as an instrument of species preservation?

"Perhaps the biological determinism motive is not justified in the case of *Homo sapiens*. Perhaps his culturally conditioned attitudes overshadow the biological base of his psyche. Well and good. The argument does not suffer if the emphasis shifts toward the cultural determinants of large-scale behavior.

Cultures have been known to become extinct when certain patterns, originally adaptive, became maladaptive. The people of those cultures knew that they were becoming culturally extinct; yet they could do nothing about it. It seems that individual awareness is of little consequence in large-scale trends.

"If this is so, is it not reasonable to suppose that individual men or so-called organizations of men are powerless to start *or* to stop wars; that wars and other large-scale processes of human history are determined by conditions too pervasive, too cosmic, to be affected by conscious effort?

"It is not easy to grant this possibility, but this is largely because we are so emotionally involved in this subject, as we once were in the question of the earth's motion. To see this clearly, consider the equally reasonable 'optimistic' view instead of the pessimistic one just stated. Suppose the human species, being endowed with an unsurpassed power of co-operation, flourishes *in spite* of periodic setbacks of wars. The notion may seem absurd against the background of continuous intraspecies mortal combat, but remember we are speaking only of the very large effects. This cohesive power may have recently increased to the point where wars have become impossible. In spite of the seeming readiness of statesmen to start wars, because of the way statesmen picture the past and the future, they are not *able* to do so: they can no longer set the apparatus in motion. They are not free to do this any more than most of us are not 'free' to commit suicide, although we have the freedom to toy with the idea. It may be easier for most people to accept this view than the opposite one. But it is no more and no less reasonable than the other. And it is equally deterministic.

"If we take a more neutral subject, we see that it is still easier to grant the operation of forces too large to control; easier even than to grant the 'optimistic' view on war, because granting the 'optimistic' view, we cannot escape the feeling that the 'pessimistic' one is also reasonable; and that one is too painful to contemplate. Take, then, the evolution of languages. Changes in vocabulary, pronunciation, grammar, etc., go on, according to their own laws (many of which have already been discovered by the linguists), and no one, no matter how 'powerful,' can do much about this process. Secular changes in language structure are good examples of irresistible secular trends in human behavior (37).

"If such irresistible trends are the rule, the things to study in large-scale human history are not patterns of decisions, motivations, power distributions, and all the other things that the social scientists and historians are ordinarily concerned with, but rather the gross statistical laws which determine the large waves of historical events. The events, seemingly governed by 'decisions,' are only small ripples on those large waves."

This is the determinist view in its extreme form.

This thesis can be neither proved nor disproved. The only honest judgment of it must be the acknowledgment of ignorance: we do not know to what extent this view is valid, nor even how to test its validity.

CRITIQUE OF DETERMINISM

We have presented the determinist view of history deliberately in its extreme form in order to convey most of its flavor. Richardson, whose approach to a theory of war we have examined, does not take this extreme position. Judging by his writings, he would not argue that war is a cosmic phenomenon, whose control by human beings is an illusion (like the illusion that many preliterate peoples entertain that they can control the weather by incantations). Richardson does imply, however, that the prevention of wars, if it does become possible, will come about only through our understanding of the "cosmic-like" forces that make for war. The closest analogues to war in Richardson's estimation are epidemics and certain dynamical systems with positive and negative feedbacks.[33] Both are characterized by certain regions of stability and instability. Epidemics, explosions, the breakdowns of dynamical systems occur when the bounds of stability are overstepped. A knowledge of such conditions has enabled man to control epidemics and to design stable dynamic systems in technology. It is even possible that increased knowledge of economic dynamics has made the control of violent economic fluctuations feasible. Richardson views the future control of violent conflicts as an accomplishment of a similar nature. He thus implicitly subscribes to the old Hegelian dictum: "Freedom is the recognition of necessity"—the knowledge of what cannot be done enables us to do the things we can.

A criticism of Richardson's approaches to large-scale conflict (taken as representative of several similar approaches to mass behavior) should be done on two levels—the conceptual and the technical. In technical criticism, questions of this sort are raised: Are the mathematical tools used in the analysis appropriate? Are the estimates of the parameters reliable? Are the quantities expressed by the variables meaningfully measurable? What role can chance be expected to play in the observed coincidences between theory and observation? Samples of such criticism were offered in Chapter II. Such and similar questions can be raised about the material of Chapters III and IV. In particular, how suitable is the bimolecular reaction model for a theory of attitude epidemics? If it is suitable, is it not essentially by-passed in Richardson's treatment, when he introduces drastic simplifications so as to reduce his nonlinear differential equations to linear ones or to the simplest nonlinear ones (the logistic equation)?

Conceptual criticism strikes deeper. It raises the question not of the competence of the method of social physics but of its relevance. Granted that the method is suitable for describing and even predicting certain phenomena, does it get at what really matters?

To see the import of this question, suppose we grant what the determinist says about the inexorable Law of Large Numbers which will always be reflected in human affairs, if human affairs are taken on a large enough scale. Suppose now we apply this philosophy to the investigation of some form of human behavior, say the make-believe conflict called chess. Suppose we are entirely ignorant of the rules of that game and that after having watched many games we still cannot find any regularity in what we observe. We are about to give up trying to understand what is going on, when the Social Physicist comes upon the scene and delivers his lecture.

"You are watching through a lens with too high a resolving power," he tells us. "You don't see the forest for the trees. To understand these events, you must get some distance. Forget the individual movements of the pieces across the board. They don't make much difference in the large range over-all effects. Only there will you find regularities. Let me show you the results of many years' research. I have tabulated some ten thousand games. Here is a depletion curve for the number of pieces left on the board. See, it can be derived from a pair of differential equations, in which the rate of depletion of each class, black and white, is assumed to be a certain function of the numbers of black and white pieces on the board. The data fit the theory with amazing accuracy.

"Here also are masses of statistics, showing the frequency distributions of moves of each type of piece; correlations between moves by various types of pieces; distributions of lengths of games; correlations of frequencies of wins by White and Black with the lengths of games; percentage of draws; distributions of the numbers of pieces left to White and to Black at the end of the game; distributions of the number of moves elapsed before the first capture; same for after the last capture . . . All these statistics are remarkably stable over several samples of one thousand games each: the numbers agree to three decimal places. This shows that chess can be studied by the methods of exact science and in some cases even by theoretical deduction, because some of the distributions can be deduced from simple postulates involving probabilities of events. Of what relevance, then, is the 'understanding' of what goes on in any particular game?"

"Yes," we would be inclined to mutter, "but is what you have studied chess?"

The student of international politics, confronted with the findings of the social physicist, even very accurate ones, may well ask the same kind of question. Granted that with refined methods, the social physicist could deduce "amazingly" accurate descriptions of the course of armament races, of war-mood epidemics, of casualty curves, etc., the student of international politics may still be unimpressed. His preoccupation is with moves and with countermoves, with threats and feints, in short with strategy. He is interested in whether Austria-Hungary had the right sense of timing when she annexed Bosnia and Herzegovina in 1908; in whether the violation of Belgian neutrality was indeed the decisive factor in bringing Great Britain into World War I; in the motivations behind the intervention on the part of Germany and the U.S.S.R. and behind the nonintervention on the part of the Western Powers in the Spanish Civil War; in the efficacy of nuclear weapons as deterrents, etc., etc.

The social physicist might ask whether the most intimate knowledge of all these matters can give the political scientist the power to predict events, and the political scientist must answer honestly that it probably cannot.

"But prediction is not the only yardstick of knowledge," the political scientist can reply. "My task is to *understand* what is going on."

"What is to understand unless it is to be able to predict? How do you know you understand, if you cannot predict?" the physics-oriented scientist persists.

"Not so," counters the other. "The prediction of the moves of chess may be quite poor; yet it is obvious what is meant by understanding chess, not only in the sense of knowing the rules but also in a deeper sense of appreciating the principles of strategy and, perhaps, the aesthetic aspect of the game. What is 'real' chess depends on whether you are the chess board, a chess piece, or a player."

This is an old, old argument between the partisans of formally rigorously stated knowledge and those of intuitive, innerly felt knowledge. In Part II we will examine a point of view, from which both of our protagonists will appear partly right and partly wrong. The position of the social physicist will be partly vindicated, as it will be shown that the sort of thinking which includes rational calculations and considerations of strategy *can* be put into a framework of mathematical theory and thus need not be relegated to "intuition." But the mathematical tools used in this process will appear to have little resemblance to the tools with which the social physicist had been working. The position of the seeker of intuitive understanding of human conflict will be partly vindicated, as it is shown that prediction in the ordinary sense is not the only criterion of knowledge and understanding. But also the intuitive approach to traditional descriptions of human affairs will be found inadequate even for "intuitive" understanding or for common-sense conclusions.

PART II
THE LOGIC OF STRATEGY

"Where are you going?"
"To Minsk."
"Shame on you! You say this to make me think you are
going to Pinsk. But I happen to know you *are* going
to Minsk."—*A JEWISH ANECDOTE*

No one today will doubt the intensity, though he may dislike
the color, of the (shall I say) sodium light cast by statistical
mathematics, direct descendant of games of chance, upon the
social sciences. Perhaps in another three hundred years'
time economic and political and other branches of moral
philosophy will bask in radiation from a source—theory of games
of strategy—whose prototype was kindled round the poker
tables of Princeton.—*R. B. BRAITHWAITE*

CHAPTER VI

GAME THEORY AND
ITS FORERUNNER,
GAMBLING THEORY

IN SOCIAL PHYSICS, most of what we feel intuitively to be of importance in human behavior has been omitted. "From the inside" the causes of our actions appear to be impulses, desires, and goals. But these impulses and goals of the individual are lost in the equations of social physics, which typically describe the actions and interactions of large "blind" masses. They describe what would happen if people did not stop to think.

In short, social physics ignores "rationality" or at least the relevance of individual rationality or even of individual consciousness to large-scale human affairs. If it poses a consciousness at all, it attributes it not to individuals but to much larger aggregates, and even there the consciousness is of a very limited kind. The Marxist "class consciousness," for example, is little more than an appetite for the largest possible share of wealth produced by society; or a conviction that the class in question is destined to become dominant.

When we think of an individual's consciousness, especially consciousness of choice, an ingredient of rationality, we have in mind something more complex. Usually, an individual is faced in a given situation with a certain number of choices, that is, alternative courses of action. Each course is likely to lead to a consequence or to one of several possible consequences. We call an individual rational if he takes into account the possible consequences of each of the courses of action open to him; if he is aware of a certain preference order among the consequences and accordingly chooses the course of action which, in his estimation, is likely to lead to the most preferred consequence. Sometimes the outcome will depend not only on the course of action that this individual will choose but also on courses of action which other individuals will choose, over whom he may have no control. In that case, the preferences of those other individuals for the different outcomes may differ from his. We usually think of an individual as rational if he takes these matters into account.

A familiar example of such rationality is seen in the way able players play games of strategy, for example checkers. For each player, there are three relevant outcomes: win, draw, and lose. A player prefers win to draw and draw to lose, and so does his opponent, except that for the opponent the outcomes are reversed. Each player then makes his choice of moves on the basis of reasoning which goes something like this: "If I do this, he is likely to do that, in which case I will have a choice of this or that . . ." We tend to think of a player as rational if he, in turn, imputes rationality to his opponent. To assume that the opponent will make the error we want him to make is not usually realistic, at least not without some evidence of the other's inferior skill.

Games of strategy, then, offer a good model of rational behavior of people in situations where (1) there are conflicts of interest; (2) a number of alternatives are open at each phase of the situation; (3) people are in a position to estimate consequences of their choices, taking into consideration the very important circumstance that outcomes are determined not only by one's own choices but also by the choices of others, over whom one has no control.

Note that the concepts involved in this definition, such as "choice," "awareness of possible consequences," "preference for outcomes," etc., have no counterpart in the framework of thought which makes up physics and, by extension, social physics. "Causality" or the impulse for immediate change, as it is understood in physics, always acts on the "here and now." The thrown stone changes its speed and direction at a given moment, because it is acted upon by a force which has a given magnitude and direction *at that moment*. The stone has no preference for any of its ultimate states, nor could it do anything about it if it had. Also in social physics a "mass" or a "system" is in a certain state, has a certain configuration, and associated with that state are "forces" which determine the immediate minute changes and so determine the next state. Concepts of choice, calculation of outcomes, and preference are extraneous to social physics.

In the last decade and a half, an entirely new mathematical approach to a theory of conflict has arisen, called the theory of games.[34] The word "game" in this context is not meant to imply a lack of seriousness (which might be associated with its usual meaning) but rather the idea that so-called "parlor games," more appropriately called "games of strategy," offer the purest examples of situations which are taken as prototypes in this new theory of conflict. In these situations, "rationality" is central. In a way, then, the theory of games is an approach diametrically opposed to that of social physics. In what follows, we shall examine the essentials of that theory, especially its relevance to the psychology and, I think, to the ethics of conflict and co-operation.

A parlor game represents a limited portion of "life" in which it is possible (in principle) to list all the things that can happen. The actual number of possible events is usually vast beyond comprehension, even in simple games, but only a fraction of these events is normally of interest. So it is not too much of an exaggeration to say that in a parlor game all eventualities can (in principle) be taken into account. The idealized player of such a game can be supposed to be "omniscient."

The limits of what can happen are set by the rules of the game. Typically, the course of the game is a sequence of "moves" made by the players in some prescribed order, which may or may not depend on the outcomes of the preceding moves. (E.g., in many card games, the play is up to the player who took the last trick; but in chess moves are made alternately without regard for the outcomes.) In many games we may imagine a fictitious player called Chance, who now and then makes his move. In game theory, the term "move" means not the actual act but the range of choices open to the player whose move it is. For example, in tick-tack-toe, the first "move" is the first player's choice of nine boxes where to put his first mark; the second move is the second player's choice of eight boxes for his, etc. The first move in chess offers twenty choices. Or, if we wish to define the first move in chess as the toss of a coin, which decides who is to play White, then Chance has the first move. This move offers just two choices, and it is Chance's only move in chess. On the other hand, in poker, if we assign to Chance the first move, which is the arrangement of the shuffled deck, then Chance has on this move about one hundred million trillion trillion trillion trillion trillion choices, because this is the number of possible ways that the fifty-two card deck can be arranged.

Wherever combinations or permutations of things must be counted, fantastically large numbers are bound to occur. This should not be of itself a major concern to the theoretician. The vastness of the numbers of combinations does not prevent him from calculating by relatively simple means the probabilities of combinations which are of interest. In poker, for example, it is a simple matter to compute the occurrence probabilities of flushes, straights, pairs, etc., and also the probabilities of filling these combinations, given the cards on hand. There are situations where "omniscience" means nothing more impressive than a knowledge of such probabilities, and "rationality" means simply taking these probabilities into account when making choices.

It would be disastrous, however, for a poker player to decide his moves (e.g., to raise or not to raise, how many cards to draw, etc.) only on the basis of these probabilities. If he did this, his manner of playing would be consistent, and his hand could be reasonably inferred from his play to his permanent disadvantage. In making his decisions, the poker player must remember that these decisions may give information to the opponent and that the opponent may put this information to use. The necessity of taking an intelligent opponent into account is what distinguishes game theory proper from the much simpler theory of gambling. This latter, much older theory offers a good vantage point for understanding the vastly more sophisticated game theory, and so we shall examine some principles of gambling theory first.

GAMBLING THEORY

In a gamble, there is, strictly speaking, no opponent, and no *strategic* skill is required in making rational gambles. The only rational act in a gamble is the calculation of odds. However, the theory of gambling can be conveniently considered as a "one-person game" or as a "game against nature." Some of the concepts fundamental in game theory (e.g., mathematical expectation, utility) can be advantageously introduced on the simpler level of gambling theory.

The theory of gambling is instructive in two other ways. First, it is an excellent illustration of how a mathematical theory of a humble origin (seemingly concerned with situations of no great significance) developed into a method which has permeated almost all branches of mathematicized science. Second, the discrepancy between the normative[35] theory of gambling and the observed gambling behavior of real people leads to a natural point of entry into the psychology of choice in risky situations.

The importance of game theory can be analogously forecast. It too has had humble beginnings ("around the poker tables of Princeton," as someone has put it) and has already started to seep through many branches of behavioral science as the embodiment of a method which has stripped "conflict of interest" to its barest essentials. Next, an attempt to derive a normative theory has led to numerous logical difficulties, paradoxes, etc., which, in the opinion of some, reveal the whole rich content of this aspect of behavior, as seen in the light of rigorous theoretical development.

ODDS

The central problem of gambling theory is to determine the odds of some event. Some such problems offer a mathematical challenge. If a pair of dice is thrown again and again, a pair of sixes is bound to occur sometime. But when? This question has no definite answer. We can only talk about the chance that the pair of sixes will occur on a particular throw or within so many throws. We can also calculate the average number of throws we can expect before the occurrence of this pair. All this knowledge is useful in making a decision of whether or not to accept a bet on the event at given odds.

Suppose, for example, one is offered even money that a pair of sixes will *not* occur by the 24th throw. Ought we accept this bet? "Common sense" reasoning might go something like this. The odds against a double six are 35 to 1. So we have a reasonable expectation of getting a double six once in every 36 throws. Should we not then expect that there is an even chance that it will come before or after the 18th throw? Therefore even money that it will come before the 24th throw ought to be a good bet. But it isn't. In a moment we will take a closer look at this situation which has historical significance. But first let us look at another.

There are 40 people at a party. Someone offers even money that no two have the same birthday. Should we accept the bet? "Common sense" analysis may suggest that we should not. The odds against two people having the same birthday are about 364 to 1. It seems that the odds against any two among forty having the same birthday should still be considerable. But this is not so. The odds are actually heavily *in favor* of a coincidence of birthdays among forty people.

Common sense is not powerful enough to deal with such problems effectively. In the seventeenth century, a French gambler Chevalier de Méré, was consistently losing by betting even money that a pair of sixes will come up on or before the 24th throw. His predicament, communicated to the mathematician Pascal, marks the beginning of systematic investigation of probability as a mathematical discipline.[36]

Chevalier de Méré, in arguing that there ought to be at least an even chance for the double six to come up by the 24th throw went beyond the simple-minded argument we made above. He tried a calculation, but, as we shall see, his reasoning was not sufficiently rigorous. He had been previously winning (on the average) by offering even money that if a *single* die is thrown, the six will come up by the fourth throw. Taking his average win as an indication that there is better than even chance for this event, he extended the argument to the pair of dice as follows. The chance of a six coming up on a single die is $\frac{1}{6}$ (correct). The chance of a double six coming up on a pair of dice is $\frac{1}{36}$ (correct). Therefore, the chance of the "favorable event" has been reduced by a factor of 6 from the first situation to the second (correct). Therefore if the run is *lengthened* by a factor of 6 ($4 \times 6 = 24$), the six-fold reduction ought to be canceled, and the odds of a double six by the 24th throw ought to be the same as the odds of a single six by the fourth throw of a single die (wrong!).

We must now show (as Pascal presumably did) that De Méré was wrong. Consider the chance of *not* throwing a six on a single throw of a single die. This is $5/6$. If we assume that whatever happens on one throw has no influence on what happens on any of the following throws, then the chance of not throwing a single six on four consecutive throws is $(5/6)^4 = 625/1296$. This is De Méré's chance of losing in the single die game. Therefore his chance of winning in that game is obtained by subtracting $625/1296$ from 1 or $671/1296$. This is more than one half, and this is why De Méré was winning with the single die. Now apply the same argument to the two-dice game. The chance of not making a double six in 24 throws is $(35/36)^{24}$. Subtracting this from 1 gives about 0.48, which is less than one half. The rigorous argument leads to a conclusion opposed to that of the common sense argument.

Now take the coincident birthday bet. Pick an arbitrary person and note that the chance that some other person's birthday does *not* coincide with his is $364/365$. Now the chance that a third person's birthday does not coincide with that of *either* of the first two is $363/365$, because only 363 days are different from both birthdays. Continuing in this way, we see that the chance that no two birthdays coincide in a party of forty is the product of these 39 fractions:

$$\frac{364}{365} \times \frac{363}{365} \times \frac{362}{365} \times \cdots\cdots \times \frac{326}{365}$$

This number is about $1/8$. Therefore, the odds against this happening (i.e., the odds *in favor* of at least one coincidence of birthdays) are about 7 to 1.

EXPECTATION

The analysis of De Méré's problem shows that De Méré should make even money bets on a six coming up by the fourth throw of a single die, but that he should not make such bets on a double six coming up by the 24th throw of two dice. On what basis can such advice be given? Later developments of probability theory showed how the probabilities of single events could be translated into "expectations" over long sequences of such events. The definition of expectation and the proofs of the relevant theorems involve a technical discussion, which we will not pursue here. Roughly, if the probability of an event in a certain context is p, we can reasonably expect that in the long run in this context, the event will occur a p-th fraction of the time. Therefore if we bet x dollars on the event, and our opponent bets y dollars on the contrary event, then we can expect to win py dollars per bet and to lose $(1 - p) x$ dollars per bet. Our net expected win in the long run will be $py - (1 - p) x$ dollars. If this number is positive, the bet is justified, not otherwise. The expectation will be positive if $py > (1 - p) x$ or if $p/(1 - p) > x/y$. Therefore, he who bets on an event of probability p can expect to come out ahead in the long run if the odds he offers are less than $p/(1 - p)$. In particular, if $p = \frac{1}{2}$, the cutting point is even odds.

Actually, this is the way gambling houses operate. In all "honest" houses, the odds favor the house by a small margin. Any margin will guarantee a long-run win. Usually, the margins are made small so as to make the bets seem attractive to the suckers. Also the conditions of many gambles are made deliberately complicated, so that the odds favoring the house are not obvious (although any reasonable person must assume that the odds always favor the house).

Is this, then, the one paramount rule of "rational" gambling: always accept bets in which the odds are in your favor and only those? Let us look more closely.

A man's life savings amount to $1000. He is offered 100 to 1 odds if he puts this amount on a single turn of the roulette wheel. The odds against any number in a single-zero roulette wheel are 36/1. If it is "reasonable" to accept bets which offer positive expected gain, the man should accept the offer. He stands to win $100,000 with probability 1/37 and to lose $1000 with probability 36/37. His expectation, therefore, is

$$100,000/37 - 36,000/37 = 64,000/37 = \$1729.72$$

This is a substantial positive expectation. Common sense, however, tells us (at least most of us will agree) that it is not reasonable to risk one's life savings in such a situation, in spite of the favorable odds.

Take another example. Practically all owners of houses carry fire insurance. This sort of insurance is essentially a wager, in which the insured bets the yearly premium against the amount for which the house is insured that his house will burn down within a year. Most of the time the insured "loses" his bet. But if the house does burn down, he "wins" it. The odds against the fire certainly exceed the odds of the bet; otherwise the insurance companies would soon go bankrupt. Therefore, according to the criterion of expected gain, taking out fire insurance is not "reasonable." Yet common sense says that it is.

A while ago, when the mathematical argument disagreed with the common-sense conclusion, we appeared to side with the mathematical argument, we hope to the reader's satisfaction. Here, however, it would be rash for us to ask the reader to accept the conclusions of the mathematical argument against those of the common-sense arguments. The difference between the two situations is of crucial importance. A thorough understanding of it will help us to understand the much more involved (but similar) arguments pertaining to game theory proper.

In De Méré's problem, we tacitly assumed that the game would continue over many throws of the dice. Therefore, the expected gain could reasonably be assumed to be the actual gain in the long run. In the single turn of the roulette wheel, however, the expected gain will certainly not be translated into actual gain. The gambler will either win $100,000 (with probability 1/37) or he will lose $1000 (with probability 36/37). In neither case will he win his "expected" $1729.72. What meaning, then, is to be assigned to this purely theoretical amount of gain? It may be the determinant of a "policy," such as gambling houses adopt. But a mathematical theory is never in a position to prescribe a *basic* policy. All mathematical theory can do is prescribe a course of action after a basic policy of betting, whatever it is, has been chosen. There are situations in which it is wise to choose the policy of betting wherever the expected gain is positive, and there are other situations where it is not wise to do so. We preferred the results of the mathematical argument in our first examples, but only because we had tacitly assumed that we should follow the policy of betting whenever the expected gain was positive. In our roulette wheel and insurance examples, we are not at all sure whether it is wise to extend this policy to those circumstances. This question is about standards of judgment, not a mathematical question.

However, mathematical arguments can sometimes help us *uncover* the standards by which we guide our actions. In other words, instead of asking, "Given these standards, how should a man behave?" we can ask "Given that a man behaves in this way, what must his standards be if he is rational?"

The following interesting gamble illustrates the point. A coin is tossed. If a head turns up, you win 1¢. If two heads turn up in succession, you win 1¢ + 2¢ = 3¢. If three heads turn up in succession, you win 1¢ + 2¢ + 4¢ = 7¢, etc. For each additional head that turns up *in a continuous run,* you win twice the amount you won on the preceding heads. Once a tail turns up, the game is over. You can start a new game, with a win of 1¢ if a head turns up the first time, etc. You may play any number of games. Question: how much should you be willing to pay for each game? Try this procedure with a coin to assure yourself that if you pay 2¢ per game, you will be ahead in a very short time. If you have patience, you can assure yourself that even at a nickel a game, you will still come out ahead eventually. What is the limit? Would you play a dime a game? Would you pay a dollar? How about a million dollars?

Note that you are guaranteed the opportunity to play as many games as you like. You may also assume that you have unlimited credit, so that you need not fear that you will be ruined before you can expect to gain. Therefore it seems that the "expected gain" criterion should apply. Now by the expected gain criterion (believe it or not, but this is what a straightforward calculation shows) you should be willing to pay *any amount* per game. No matter what you pay, even if a million dollars per game, *eventually* you ought to come out ahead. This is so because eventually you are bound to get a very long run of heads, in which your winnings, doubled with each head, will mount so astronomically that all your losses will be wiped out. This event will happen no matter what losses have been accumulated. Of course *when* this will happen will depend on how much you pay per game. If you pay a fairly large amount, this may come after the sun has become a ball of ashes; so this knowledge that you cannot possibly lose in the long run has little practical value. But the mathematical point of view is such that the purely logical aspects of the problem are investigated first without the encumbrance of practical considerations. It is always possible to take the practical considerations into account later. It keeps our thinking clear to keep them out for the time being.

UTILITY

The Swiss mathematician Daniel Bernoulli posed the following problem inspired by the hypothetical game just described (6). What rule besides the expected gain rule can we propose in the light of which it will appear reasonable to pay a moderate amount for each game of this sort but unreasonable to pay a large amount? From this question, the notion of utility was born. The notion has had a lively history of philosophical controversy. John von Neumann, the creator of game theory, rescued this concept from near-oblivion into which it had fallen and has used it as one of the cornerstones of game theory. But let us return to the ideas of Bernoulli.

Bernoulli argued as follows. In gains and losses, it is not the money that counts. It is what money is worth to you. The more money a man has, the less a given increment of money is "worth" to him. In fact, the worth of an increment ought to be inversely proportional to the amount of money a man already has. Therefore, gains and losses ought to be calculated relative to the capital on hand. This puts a "law of diminishing returns" on gains in terms of what the gains are "worth." Under this assumption, Bernoulli was able to show that there is an upper limit to how much one ought to pay for each play of the St. Petersburg Game (as the game described above came to be called) if the expected *utility* (as distinguished from the money gain) was to remain positive.

Bernoulli's assumption that the worth of an increment is inversely proportional to the amount on hand leads to the conclusion that the utility of money is proportional to the logarithm of the amount of money.[37] If we make this assumption, we get a different standard of "rationality" for gambling situations. For example, the man with \$1000 to his name, who is offered 100 to 1 odds on the roulette wheel can calculate the amount he can bet and still break even in terms of expected *utility* return (instead of money return). To do this, he should take for the alternative outcomes his respective utilities of the amounts of money in his possession following a win or a loss. If he bets x dollars, these will be $\log (1000 - x)$, if he loses, and $\log (1000 + 100x)$, if he wins. To break even in utilities, the expected utility following the gamble should equal the utility of what he has before the gamble. This leads to the following equation:

$$\frac{36}{37} \log (1000 - x) + \frac{1}{37} \log (1000 + 100x) = \log (1000)$$

$$(50)$$

You may verify that if $x = \$50$, the left side of this equation is already slightly less than the right side. In other words $\$50$ is already a little too much to bet to break even in expected utility (compared to the utility of the capital on hand). Bets less than about $\$50$, however, give a positive expected utility and so are justified.

We can also calculate the amount he should bet if he wants to maximize his expected utility. This is done by calculating the rate of change of the left side of equation (50) with respect to x and setting this rate equal to zero. The resulting expression solved for x gives the point at which the expected utility stops increasing and begins to decrease, that is, reaches its maximum. We have accordingly

$$\frac{d}{dx} \left[\frac{36}{37} \log (1000 - x) + \frac{1}{37} \log (1000 + 100x) \right]$$

$$= -\frac{36}{37} \frac{1}{1000 - x} + \frac{1}{37} \frac{100}{1000 + 100x} = 0$$

$$x = 17.30$$

According to this scheme, the best decision is to bet $\$17.30$, which, on the face of it, seems not unreasonable. It is *the* best decision if the utility of money is logarithmic, as Bernoulli argued, and if one sticks to the policy of maximizing the expected utility return.

The importance of the utility idea is not that it proposed a policy of risk taking which seemed more in line with common sense than a policy based on the mathematical expectation of money gains. Nor should Bernoulli's logarithmic functions be viewed as a "psychological discovery" that "satisfaction is proportional to the logarithm of the gain."

No, the importance of Bernoulli's idea is in the following question, which it suggests: *Is* there a psychological measure of satisfaction, which, if assumed, will explain the actual behavior of people in risk situations? In other words, suppose that we observe that people do *not* bet consistently so as to maximize expected money returns, even if long-run expectations are justified. Can it be that there is something else which they are trying to maximize, some sort of satisfaction which is partly connected with the actual money return but may not be proportional to the expectation and may be connected with other things, for example, *being* in the risk situation, playing against big odds, etc.? Certainly there is more to winning a pot than the amount in the pot. There is the jingling of the coins, the admiration of the onlookers, the feeling of being "lucky," etc. Perhaps if all of these things are taken into account in some way, the gambling behavior (and more generally all risk behavior) of people can be explained in terms of maximizing some quantity. And if this quantity is different in different people but can be determined for each person or for each class of people, it seems worth while to try to do so: the discovery would be an important psychological finding.[38]

MAXIMIZATION OF UTILITY

The existence of such a quantity, called utility, is assumed in game theory. Specifically, it is assumed that various outcomes (results of choices among alternative courses of action) have different amounts of this quantity associated with them. If the various outcomes are the different payoffs which may accrue in a game, then the mathematical relation between the amount of the actual payoff (if it is measurable) and its utility constitutes the "utility function" of the individual concerned.

Bernoulli, we have seen, assumed that the utility function of money is a logarithmic one. In principle, any kind of function might have been chosen.

It is further assumed in game theory that in every game situation (including gambles) the objective of a "rational" individual is to maximize the utility expectation accruing to him consistently with the constraints of the situation, that is, to get as much of this utility (or of its expectation) as it is possible to get, taking into account the efforts of all the other "rational" participants of the game, who are trying to do the same.

When the possibility of applying game theory to real life is brought up, many point out that this fundamental assumption of game theory reflects only the brutal side of human nature. Is not charity, co-operation, compassion, solidarity, etc., as much a part of being human, such people are likely to ask, as competitiveness and acquisitiveness? To this there are two things to say in reply. First, the "maximization of one's own utility" may have nothing to do with selfishness of the anti-social type. Nothing is said about *how* the outcomes are valued in terms of personal utility. To take an example, suppose an adult plays checkers with a child and prefers to have the child win. There is no contradiction between this charitable impulse and the maximization of utility. We simply assign the maximum utility of the adult to his loss of the game instead of to his win. He can still play so as to obtain this maximum. Or suppose a solidarity of feeling in a group dictates a unanimous decision that certain scarce commodities be rationed only to children and the aged. Then *this* distribution of the commodity commands the maximum utility of each individual, not the one where everything is given to him alone. In other words, the ordering of utilities is always *tautological*. *Whatever* is preferred (whether it seems selfish or altruistic from certain points of view) is assigned the higher utility.

The second point is that often scientific investigations must set aside all questions of morality in order to arrive at some truth. This does not mean that scientific ethics condones immoral acts, nor that there are no limits on what may be actually done in the pursuit of truth. By "setting morality aside" we mean simply pursuing the consequences of assumptions to whatever conclusions they will lead. And so, if we choose to make the assumption that people will behave selfishly and ruthlessly in a given situation, we are bound to derive the consequences of such assumptions. Whether the assumption is justified in real life or not, it is certainly justified in parlor games as they are played among equals. Indeed, the social value of parlor games may be in the very fact that they provide opportunities for completely ruthless behavior in situations which (for mature persons) are sufficiently insulated from real life. "Sportsmanship," that is, the ability to take defeat in games philosophically, is, in a way, a measure of maturity.

It is nevertheless instructive to see to what extent the ruthlessness of parlor games is duplicated in real life conflicts, for example, in economic competition, in politics, and in war. Some feel that the total ruthlessness of the game of strategy is never completely carried over into life situations, not even in war. If this is so, it can be demonstrated only by a thorough analysis of the logical consequences of total ruthlessness.

THE UTILITY SCALE

So much for the assumption of maximization of utility. Its tautological character might lead one to believe that the problem of assigning utilities is solved as soon as the preferences of an individual with respect to a set of outcomes are discovered. The problem, however, is more involved. An ordering of preferences implies an ordering of utilities. But game theory needs more than just an ordering of utilities. The game theorist must assume that he knows also the ratios of the differences of pairs of utilities.

The meaning of this requirement is easiest to demonstrate by an analogy with temperature. It is easy to decide which of two bodies is warmer by just feeling them (provided the difference of warmth is not too small). A set of bodies can be arranged without difficulty in order from the coldest to the warmest. But this knowledge still does not enable us to answer these questions: "Is the difference in warmth between bodies A and B greater than the difference between B and C? What is the ratio of these two differences?" We can answer these questions if we have a temperature *scale,* such as is provided on a thermometer.

Note, however, that there are several such scales. Therefore, it makes no sense to say what the "real" numerical value of the temperature of a body is. The human body registers normally 98.6 on the Fahrenheit scale, but 37 on the Centigrade scale. Neither the zero point nor the size of the degree of the two scales is the same, and so the actual numerical value of the temperature and even the ratios of such numerical values must always be related to a particular scale. For example, the ratio of the temperature of boiling water to that of the human body on the Fahrenheit scale is $212/98.6 = 2.15$; but on the Centigrade scale the same ratio is $100/37 = 2.70$. However *the ratio of two temperature differences* on the two scales will always be the same. For example, let C_1 be the temperature of boiling water on the Centigrade scale, C_2 the temperature of the human body, and C_3 the temperature of freezing water. Then the ratio of $C_1 - C_2$ to $C_2 - C_3$ is $(100 - 37)/(37 - 0) = 1.70$. If F_1, F_2, and F_3 are the corresponding points on the Fahrenheit scale, the ratio of the corresponding differences is $(212 - 98.6)/(98.6 - 32) = 1.70$. We say that the ratio of temperature differences is *invariant* with respect to the different temperature scales. Such scales are called *interval* scales.

The sort of utility measure required in game theory is an interval scale. The zero point and the unit of this scale may be arbitrary. That is to say, it may not be possible to determine the "true" values of utilities by any conceivable experiment, but this is irrelevant. What we *must* be able to determine is the ratio of each pair of utility differences. Then we can assign a zero point and a unit at pleasure. The invariance of ratio differences means that we can apply a "linear transformation" [39] to any utility scale without disturbing any of the experimental results.

Another consequence of the fact that utility scales, as they are used in game theory, are interval scales is that utilities of different people for some outcomes cannot be compared. For example, the well-known rationalization of physical violence used by many parents, "It hurts me more than it hurts you," has no meaning in this context. There is no way of comparing "hurts" of two different individuals. But it would make sense to say, "The ratio of the difference between my regret today and my regret yesterday to the difference between my regret of last Sunday and that of last Friday is twice the analogous ratio of your differences of regrets." Even though we may think that we know what the first statement means and may feel that the second is gibberish, in the light of the meaning of utility, as it is used in the theory of games, the second statement makes sense, and the first does not. An analogy with temperature will make this point clear.

Suppose I talk about the weather with a Martian and I am not sure whether the Martians use the Fahrenheit scale or the Centigrade scale or the Reamur or the Kelvin scales to measure their temperatures. Indeed, it is quite unlikely that the Martians use any of these scales. But it is less unlikely that if they measure temperatures at all, they make their thermometers as we do. That is to say, we may assume that they fix two points (on our thermometers these are usually the freezing and the boiling points of water, but if the Martians have no water, they will use another substance) and subdivide the "thermal distance" between these points into degrees. The assignment of numbers to the two reference temperatures fixes the zero and the unit of the scale. I am saying, therefore, that I can reasonably guess the method which the Martians use to measure temperature, but I do not know either the zero point or the size of their degrees. Now I ask the following question. Can I tell anything to the Martian about our temperature (or can he tell us) that makes sense? Yes, some communications about temperature will make sense to both of us, regardless of the scales we use, but other communications will not.

Assume that the Martian tells me that the temperature on Mars is 32°. This tells me nothing. On the Fahrenheit scale it would be just freezing; on the Centigrade scale it would be hot; on the Reamur scale still hotter; on the Kelvin scale it would be incredibly cold. Nor does this statement make sense: "It is twice as warm today as it was yesterday." But the following statement would make sense: "Our thermometers rose twice as much today between sunrise and noon as they did yesterday in the same period." It makes sense, because if it is true, it would be true no matter what temperature scale was used.

Now comparing utilities of different people is like comparing temperatures on different (unknown) scales. Characteristically, this problem has usually brought ethical questions into the picture. For example, what does it mean to say that one man has sacrificed more than another has gained, if the measures of inner satisfactions are to be applied? Utility has been so defined in game theory as to avoid such questions. To the extent that it is possible to develop game theory on the basis of utility measured on an interval scale, ethical questions pertaining to comparison of interpersonal utilities need not be raised. Eventually, however, the end of the line is reached, and such questions become unavoidable. But then the consideration of such questions enters *perforce,* not because of prior commitments, and hence the questions command more attention in a scientific investigation than they would otherwise.

In closing our discussion of utility, we will briefly indicate how the utility function of an individual can be in principle established on an interval scale.

To fix ideas, let the returns of some game (or some other situation) be in money. Suppose we offer a man a choice of (1) $100 or (2) a fifty-fifty chance of getting $50 or $150.[40] If he is indifferent between the alternatives (1) and (2), then the difference of utilities between $50 and $100 is for him equal to the difference between $100 and $150. But suppose he prefers (2), that is, the gamble. In this case, increase the prize which is offered to him with certainty, say to $110. If he still prefers the gamble, increase it farther. Somewhere along the line, he should change his mind so as to prefer the certain prize, because it stands to reason that he will not prefer the gamble if the *certain* prize is $150.[41] Therefore, at some point before this figure is reached, he will become indifferent between the certain prize and the gamble. Suppose this point is at $120. We assume that each amount has a certain utility for him and that he is trying to maximize his expected utility. Therefore, indifference between the certain $120 and the even chance to get $50 and $150 implies the following equation:

$$u\,(120) = \tfrac{1}{2}\,u\,(50) + \tfrac{1}{2}\,u\,(150) \qquad (51)$$

(Read: The utility of $120 is the same as half the utility of $50 plus half the utility of $150.)

The left side represents the utility (to our man) of $120.

The right side is the expected utility of the gamble. Multiplying each side by 2, we can write equation (51) as

$$2\,u\,(120) = u\,(50) + u\,(150) \qquad (52)$$

or

$$u\,(120) - u\,(50) = u\,(150) - u\,(120) \qquad (53)$$

In other words, the difference between the utility of $120 and that of $50 is equal to the difference between the utility of $150 and that of $120. If we plot the three points so obtained, that is, utility vs. money, the utility curve will appear steeper at the larger money amounts. For this man, the "law of diminishing returns of utility" happens to work in reverse: the more money he has (in this range) the more the increments are worth to him (a quantitative description of greed).

Of course we have established only three points on the man's utility function. To get a fairly complete curve, we must get many points in between. We may find the resulting curve quite erratic. But if the ordering is consistent, the utility function can be in principle established, no matter what the preferences are. For example, there is nothing in utility theory that says that the utility of money increments beyond a certain amount cannot become negative. It is even reasonable to suppose that they do sometimes become negative. Suppose, for example, it were possible to offer a man any amount of money he chose to name. No matter what figure he names, we would have to assume that increments beyond that figure cease to be positive (possibly become negative) for him, because utility is defined in such a way that every decision is made in view of maximizing utility. (It would be interesting to find out what would be the distribution of the "optimum amounts" named in a large sample of some population.)

The method of determining the utility function can be extended to any situation if only preferences can be established among hypothetical gambles involving the outcomes in question. For example, questions of the following kind should always be answerable, if a utility function is to be established: "If, as you say, you would rather be King of Denmark than remain a bachelor and would rather remain a bachelor than see the outbreak of a nuclear war, which would you prefer, to remain a bachelor for certain, or a gamble, where the chances are 99 for you to become King of Denmark vs. 1 for the outbreak of nuclear war (all situations being mutually exclusive)?"

To the extent that such questions are consistently answerable, the events involved in them can be assigned utilities on an interval scale and so a utility function can be defined. The zero point and the unit of this function will, as has been indicated, remain undefined. These can be chosen arbitrarily and the resulting new function will still be consistent with all the answers given to the preference questions. While this gives us freedom in choosing a particular utility scale for some individual, it prevents us from comparing utilities of different individuals.

For most of game theory, this definition of utility is sufficient, and we shall adopt it until further notice. We are now ready to examine some situations pertaining to game theory proper.

CHAPTER VII

ENTER THE FOE

RATIONALITY, we have seen, in the context of making decisions, involves calculations of this sort: "If I do this, that will happen . . . , if I do that, this will happen . . . Since I prefer this to that, I will do this . . ."

Here it is assumed that the consequences of each action are certain. If they are not certain, we can still define rational decision if the probabilities of the outcomes associated with each choice of action are known. For then we can calculate the various expected returns (in terms of utility) and compare these returns. Note that if to each action there corresponds a simple, certain outcome, the exact utility measure is unnecessary: a simple ordering of preferences among the outcomes will determine the choice of action. But if several outcomes may result from some actions, and only their probabilities are known, this ordering of preferences is not enough: one must be able also to order the preference of various *risky* outcomes, and this can be done only if an interval scale of utility is assigned to the outcomes. The probabilities then become weightings in the averaging over the utilities, and the whole decision problem is recast in terms of these averages. But it still remains the same kind of problem.

All this makes sense if in any given situation the world which the decision-maker is facing is *given*. That is to say, the connections between the acts and the consequences and the relevant probabilities are fixed and knowable. The problem of the decision-maker is often to act so as to maximize some number (the expected utility return). Such problems have been long familiar to mathematicians, and routine techniques are available for solving them.[42]

The picture changes radically when the decision-maker faces an opponent who is also rational and informed of all relevant facts (probabilities, etc.), who can also make choices affecting the outcome of the situation, but whose interests (i.e., his ordering of preferences of the outcomes) are not the same. Game theory is concerned with problems of this sort. The associated situations (which we shall soon define more carefully) are called games of strategy or simply games.

There may be any number of players, and the interests of any of them may partly coincide and partly conflict. Also the players may or may not be able to communicate with each other. The simplest possible case is of two players whose interests completely coincide and who can communicate freely. This case is not interesting, because these two players may as well be treated as one (against the "world"). We then have a single decision-maker, whose problems we have touched upon in the preceding chapter.

THE ZERO-SUM GAME WITH SADDLE POINT

The next simplest case is where there are two players, whose interests are diametrically opposed. This situation is called the two-person zero-sum game. Its analysis is the simplest and, in the opinion of some (but not all), is the most basic problem of game theory. The whole remaining theory was originally formulated on the basis of this analysis. Much of the recent critique of game theory, as we shall see, is predominantly a discussion of whether this analysis (unimpeachable from the point of view of its own logic) is a good foundation for a general theory of games.

Suppose first that the outcomes are certain. Suppose also

that each of two opponents in a zero-sum game is to make just one choice among several alternatives, each being ignorant of the choice the other is going to make. Each pair of choices so made determines a payoff to each player. The game is called zero-sum if each of these payoffs is the negative of the other.

Call the players A and B. Player A will have to reason so: "If I do this *and* B does that, this will happen; but if I do this (the same 'this') and B does that (a different 'that'), then that will happen, etc." Player A must take all *pairs* of choices into account. Evidently, the number of such pairs is the number of A's choices multiplied by the number of B's choices. Note that neither player can affect any particular outcome. Although each controls his own choices, he does not control the choices of his opponent. If the probabilities of the opponent's choices were known, the problem would reduce to a gamble, that is, a game against a device (like a pair of dice, a roulette wheel, etc.) whose "habits," meaning the probabilities of its "choices," are known. But in a real two-person game, A has no right to assume that B makes his choices by drawing lots. The assumption of game theory is that the players are rational. Player A should therefore assume that B reasons exactly as he himself does: "If I do this and A does that, this will happen, etc.," taking into account that B's preferences for the outcomes are opposed to his own. Are problems involving such choices "solvable"? And what does it mean for them to be "solved"?

Certainly a "solution" in the old sense of maximization of utility cannot be expected, because what happens to be the best possible outcome for A is the worst possible outcome for his opponent, if the interests are diametrically opposed.

Is there any outcome, which is determined by the game itself, which is, in some way, "forced," that is, bound to arise if a certain line of reasoning is pushed to a compelling conclusion? It is in this sense that the "solution" of such a game is offered. Roughly, the solution will be an outcome which both players can force and which cannot be hoped realistically to be improved upon from the standpoint of either player. This solution (called the *minimax,* or, more recently, the *maximin*) is the best each player can do for himself in the face of the opposition of the other player. It is therefore conceptually analogous to an equilibrium attained by two opposing forces. Let us see how this comes about in a simple example.

Suppose A has two choices of action, a_1 and a_2, and B also has two choices, b_1 and b_2. There are therefore four possible outcomes: the choice pairs, (a_1, b_1), (a_2, b_1), (a_1, b_2), and (a_2, b_2).

These outcomes can be represented on a 2×2 grid or a matrix. A zero-sum game is one in which A's gain is B's loss, and vice versa. Therefore, we only need to enter A's gains (positive or negative) into the boxes of the grid, understanding that B's gains will be the same numbers with the opposite sign attached. Let the payoffs for the four outcomes of our game be as represented in Matrix 1:

$$\begin{array}{cc} & \begin{array}{cc} b_1 & b_2 \end{array} \\ \begin{array}{c} a_1 \\ a_2 \end{array} & \begin{bmatrix} 4 & 2 \\ 5 & -3 \end{bmatrix} \end{array}$$

Matrix 1

This means that if A chooses a_1, and B chooses b_1, A gains (B loses) 4; if A chooses a_1, and B chooses b_2, A gains (B loses) 2; if A chooses a_2, and B chooses b_1, A gains (B loses) 5; if A chooses a_2, and B chooses b_2, A loses (B gains) 3.

We see that the best outcome for A is a gain of 5; the best outcome for B is a gain of 3. Further, A can *guarantee* himself a gain of 2. If he chooses a_1, he is sure to get at least 2, and possibly 4 if B is so foolish as to play b_1. Of course A would like 5, which is in the a_2 row, but he knows it is foolish of him to choose a_2 in the hope that B will choose b_1. For why should B choose b_1? On the contrary, A is certain that B will choose

b_2, because B is better off with b_2, *no matter what A does.* Being certain of this, A chooses a_1, because that is where he is best off, given that B chooses b_2.

Therefore, we expect that (a_1, b_2) will be the pair of choices. A's gain is 2. He is assured this gain by the structure of the game, and B can do nothing about it. The best B can do is see to it that A gets *no more* than 2 (by avoiding b_1). He is therefore also assured of the "best" possible outcome (the "least worst," from B's point of view, but mathematically speaking, it is the same thing).

The pair of choices (a_1, b_2) is the solution of this two-person game. Its payoff, 2 to A, whose point of view we have arbitrarily chosen, is called the *value* of the game. The value is conventionally taken to be the value to A. From B's point of view, the value is, of course, —2.

The game just described is particularly simple, because the choice of one of the players (B's) is obvious. He is not even tempted to choose b_1, because there is nothing for him in the column which is not bettered in the corresponding entry of the other column. Therefore, B need not even try to figure out what A is likely to do. A, on the other hand, must resist the temptation of choosing a_2 (with its luring gain of 5 in b_1), and this he does by assuming B's point of view and rationality.

The case where both players must resist temptation is given by the game shown in Matrix 2:

$$
\begin{array}{c} \\ a_1 \\ a_2 \\ a_3 \end{array}
\begin{array}{ccc} b_1 & b_2 & b_3 \end{array}
\left[\begin{array}{ccc} 8 & -5 & -10 \\ 0 & -2 & 6 \\ 4 & -1 & 5 \end{array} \right]
$$

Matrix 2

Here, as we see, A faces the temptation of choosing a_1, because his greatest payoff (8) lies there. B might be tempted to choose b_3, because his greatest payoff (10) is there. If both yield to the temptation, then B's hopes are realized, because the outcome (a_1, b_3) yields him 10. But if B is rational and imputes rationality to A, he will not be tempted to choose b_3, because he will not assume that A will yield to temptation. The risk for A in playing a_1 is too great.

What A might try to do is to minimize the risk. To do so, he will examine the worst possible result in each row. In Matrix 2, these are respectively —10, —2, and —1. Then he will choose (as a tentative decision) the row in which the worst possible outcome is the *least* worst of the three. Clearly, this is a_3. This decision is still tentative, and A goes on to reason so.

"Suppose B knows of my policy of minimizing risk. Then he will suppose that I will choose a_3. What is *his* best choice in that situation? Clearly, his best is b_2, because there he gains 1, whereas he loses 4 and 5 in b_1 and b_3 respectively. Now suppose he does come to that decision on the basis of what he supposes *I* will do. What is *my* best choice in the light of *that* knowledge? Clearly, my best choice is still a_3, because that is where I stand to lose least if B chooses b_2. But a_3 was already my tentative choice on the basis of minimizing risk, I see, therefore, that assuming my decision and assuming that B acts on the assumption that I have acted on that decision, the decision is still the best I can do. Hence my choice is a_3."

If we follow B's reasoning, as he takes his opponent's reasoning into account, we see that he too will come to the same conclusion that he must choose b_2. Therefore (a_3, b_2) is an outcome which, in a sense, enjoys a certain stability: various chains of reasoning converge on it. This outcome is called the *maximin* solution of this game.[43] The reasoning in this game is somewhat more involved than in the preceding, because both players must take the reasoning of the opponent here, while in the previous game B saw that he had to choose as he did no matter what A chose to do.

The most important feature of both these games is the finality with which the conclusion is reached. That such is not always the case will become all too apparent later and will lead to complications and enrichments of game theory, bringing it more closely to problems associated with typically human affairs. The finality of the solution in the two games examined is a consequence of two conditions satisfied by the games. Both are zero-sum games (that is the sum of the two payoffs in each outcome is always zero), and both matrices which describe them have "saddle points." A saddle point is an entry in the game matrix which is the smallest in its row and the largest in its column.[44] In the game represented by Matrix 1, the saddle point entry is (a_1, b_2); in that represented by Matrix 2, it is (a_3, b_2).

From A's point of view, this entry represents the worst that can happen to him if the corresponding row is chosen (i.e., the worst that B can do to him if A's choice is fixed to that row), and it is also the best that can happen in the corresponding column (i.e., the best A can do if B's choice is fixed to that column). It can be shown mathematically that whenever such a saddle point exists in a matrix, the following conclusions are true.

1. The saddle point entry has exactly the same significance for B that it has for A.

2. If there are several saddle points in the matrix, the entries in all of them are equal.

3. If there are two saddle points, say (a_1, b_2) and (a_3, b_4), then if the row or column designations are interchanged in the two pairs, the resulting pair will also be a saddle point, indeed with the same payoff. That is, if (a_1, b_2) and (a_3, b_4) are saddle points, then (a_1, b_4) and (a_3, b_2) are also saddle points with the same payoff entries.

Thus, even if there is more than one saddle point, there is no difference in the outcomes of the game as far as the payoffs are concerned, no matter which saddle point is the outcome. Each player, choosing his co-ordinate (row or column) may choose indifferently among all those which contain a saddle point. No matter which two co-ordinates are combined into a pair, the payoffs to the two players will be respectively the same. These payoffs are called the *values* of the game to the players. (The value to A is taken as the value of the game.)

If a zero-sum game has a saddle point, we have seen that the outcome at that saddle point is "stable," and that therefore the game has a value in the sense described above. It follows that the examination of the payoff matrix of a zero-sum game with a saddle point tells us the one and only way in which the game can end (as far as the payoffs are concerned) if *both* players do the best they can.[45] It follows that for such rational players there is no point in even playing such a game. This conclusion is actually warranted in real life in the case of very simple games of this sort, such as tick-tack-toe. If win, draw, and lose are designated by the payoffs of 1, 0, and —1, then the payoff matrix of tick-tack-toe will turn out to have a set of saddle points, all with entry 0. This means that in this game, each player can guarantee for himself a draw, that is, each can prevent the other from winning. Therefore, barring mistakes, which rational players do not make, every game of tick-tack-toe must end in a draw, and hence there is no point in playing it. Indeed, adults do not play this game. Even if the determined outcome were not a draw but, say, always a win for the first player, there would be no point in playing the game. If it were for some reason *necessary* to play it, the players could save themselves trouble by simply declaring that it has been played with the determined result: the "value" of the game paid by B to A.

Checkers, too, is a game in which the outcome is in principle determined. It is known that each player in checkers can guarantee a draw for himself. That is why in contemporary checker tournaments the first moves are usually decided by lot. If the players could choose the first moves, the game would be sure to end in a draw. Determining what the first moves shall be by lot does not change the determined character of the game, but it starts the game from positions which have not been completely investigated, and so interest in the game is maintained.

It is also known that chess is a game with a saddle point, but it is not known at this date (1960) what its value is—whether a win is guaranteed to White or to Black or whether a draw is guaranteed to both players (although most chess players would guess the last alternative).

Even if the value of chess were known, the game would still be played for many generations to come. It is one thing to know that somewhere "there exists" for both players a best way of playing a game and quite another thing actually to discover the way to play.

The foregoing discussion now leads to some questions which may have already occurred to you.

1. What can be said about games without saddle points? How will rational players play these?

2. What can be said about non-zero-sum games, in which what one player wins, the other does not necessarily lose?

3. What can be said about games with more than two players?

All these matters will be discussed in what follows. First, however, I raise another question, which possibly has also already occurred to you. Is it not a terribly drastic simplification to treat the logic of games as if only one set of choices of action were open to each player? Do not all games of interest involve *successions* of choice situations, and moreover, do not successive choices depend on what has happened before? If we try to extend the theoretical treatment to these more realistic cases, will we not get bogged down in prodigious complications?

The answer is essentially the content of the next chapter, but its gist will be given now. The total number of choices of action in a game of strategy, as these choices are usually conceived (e.g., choices of how to move in a particular situation in a game of checkers), is irrelevant to the logic of the game in which the final outcomes are of central interest. We shall see in the next chapter that *all* of the potential choices can be "collapsed" into a single choice. The course of action so chosen is called a *strategy*.

CHAPTER VIII

THE MEANING OF STRATEGY

LET US INVENT A GAME so simple that it can be analyzed in its entirety. Suppose there are just three moves. On the first move, the first player A has two choices: he may say "1" or "2." On the second move, the second player B has three choices: "1," "2," or "3." On the third move, A has again two choices, "1" or "2." It follows that the whole game can be played in just 12 different ways: $2 \times 3 \times 2 = 12$. To each of these 12 ways we will assign a payoff, a certain amount to be paid by B to A, which may also be negative, in which case A actually pays B, or zero.

Now we need a rule for the assignment of payoffs. We shall make this rule somewhat involved, so that it will not appear immediately obvious to either player how best to play. The rule will be the following: If the three numbers chosen by the players on their three moves were x, y, and z, the payoff to A shall be the quantity $[xyz - (x + y + z) + y^2]$, if this quantity is odd; but if it is even, then the payoff to A is the same quantity with its sign changed. Table 2 tells the whole story.

Figure 8 is another representation of the same game. The letters at the nodes of the "game tree" indicate whose move it is. The numbers on the branches are the choices available on that move. The numbers at the end points are the payoffs to A. The payoffs to B are, of course, the same numbers with the opposite sign.

Table 2

x y z	(xyz)	(x + y + z)	[xyz − (x + y + z) + y²]	Payoff to A
1 1 1	1	3	−1	−1
1 2 1	2	4	2	−2
1 3 1	3	5	7	7
1 1 2	2	4	−1	−1
1 2 2	4	5	3	3
1 3 2	6	6	9	9
2 1 1	2	4	−1	−1
2 2 1	4	5	3	3
2 3 1	6	6	9	9
2 1 2	4	5	0	0
2 2 2	8	6	6	−6
2 3 2	12	7	14	−14

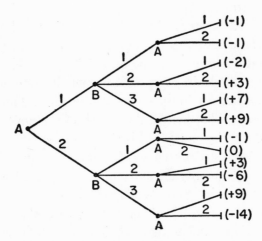

Figure 8. The three-move game in extensive form, showing the game tree. The letters at the nodes indicate whose move it is. The numbers on the branches indicate the choice of move. The numbers in parentheses indicate payoffs to A.

A glance at the tree immediately reveals that A should not choose "1" on his first move. If he does, B's choice of "1" will cause A to lose 1, whatever A does on the third move. B would be foolish to counter A's "1" with "2," because A would win 3 with "2" on the third move. Since A cannot suppose that B is foolish, A's first choice should be "2." To this B can only reply "1." To reply "2" would give B a loss of 3, and "3" would cost him 9. After B replies "1," A will, of course, choose "2." The payoff is zero. You may check to see that neither player can win more.

COLLAPSING THE GAME TO ONE WITH A SINGLE DECISION BY EACH PLAYER

The problem now is to reduce all the combinations of successive choices to a single choice among a set of alternatives to each player. If this is done, the game matrix can be written down, and the saddle point will become immediately evident. To do this, the creators of game theory introduced the notion of "strategy."

A "strategy" in game theory is a technical term with a precise meaning. It means a complete program given by a player before the game begins (say to a referee), stating what he will do in every conceivable situation in which he may find himself in the course of the game. This means he has to specify what he will do at each of the nodes of the game tree where the move is his. The referee, in possession of each player's stated strategy (including Chance's), can then state unambiguously the outcome of the game. Under these circumstances, the game "collapses" to one where a single choice (of a strategy) is to be made by each player, and the game is over as soon as these choices have been announced by the referee. Here is an example of a *single one* of A's strategies in the three-move game just described.

A: I will choose "1" on the first move. If B takes "1," I

will take "1" on my last move; if B takes "2," I will take "1"; if B takes "3," I will take "2."

We see that this is not a very good strategy. A will lose 1 or 2 if B takes "1" or "2" respectively. He may win 9, if B should take "3," but A cannot count on this. Nevertheless it is *a* strategy. It tells everything that A will do whenever A has any choice of action.

Let us see what one of B's strategies may look like. He has just one move with three choices. So he must specify one of the three, but each under two contingencies, namely, in case A chooses "1" or "2." Here is an example.

B: If A chooses "1," I will choose "3"; if A chooses "2," I will choose "1."

Now let us combine the two strategies. Together they will determine the outcome of the game. A has committed himself to "1" on his first move. B has committed himself to "3" if A chooses "1." But A did choose "1." Therefore B will choose "3." B's commitment to "1" in case A chose "2" is irrelevant here, because A did not choose "2." Turning back to A's strategy, we recall that he chose "2" on his last move if B should take "3." This gives A a payoff of 9. We had said that this strategy of A was not wise, but it turned out well for him, because B's strategy was even less prudent.

Clever or foolish, every such specification is a strategy. And a pair of such strategies, one chosen by each player, completely determines the outcome of the game.

Let us now see how many different strategies A has available in this game of 3 moves and 12 outcomes. We see that he can associate 1 of 2 choices of his last move with each of B's 3 choices. This can be done in 8 different ways. Moreover, he has 2 choices on his first move, which can be made independently of these 8 ways. Therefore, A has 16 strategies. Similar calculations show that B has 9 strategies. All of the strategies are listed and numbered in Table 3.

Table 3

A's 16 strategies

Strategy	First Move	Last Move
1.	1	1, regardless of B's choice
2.	1	1, if B chooses 1 or 2; 2 otherwise
3.	1	1, if B chooses 1 or 3; 2 otherwise
4.	1	1, if B chooses 2 or 3; 2 otherwise
5.	1	2, if B chooses 1 or 2; 1 otherwise
6.	1	2, if B chooses 1 or 3; 1 otherwise
7.	1	2, if B chooses 2 or 3; 1 otherwise
8.	1	2, regardless of B's choice
9.	2	Same as strategy 1
10.	2	Same as strategy 2
11.	2	Same as strategy 3
12.	2	Same as strategy 4
13.	2	Same as strategy 5
14.	2	Same as strategy 6
15.	2	Same as strategy 7
16.	2	Same as strategy 8

B's 9 strategies

Strategy	Second Move
1.	1, regardless of A's choice
2.	1, if A chooses 1; 2 otherwise
3.	1, if A chooses 1; 3 otherwise
4.	2, if A chooses 1; 1 otherwise
5.	2, regardless of A's choice
6.	2, if A chooses 1; 3 otherwise
7.	3, if A chooses 1; 1 otherwise
8.	3, if A chooses 1; 2 otherwise
9.	3, regardless of A's choice

From the complete listing of the two sets of strategies available to each player, we can now construct the game matrix, which in this case will have evidently $16 \times 9 = 144$ entries, as shown in Matrix 3:

	b_1	b_2	b_3	b_4	b_5	b_6	b_7	b_8	b_9
a_1	−1	−1	−1	−2	−2	−2	−7	−7	−7
a_2	−1	−1	−1	−2	−2	−2	9	9	9
a_3	−1	−1	−1	3	3	3	7	7	7
a_4	−1	−1	−1	−2	−2	−2	7	7	7
a_5	−1	−1	−1	3	3	3	7	7	7
a_6	−1	−1	−1	−2	−2	−2	9	9	9
a_7	−1	−1	−1	3	3	3	9	9	9
a_8	−1	−1	−1	3	3	3	9	9	9
a_9	−1	3	9	−1	3	9	−1	3	9
a_{10}	−1	3	−14	−1	3	−14	−1	3	−14
a_{11}	−1	−6	9	−1	−6	9	−1	−6	9
a_{12}	0	3	9	0	3	9	0	3	9
a_{13}	0	−6	9	0	−6	9	0	−6	9
a_{14}	0	3	−14	0	3	−14	0	3	−14
a_{15}	−1	−6	−14	−1	−6	−14	−1	−6	−14
a_{16}	0	−6	−14	0	−6	−14	0	−6	−14

Matrix 3

The saddle point entry is at (a_{12}, b_1). It prescribes strategy 12 to A and strategy 1 to B. The saddle point entry is 0, as we would expect from our preliminary analysis.

The great importance of the strategy concept is that it does allow the game theorist to "collapse" the sequence of choices to be made in the course of a game into a single choice among all the available strategies by each player.

Before the logic of this "collapse" actually sinks in, most people cannot get rid of a feeling that a player, by choosing a strategy in advance of the game, somehow unnecessarily "commits" himself, gives up some freedom of choice or flexibility, and thus places himself at a disadvantage. This feeling, however, is illusory. It stems from the difficulty of imagining how all possible situations can be conceived in advance. Of course, the practical difficulty of "foreseeing everything" is enormous. But we are dealing not with the practicality of strategic decision but with its logic. Logically speaking, a commitment to a strategy does not sacrifice any freedom of action. Freedom of action is sacrificed in a rigid commitment only if unforeseen circumstances make a change of policy imperative. But there are *in principle* no unforeseen circumstances in a game of strategy. Everything that can possibly happen in such a game can be *listed,* because the rules of the game prescribe everything that can possibly happen, and therefore everything can be foreseen.

Therefore, in principle the game can be reduced from its so-called "extensive" form, as pictured by the game tree, to the so-called "normal" form, as pictured by the payoff matrix. What we did with our game of choosing numbers could be done in principle with tick-tack-toe, poker, bridge, checkers, chess, or any other game of strategy.

The qualification "in principle" is essential, because the practical difficulties multiply very rapidly as the games cease to be trivial.

Take tick-tack-toe. How many different ways are there of playing it? The first player has 9 choices where to put his "X." The second player has 8 choices where to put his "O." The first player then has 7 choices, etc. Assuming that the game lasts 5 moves, that is, the least number of moves in which the game can be won (and usually sufficient to make the outcome obvious), the number of ways the game can be played is $9 \times 8 \times 7 \times 6 \times 5 = 15{,}120$.

Now let us estimate the number of strategies. Player A has 9 initial choices. On the third move (which is again his) he may associate any of his 7 replies to any of B's 8 choices on B's second move. This can be done in 7^8 different ways. The fifth move is again A's. Here he can associate 5 replies to any of B's 6 choices on B's fourth move. This can be done in 5^6 different ways. Therefore, to play the first 5 moves, 3 by A and 2 by B, there are open to A $9 \times 7^8 \times 5^6$, or almost a trillion different strategies, if the symmetries of the tick-tack-toe grid are not taken into account. Taking symmetries into account reduces this number drastically, but then the description of the game becomes much more involved.[46]

To drive home the idea about the enormous number of strategies even in simple situations, let us take a brief look at the first exchange of moves in chess. Assuming that the entire game of chess consists of *only this exchange of first moves,* the number of strategies open to Black is so large that if the strategies were written out 100 to a page on paper stacking up 100 sheets to an inch, the stack of paper so filled would be 40,000 light years thick.[47] The number of *situations* which can result from the first exchange of moves is only 20 $\times$ 20 = 400. It is important to keep in mind that the number of strategies is usually many magnitudes larger than the number of situations that may occur in a game. The number of strategies is usually hyper-astronomical and cannot be realistically imagined.

In spite of its trillion strategies, however, tick-tack-toe is so simple that it is a routine matter to program a computer to play a perfect game. This is because all the relevant instructions (i.e., foreseeing all the relevant eventualities) can be formally described in a few rules, which guide the program. You can readily verify, for example, that A's best move is the center. Also if B takes anything but a corner in reply, A is bound to win. If B takes a corner square, A's best next move is the corner at the opposite end of the diagonal, etc. Two computers playing each other will, of course, always draw. A more futile conflict is difficult to imagine.

SOME ETHICAL CONSIDERATIONS

It may seem like a *tour de force* to derive a moral from our analysis of the simplest possible games of strategy, but let us try.

I think the analysis offers an insight into *some* forms of

human conflict. One of the great chess players glorified chess as a form of conflict consistent with human dignity, that is, one in which the intellect and not brute force was the decisive factor. If "morality" in chess is too farfetched, one can still speak of taste or aesthetics in chess. The games that have gone down in history are the "elegant" games, those in which decisions were reached with a minimum of "bloodshed," or else those in which the side that suffered the greatest "casualties" has won (a sort of triumph of right over might). More pertinent to our discussion is the common practice among experts to *concede* games or to agree on a draw as a result of insight into the logic of the situation. I submit that this practice is a reflection of a certain moral principle, characteristic of gamelike conflict as opposed to fightlike conflict. The principle has to do with imputing rationality comparable to one's own to the opponent. On the basis of this mutual respect, agreement is possible, even though the interests of the players are diametrically opposed.

There was a time when war was considered a gentleman's game, and gamelike standards prevailed in the conduct of warfare. Certain positions were considered "untenable," and when armies found themselves in such positions, they surrendered. If neither side could obtain an advantage, negotiations often were initiated and sometimes ended in the acceptance by both sides of *status quo*. These attitudes were also reflected, of course, in the treatment of prisoners, especially of gentlemen prisoners.

Although it can be argued that this gamelike morality of eighteenth-century warfare was superior to the morality of modern "total war," some moral philosophers take the opposite view. Tolstoy (120, Vol. 3, pp. 297–98), for example, speaking through his hero, Prince Andrei,[48] argues as follows:

No captives taken! This alone would change the whole war and would make it less cruel. We have only been playing at war,—that is bad. We are acting the magnanimous persons. This magnanimity and sentimentality is like the magnanimity and sentimentality of the young lady who feels nauseated when she sees some one killing a calf: she is so good that she cannot see blood, but she devours this calf with relish when it is properly seasoned. We are told about the rights of war, about chivalry, parliamentarism, sparing the unfortunate, and so forth. Nonsense . . .

If there were no magnanimity in war, we would go into it only when it was worth while to go to a certain death. Then the intensiveness of the troops would be different . . . Then all these Westphalians and Hessians, whom Napoleon is leading would not follow him to Russia, and we ourselves would not go into Austria or Prussia to fight, not knowing why. War is not a pleasantry, but a very nasty piece of business, and one has to understand it, but not play war . . .

Such attitudes prevailed in Russia ever since the Napoleonic invasion, and curiously enough were a great shock to the German invaders of 1941. The recurring theme in the German accounts of the first months of that war was that the Russians simply did not know that they were beaten. This to the German military, who still thought mainly in terms of gamelike characteristics of war (they too were to change their attitude shortly), was gross immorality, an affront, like the affront which a chess player feels when his clearly beaten opponent refuses to concede. This attitude can be and usually is rationalized by the party which considers itself victorious: it is immoral to shed blood "uselessly," that is, without strategic advantage. The Russians did not feel this way. For them the war was not a game but a fight, completely dominated by an all-consuming hatred for the enemy. Strategic considerations were important, of course, for the effective conduct of the war, but they were never to be the determinants of the answer to the question of whether to continue to fight.

Still, when the Russians found themselves in a *winning* position at Stalingrad, they too used the "useless bloodshed" gambit. The German lines were deluged with leaflets, on which the Russian and German positions were outlined on a map, and a reasoned military argument was offered to the effect that the German position was hopeless. In other words, when they were winning, the Russians spoke the game language—the common language of military men, to all of whom maps have the same meaning and all of whom are expected to make similar decisions on the basis of similar evidence.

The comparative "morality" of fightlike and gamelike wars is an interesting ethical issue, but for the present we must continue with our investigations of game theory proper, which has a great deal more to offer of relevance to the abstract and general treatment of conflict.

CHAPTER IX

THE STRATEGY MIXTURE

WE HAVE SEEN how in certain games each player's choice of a single strategy completely determines the outcome of the game. This is true if Chance plays no part. If Chance does intervene in the game, then the outcome of a particular play of the game is not completely determined by the other players' choices of strategy. However, if the probability distribution of Chance's choices is known, we can enter into the payoff matrix the *expected* payoffs to each player. It is as if the payoffs were now not in "cash utiles" but in lottery tickets, each with a chance to win so much with probability so much. If, as is always supposed in game theory, the expected utilities are assigned as the actual utilities to such tickets, the intervention of Chance makes no difference in the strategic structure of the game. We have eliminated Chance by replacing the uncertainty of actual payoffs by the certainty of the payoff expectations.

The situation is more involved if players are able to hide their moves from each other. In tick-tack-toe and in chess, this is impossible. Each move is under the scrutiny of the opponent, and the entire game is always reconstructible. But in other games, this is not so. In poker, for example, the exchange of a number of cards in a player's hand for a number drawn from the deck is a move. But which cards have been discarded (the player's choice) and which drawn (Chance's choice) is known only to one player.

Games in which no choices are concealed from anyone (like chess and checkers) are called games of perfect information. It is shown in game theory that the payoff matrices of zero-sum games of this sort always have saddle points. Games which are not games of perfect information may not have any saddle point in their payoff matrix. Then the straight-forward choice of strategy (the maximin), which, we have said, constitutes the solution of the two-person zero-sum game, cannot be applied, at least not in the same way. There is, however, a way of re-establishing the maximin solution for a two-person zero-sum game, even if it has no saddle point. The method is revealing of some interesting aspects of the game-like conflict, and so we will examine it.

ANOTHER GAME WITH PERFECT INFORMATION

Consider first a game of the type examined in the last chapter. To make the reasoning easy to follow, we will make it an even simpler game. Here A has two choices on his first move: Right or Left. Then B has the same two choices on the second move; then A again. The outcomes are given in Table 4.

Table 4	Move:	1	2	3	Payoff to A
		L	L	L	—1
		L	L	R	2
		L	R	L	1
		R	L	L	2
		L	R	R	0
		R	L	R	4
		R	R	L	0
		R	R	R	—5

All the strategies are shown in Table 5.

Table 5

A's strategies

Strategy	First Move	Last Move
1.	L	R, regardless of B's choice
2.	L	Do what B does
3.	L	Do the opposite of what B does
4.	L	L, regardless of B's choice
5.	R	Same as strategy 1
6.	R	Same as strategy 2
7.	R	Same as strategy 3
8.	R	Same as strategy 4

B's strategies

Strategy	Second Move
1.	R, regardless of A's choice
2.	Do what A does
3.	Do the opposite of what A does
4.	L, regardless of A's choice

The payoff matrix is shown in Matrix 4:

	b_1	b_2	b_3	b_4
a_1	0	2	0	2
a_2	0	—1	0	—1
a_3	1	2	1	2
a_4	1	—1	1	—1
a_5	—5	—5	4	4
a_6	—5	—5	2	2
a_7	0	0	4	4
a_8	0	0	2	2

Matrix 4

The saddle point is the entry (3, 1). A can guarantee himself a win of 1 by playing his strategy 3.

But now suppose that B can conceal his move from A. Thus, when A has to make his choice on the third move, he does not know whether B has moved Right or Left. In that case we see that strategies 2, 3, 6, and 7 are no longer open to A, because in these strategies, A's choice on the third move depends on B's choice on the second. But A does not know now what B did on the second move and therefore cannot be guided in his choice on the third. However, we see that strategies 1, 4, 5, and 8 are still open to A, because in these strategies A's choice on the third move does not depend on B's choice. In this new game (new, because the rules have been changed) the payoff matrix will now be as in Matrix 5 (where A's strategies have now been relabeled 1, 2, 3, and 4):

	b_1	b_2	b_3	b_4
a_1	0	2	0	2
a_2	1	—1	1	—1
a_3	—5	—5	4	4
a_4	0	0	2	2

Matrix 5

Here A's maximin seems to be 0 (the largest of the minima of the rows), but none of the 0 entries is the maximum of its column and therefore is not B's maximin. There is no saddle point, and our whole theory of choosing the best strategy, which in the game with the saddle point applies to both players, fails.

A GAME WITHOUT A SADDLE POINT

We shall now proceed to get around this difficulty. For our examples we take games with only two strategy choices to each player. They can illustrate the principles to be discussed as well as the more complicated games and have the advantage of simplicity.

Take the following example:

$$
\begin{array}{c}
\begin{array}{cc}
b_1 & b_2
\end{array} \\
\begin{array}{c} a_1 \\ a_2 \end{array}
\begin{bmatrix}
0 & 2 \\
3 & —1
\end{bmatrix}
\end{array}
$$

Matrix 6

How shall such a game be played? Let us take A's viewpoint. He would like 3; so a_2 is tempting. But —1 threatens there. For security's sake, a_1 is more attractive; it guarantees 0. The maximin principle would indicate a_1, since 0 is the better of the two worse outcomes. It seems, then, that a_1 should be A's choice.

Now consider B's view. He would like to win 1, and he would play b_2, if he could count on A's playing a_2. But he suspects that A will probably play a_1, because that is where A's maximin lies. If he were sure of A's playing a_1, he would play b_1. But then another suspicion enters B's mind. Suppose A is aware of his (B's) reasoning as far as it has gone. That is, suppose A has guessed that B will play b_1. Might he not on that assumption play a_2 and win 3? If B could only be sure of that, *then* he would play b_2 and win the most he can in this game. But wait. Suppose A has followed *so* far. Will he not play a_1 (to save himself), so as to win 2? But if he does, B should play b_1 . . .

We are going around in circles. Ordinary logic will not suffice to establish a "rational" strategy for either player.

Here game theory could have toppled over if a theorem had not been proved which saved the foundations. Suppose each player plays each of the strategies open to him at random but in some definite ratio of frequencies. For example, suppose A plays a_1 35 per cent of the time and a_2 65 per cent of the time. We say that he is "mixing" his strategies in 35:65 ratio. The minimax theorem of von Neumann then asserts the following (125): There is a definite ratio of strategy mixture (call it a strategy "recipe") for each player, which has all the properties of a maximin (minimax). It will guarantee the most each player can get in the sense of long-run expected payoff, if the opponent follows the same policy, that is, uses *his* maximin strategy recipe. If the opponent departs from the maximin mixture, he can do no better but may do worse, if the first player sticks to his maximin mixture.

The procedure for finding the best mixture is quite simple in zero-sum games with two strategies to each player (the 2×2 games), but becomes much more involved in larger games. The procedure for 2×2 games is as follows (133). Find the absolute difference between the corresponding entries in the two columns. In the case of the example we are considering, these differences are (2, 4). Note the ratio of the second difference to the first. This is 4:2 or 2:1. This ratio will determine the relative frequencies of a_1 and a_2 for A in his strategy mixture. That is, the best mixture for A is to play a_1 66⅔ per cent of the time and a_2 33⅓ per cent of the time. To get B's mixture, we find the absolute differences of the corresponding members of the two rows. In our case these are (3, 3). Therefore, B should play b_1 and b_2 with equal frequency. Obviously, each player should conceal from the other the particular strategy he will play on a particular play of the game. He should "randomize" his strategy choices.

Let us now see what the results will be over many plays. Whenever B plays b_1, A will win 0 two-thirds of the time and 3 one-third of the time. Hence, A will win on the average $0 \times \frac{2}{3} + 3 \times \frac{1}{3} = 1$. Whenever B plays b_2, A will win 2 two-thirds of the time and will lose 1 one-third of the time, that is, will win $2 \times \frac{2}{3} - 1 \times \frac{1}{3} = 1$. No matter what B does, A will win on the average 1 unit (of whatever he is winning) per game. B will lose 1 unit per game. The value of the game is 1 to A. Neither can do anything to improve his situation. If one should depart from the policy of the best mixed strategy, the other could cash in. In a 2×2 game he could take advantage of this departure only by departing himself from his best mixture, but if this departure were found out by the opponent, the opponent could gain, but also only by departing from his best mixture, which, if discovered by the other . . . (the circular reasoning starts again).

However, in games with more than two strategies available, a player can benefit by the opponent's departure from the maximin mixture even if he stands pat on his own maximin mixture. It is in this sense that the maximin mixture is the safest for each player.

BUTTON-BUTTON

The role of the best-mixed strategy can be seen clearly in the very simplest game requiring mixed strategies. Button-Button will do. A conceals a button in one of his hands, and B tries to guess in which. If B wins a penny for every guess and loses a penny for every miss, the payoff matrix of the game is (assuming $1\cancel{c} = 1$ utile) given in Matrix 7:

$$
\begin{array}{cc}
 & \begin{array}{cc} \text{B guesses} \end{array} \\
 & \begin{array}{cc} \text{Left} & \text{Right} \end{array} \\
\begin{array}{l} \text{A hides } \text{L.H.} \\ \text{button in} \\ \text{R.H.} \end{array} &
\begin{bmatrix} -1 & +1 \\ +1 & -1 \end{bmatrix}
\end{array}
$$

Matrix 7

A's best strategy (calculated by the method described above) is to hide the button *randomly* with equal frequency in each hand; B's best strategy (calculated by the same method) is to guess randomly each hand with the same frequency. The departure of either from this strategy may cost him money. For if A favors the right hand, and B discovers this, then B may guess "right hand" every time and be correct most of the time. But then if A discovers *this* maneuver, he will switch to favoring the left hand and thus make B wrong until B realizes what has happened. But if B discovers *this* stratagem . . .

We cannot say with whom the ultimate advantage will be unless we can put different limits on each player's perspicacity, which we do not do within the framework of game theory.[49]

We are thus forced to prescribe to each player the respective mixed strategies. These give each the maximin value of the game, in this case zero.

Note that in these games of mixed strategy both skill and chance play a part. The skill is in the business of discovering the best recipe of strategies. The *particular* strategy to be selected on each play of the game is determined by a chance device. Thus, the outcome of any single play of the game may be anything consistent with the pairs of choices included in the two strategy mixtures. Over long runs of many plays, however, the outcome is determined to the extent that the probability of an event determines its relative frequency in a large number of occurrences.

APPLICATIONS TO SECURITY

There is much to learn from two-person zero-sum games without saddle points. To begin with, everything we said about the games with saddle points is true for these games also, if the equilibrium pair of pure strategies (as the available strategies of a game are called) is replaced by equilibrium pairs of strategy mixtures. But there is more about these games which is instructive.

The notion of "security" (in a sense akin to security against an enemy's military intelligence) is introduced for the first time. In the case of pure (not mixed) strategy equilibrium, each player may just as well have told his opponent his "best" strategy. Indeed, the opponent knows it already from his own calculation. Thus, there is no problem of "security" in the zero-sum game with saddle point. The reason chess players do not disclose their plans to each other is because they are nowhere near to calculating complete strategies for the entire game. If they could, the game would not be worth playing. When a situation does arise where all the possibilities are foreseen, such information is often conveyed, most frequently, of course, by the player who sees a sure win for himself. The prospective loser may not wish to do this in the hope that the opponent has not been able to calculate the sure-win strategy, but not because such a strategy is in principle unknown to him.[50]

When the prospective winner in a game of chess says, "I can force checkmate in five moves," this means that *whatever* the other may do, a checkmate in at most five moves is inevitable. When the loser sees this, the game will surely be broken off. We may look at it this way: when such a position is reached, we may imagine that the two players are starting a game with the position given as initial. This game can be foreseen to its end and is therefore not worth playing.

In games where mixed strategies are used, the situation is more complicated. Each player can still tell the other his *mixture,* but he would be at a disadvantage if he told him the specific strategy he was going to use on a particular play, because the other can always take advantage of this knowledge.

To see this, consider the following hypothetical military situation. A truck carrying munitions passes over either of two roads every day. Road #1 is good, and Road #2 is poor. The enemy sends a detachment to ambush the truck. The detachment has a choice of blocking Road #1 or Road #2. Each of the opponents has two strategies; so this is a 2 × 2 game. The outcomes are as follows. If the truck goes on Road #1 and is ambushed, the chances of rushing through the ambush are pretty good, but, of course, not perfect. If the truck goes on Road #1, and the enemy is on Road #2, the truck will surely get through, and the ambush runs risks on the bad road. (This is the best outcome from the truck's point of view.) If the truck runs on Road #2, and the ambush is on Road #1, there is no danger of ambush, but the truck risks breakdown on the poor road. If both take Road #2, the chances of the truck's getting through are meager.

The truck, therefore, prefers the pairs in this order: (t_1, a_2); (t_2, a_1); (t_1, a_1); (t_2, a_2), where t indicates the truck's choice of road and a that of the ambush party. To make the picture complete, we should evaluate the four situations also from the ambushing party's point of view. In general, one would expect the opposing sides in a war to have reversed preferences. In a zero-sum game, however, more is required: the utilities of the two players for each payoff should actually add up to zero. Although such strict opposition of interests cannot always be expected, we shall assume that this is the case. Accordingly, we have a matrix of a zero-sum game, with payoffs to the truck as follows:

$$
\begin{array}{c}
\quad\quad a_1 \quad a_2 \\
\begin{array}{c} t_1 \\ t_2 \end{array}
\left[\begin{array}{cc} -1 & 5 \\ 3 & -5 \end{array} \right]
\end{array}
$$

Matrix 8

Since there is no saddle point, this is a game of mixed strategy. The best strategy recipes are as follows. The truck chooses the two roads in the ratio 4:3; the ambush chooses the two roads in the ratio 5:2. The value of this game to the truck is $5/7$. In other words, this sort of tactics, where each does his best, will in the long run pay off $5/7$ utiles (whatever these may be in this context) per run to the truck. It is assumed that each truck destroyed is replaced by another. Neither the truck nor the ambush detachment can improve their respective chances.

Now let us see what "military security" can mean in such a context. Certainly it would be folly for either side to reveal to the other which road they are going to use *on any particular run*. But there is no disadvantage in revealing the relative chances of using the one or the other road. In fact, either side can figure out what relative frequencies the other side is going to use for the two roads. To try to evade by using a different strategy mixture can only be of disadvantage to the evading side. There is no point at all in trying to delude the enemy on *that* score. Such attempts can only backfire.

IMPLICATIONS FOR THE ONE-SHOT PLAY

Admitting now the "reality" of this sort of evaluation (i.e., admitting that the expected utility of the long-run effects can be calculated), let us ask a somewhat embarrassing question. How does one play the "mixed strategy" in a single play of the game, and what is the justification for doing so?

The first part of the question is easy to answer. The second part leads inadvertently to philosophical and even ethical questions, with which, as we shall see, game theory is blessed (or plagued) throughout.

In answer to the first question, put seven cards into a hat, four marked with crosses. Pull one out; if there is a cross on it, use the good road; otherwise the poor one. The ambushing party should mark five cards with crosses and proceed the same way.

To answer the second part of the question is not simple. It *becomes* simple if the notion of utility is extended to risky outcomes. In this case all the dispatcher has to do is rank order all possible risky outcomes in the order of his preference. If he assumes that the enemy has ordered the same risky outcomes in the reverse order (as is the case if the game is zero-sum), then the prescribed strategy mixture insures that the truck dispatcher will 'get' the best risky outcome he can under the constraint of the situation. This way of putting it presents a decision problem to the decision maker hardly less complex than the original one.

How does one go about rank-ordering all possible risky outcomes, which are infinite in number? A much simpler way of putting it is to say that the strategy mixture will guarantee $\frac{5}{7}$ utiles. *If these utiles can be added,* that is if they can be accumulated in repeated runs, then *in the long run* the largest number of utiles will be accumulated which the situation permits. If the utiles were originally calculated in terms of trucks that got through, trucks lost, men lost, etc., the long term result can be translated back in these terms. The truck dispatcher can expect that after so many runs so many trucks will have gotten through, so many lost, so many men will have been lost, etc.

But what if there is no long run? Where there is no long run (as in one-shot games), the expected utility idea must be considered simply as an extrapolation of a long run policy. It has the virtue of being an unambiguous rule. It seems the best one *can* do.

Actually, in all life situations where ambiguities and uncertainties are inherent, operating procedures must be reduced to certain rules. There is no end to how much precaution could be taken to insure the safety of personnel in a hazardous operation, for example, in flying. Yet ordinarily only "reasonable" precautions are taken. Passenger planes, for instance, do not carry parachutes. Situations where parachutes might save some lives are exceedingly rare on passenger flights. How rare must they be to justify the elimination of parachutes? No one will venture to say. Yet the decision to equip or not to equip passenger planes with parachutes must be made. Behind such a decision there are always explicit or, more frequently, implicit estimates of probabilities. No operating procedure in industry, government, or education is designed to insure the best decision in each individual case. But the hope is that a fairly rational procedure gives good results in the long run.

The same kinds of rules are then also extended to situations where there is no "long run," because one needs *some* operating rule. Without operating rules (and these must always be to a certain extent arbitrary) no decisions at all are possible.

This, I suppose, is the spirit of the game-theoretical prescription of how to play zero-sum games without saddle points. Rules are derived from certain rationalizations, based on expected long-run optimum payoffs. The long-run expectations mean nothing in the individual case, but the rules at least make rationalizable decisions possible. This is important in situations where no decision may be worse than a bad decision.

ANOTHER ETHICAL PROBLEM

Consider now the truck dispatcher with his numbers in the hat. Three times out of seven, he will draw the poor road, on which the chances of survival are very poor in two cases out of seven. He must feel bad about sending the men down that road. But he must do it, because otherwise the enemy, if he can ascertain that the good road is always used, will always send the ambush there and will have a greater chance to come out ahead. The bad road must be used now and then to decoy the enemy, and the frequency with which it is most profitably used is given by the maximin mixture.

The strategic prescriptions of game theory in two-person zero-sum games are no different in principle from the prescriptions of a business adviser to a firm as to how best to allocate investments so as to maximize expected returns, within the constraints of not exceeding a certain risk, or how to design a set of procedures so as to maximize efficiency defined in some way within the constraints of not impairing morale beyond a certain tolerance limit.

Game theory extends these methods to apply to situations where an intelligent and usually malevolent opponent is operating. The acceptance of the game-theoretical prescriptions (as in the case of any expert advice) would ordinarily depend on the acceptability of the "rationales."

The real difficulty is to define and estimate "utilities," which game theory simply takes for granted. Except where money or some other easily measurable commodity can be taken to be equivalent to utiles or at least related to utiles in an ascertainable manner, the determination of utilities or even a proof of their existence is a most difficult matter. It is all very well to say that getting a truck through (with lives and supplies) is worth so much as against not sending it and against sending and losing it. Ordinarily, no commander will be able to assign consistent utility values to such events, let alone the totally intangible ones, like "morale" or commendation by higher authority. But perhaps the absence of such measures is due precisely to the absence (until recently) of a theory which could put such measures to use. After all, until the thermometer was invented, the terms "cold" and "hot" were held by most philosophers to be "qualitative," not "quantitative" terms, and the idea of measuring *exactly* how much hotter one thing was than another (the way one measured lengths and weights) might have seemed a silly idea, if it occurred (which it apparently did not until the possibility of such measurements suggested itself).

The very idea of mathematical expectation, now freely used in actuarial work, in business risks, etc., is, when one comes to think of it, an extremely abstract concept. To realize this, try to explain the meaning of mathematical expectation associated with a risk to a child or to a preliterate. Yet policies based on such expectations, even when long-run effects do *not* come into consideration, are held to be rational policies.

"Calculated risk" has become a common expression with policy-makers. It must be noted that with most policy-makers in our public life, "calculations," as they apply to risk, carry only a metaphorical meaning. Risks are very seldom "calculated": instead decisions are made according to one's biases and then rationalized. Game theory is, among other things, an attempt to make the pretended calculations of policy-makers actual calculations, where the policy-maker is obliged to make his *a priori* assumptions and valuations explicit. It invites an attempt to make the public decision processes open to public scrutiny.

CHAPTER X

WHAT IF THE OPPONENT IS BOTH FRIEND AND FOE?

A SCIENTIFIC THEORY often appears as an extension or a sharper formulation of problems with which people had already been preoccupied on the common sense level. So it was with game theory. Take the notion of strategy. In human affairs, concern with strategy usually means concern with effective strategies in specific situations. The chess player and the football coach, the military commander and the speculator have developed, on the basis of their experiences, certain "heuristics," or rules of operation. Sometimes these rules could be fairly explicitly stated, sometimes not. Thus chess players agree that it is advantageous to have firmly placed pawns in the center of the board, rooks on open files, etc. But none of these rules is without exceptions. If the exceptions are enumerated, we have amended rules. But there are limits to what can be said in words. The expert's "knowledge" usually exceeds his ability to explain what he does and how he does it.

Game theory did not provide a practical way of finding good strategies in any of the commonly known games. Such games are too complicated to yield to complete description in "extensive form," that is, in terms of their game trees. But game theory sharpened the concept of strategy so as to use it as a *springboard* to jump to a more general level of analysis. Specifically, it has shown that *given* a listing of all possible strategies available to each of the opponents, there is, in principle, a way of choosing a *prudent* strategy in a zero-sum game. It may be entirely too difficult actually to find this "prudent" strategy, but proof of its existence gives us an important insight into the logic of all zero-sum games.

Moreover, in the solution of this problem (proof of the existence of the prudent strategy, the maximin), a new concept had to be introduced, namely, that of mixed strategy. This concept, in turn, led to interesting philosophical questions concerning the nature of "prudence" in situations involving risk, the exact role of "security" (concealment of intelligence from the opponent by keeping *oneself* ignorant); and even ethical overtones were introduced in the course of discussion.

As we continue to investigate more and more general game situations, for example, games which are not zero-sum or games with more than two players, we shall often be "forced to the wall," so to say, that is, faced with the necessity of giving precise definitions of terms which because of their common occurrence are thought to be universally understood. "Prudence" is one of them. "Equity" is another. We shall be forced to distinguish between individual and group rationality, among various conceptions of "social welfare"; we shall need to disentangle parallel and conflicting interests when these occur together, etc. In short, we shall be led to a multitude of questions with which philosophers, religious leaders, statesmen, and social scientists have been preoccupied for centuries. But the game-theoretical approach will differ from the usual approaches to such questions in one vital respect. It starts from positions of clarity. To be sure, as more complicated cases are examined, ambiguities will make themselves felt. However, the *ambiguities themselves* will be clear, which is more than can be said for the ambiguities unavoidable in common sense approaches to problems involving values. To be specific, our ambiguities and difficulties will appear as consequences of extending the range of applications of concepts beyond the region where their meaning is clear-cut. It will then be instructive to see what happened: just how did a clear meaning become unclear.

MIND-READING AND THE BATTLE OF THE WILLS

We shall now examine the extension of game theory to the two-person non-zero-sum game. It will be recalled that in the zero-sum game, what A wins B loses, and vice versa—that is, the sum of the payoffs is always zero, no matter what the outcome. The results of the zero-sum game theory apply equally to the two-person constant-sum game, that is, where the sum of the payoffs is always the same. For clearly in this situation the interests of the two players are still directly opposed: the more one wins, the less the other can win (or the more he must lose).

But now we consider games in which the payoff sums are not the same for all outcomes. The representation of such games in normal form will not be quite so simple as that of the zero-sum games. In the latter, only one number had to be entered into each box of the matrix, namely the payoff to one of the players, because the payoff to the other was always the same number with the opposite sign attached. But now both payoffs must be entered. We shall do this. Each of the two numbers now represents the payoff to each player respectively.

As our first example, consider the following game:

$$\begin{array}{c} & b_1 \quad\ b_2 \quad\ b_3 \\ \begin{array}{c} a_1 \\ a_2 \\ a_3 \end{array} & \left[\begin{array}{ccc} 1,3 & 0,0 & 0,0 \\ 0,0 & 2,2 & 0,0 \\ 0,0 & 0,0 & 3,1 \end{array}\right] \end{array}$$

Matrix 9

Remember that in the zero-sum game the strategies were chosen by the players in secret. True, in games where pure maximin strategies were available, it was shown that this security problem does not exist. If the most prudent strategy was chosen, this fact could well be communicated to the opponent. But where mixed strategies are involved, the security problem does exist. Only the strategy mixture could be safely revealed, not the specific pure strategies of the individual plays of the game.

Let us see whether a security problem exists in the game shown in Matrix 9. As usual, we will take A's point of view. For A the best outcome is (a_3, b_3). Should he then choose a_3? Only if he has a reasonable expectation that B will choose b_3. But can he expect this?

B would like the outcome to be (a_1, b_1). So he might want to choose b_1. However, the outcome (a_3, b_1) is bad for both, since the payoff there is $(0, 0)$. Clearly, the problem here is the opposite of the problem posed by military security. It is in the interest of both players to "get together"—to agree on a joint choice of strategy.

To make the example concrete, let the strategies open to each player be choices of vacation sites, assuming that the players are a couple who enjoy each other's company but have different tastes. Let a_i $(i = 1, 2, 3)$ represent A's choices of mountains, seashore, and ocean voyage respectively, while b_i $(i = 1, 2, 3)$ will stand for the same choices by B. Let A be the man and B the woman. Since each gets a positive payoff only if the partner is along (i.e., if both choose the same vacation), it seems clearly to their advantage to come to an agreement beforehand instead of choosing in ignorance of each other's choice. In the latter case, there is always a chance that they will go off separately, and both will be the losers.

Suppose, then, they can communicate. What is likely to happen? Our intuitive feeling of "fairness" suggests a compromise. Let them both go to the seashore, splitting the difference in preference, as it were. Well and good. Suppose, however, the man is not interested in a "fair compromise" but is intent on having his own way. He may then announce:

"My dear, I have just arranged for an ocean voyage for myself. You are, of course, more than welcome to come along. In fact, I have already arranged for your reservations. But of course the final decision is up to you."

In other words, take it or leave it. What is the woman to do? To go along is the "best" she can do in view of the payoff matrix. "Fairness" goes by the wayside. She can, of course, "teach him a lesson" by going off by herself, but she will be a loser too if she does. Besides, we did not say anything about the possibility of the situation arising again in the future. (Lessons are no good unless they can be used in future situations.) For all we know, there may not be a next time. We may suppose, then, that the woman, faced with a *fait accompli* of this sort, capitulates. But need she capitulate if she is faced only with a threat? Suppose the man says,

"My dear, whatever you do, I will go on the ocean voyage."

Should she believe the ultimatum? Or should she counter with,

"It is up to you, dear. Whatever *you* do, I am going to the mountains."

The game has been reduced to a battle of wills, not wits. In other words, the clear-cut game of strategy situation has been carried beyond the depth of game theory. Psychological or other considerations must be invoked to solve the induced "bargaining problem." Much work in the extensions of game theory has been done related to bargaining (12, 73, 81, 104, 105). We shall give brief indications on the nature of this research in the next chapter. For the time being, let us return to our couple jockeying for position.

Suppose now they *cannot* communicate. They are making arrangements separately, hoping that the arrangements will coincide and also hoping for the best payoff.

The man may now reason as follows. "I'd like to go on that ocean voyage, but she likes mountains best. It won't do me any good to be bullheaded. It might if I could *tell* her that I will go to sea no matter what she does. But I can't tell her, so I can't force her to come along, and since she likes the ocean voyage least, there is little likelihood that she will choose it. Now will she choose the mountains? Hardly. She will be afraid that I will not choose the mountains, for she knows that I like the mountains least. The one and only alternative left is the compromise at the seashore. It is reasonable to suppose that both of us will come to the same conclusion and that both will conclude that the other has come to the same conclusion and also that the other is aware that the other has come to the same conclusion, etc."

Here, then, is a situation reminiscent of the equilibrium pair of strategy choices. The equilibrium has something to do with the "symmetry" of the game. The choice (a_2, b_2) is somehow "special," because of its central position in a symmetrical payoff scale. The players may well choose it as the best chance of making the same choice. The silent communication made possible by the symmetry is just sufficient to allow them to avoid going separately but not sufficient to allow them to abuse the communication privilege by threatening each other with unilateral action.

Of course, it may happen that each will try to please the other, as the couple in O. Henry's story did ("The Gift of the Magi"), and both will be the losers in the result (not counting the satisfaction of knowing that each thought of the other first: this has not been included in the utility payoffs). We shall bypass the difficulty occasioned by misplaced altruism.

THE ROLE OF THREAT IN BARGAINING

The moral of the foregoing example (we shall always try to squeeze a moral out of the various aspects of game theory, which on the face of it appears quite amoral) is that the role of communication in situations involving a mixture of parallel and opposite interests is an ambivalent one. On the one hand, the possibility of communication may serve to lead the players to a quick "equitable" solution and to avoid misinterpreting each other's intentions; on the other hand the absence of communication may *force* an "equitable" solution simply because neither party has a chance to intimidate the other.

To see this clearly, consider the policy of "brinkmanship," publicized some time ago as a basis of enlightened foreign policy. The brinkmanship gambit depends essentially on saying to the opponent, "This is an issue on which we must have our way or else we go to war. We know that we may stand to lose everything in a war. But so do you. You will lose much less if you yield on this issue than if you fight. Therefore it is in your interest to yield." (The game of "chicken," played in some teenage circles, is analogous.)

The effectiveness of this gambit depends entirely on how firmly the opponent believes what you are saying. If he disbelieves you, both you and he lose. Effective communication (the ability to communicate so as to be believed) is essential in any policy based on threats.

But if there is no way to communicate the threat, the game on the brink cannot be played at all, and the danger of mutual annihilation may be actually less than if communication is possible. A gunman is helpless when faced by a victim who has no idea of what the gunman wants. The worst situation arises when threats are understood but not *believed*. Hence the ambiguity of the role of communication in the policy of threat.

In a policy of *conciliation,* on the other hand, the role of communication is crucial. Suppose, for example, Jedesland (cf. Chapter I) firmly resolves that it will never commit aggression against Andersland. If only Andersland could believe it, it too could make such a commitment (assuming war is disastrous to both). But belief in the other's intentions depends on intangibles. In a situation of mutual suspicion trust is hard to come by, because of the disaster that threatens if trust is misplaced. The outcome depends essentially on the communication process, not only on the formal structure of the game.

HANGING TOGETHER AND SEPARATELY

A typical illustration of how lack of mutual trust, coupled with perfectly "rational" considerations, leads to disaster is given by the now well-known two-person non-zero-sum game, nicknamed the Prisoner's Dilemma. The name derives from the anecdote used to illustrate the mixed motives which underlie the game.

Two suspects are questioned separately by the district attorney. They are guilty of the crime of which they are suspected, but the D.A. does not have sufficient evidence to convict either. The state has, however, sufficient evidence to convict both of a lesser offense. The alternatives open to the suspects, A and B, are to confess or not to confess to the serious crime. They are separated and cannot communicate. The outcomes are as follows. If both confess, both get severe sentences, which are, however, somewhat reduced because of the confession. If one confesses (turns state's evidence), the other gets the book thrown at him, and the informer goes scot free. If neither confesses, they cannot be convicted of the serious crime, but will surely be tried and convicted for the lesser offense.

In these terms, letting a_1 and b_1 stand for "confess" and a_2 and b_2 for "not confess," we represent the game by the following matrix of payoffs. As usual, the first entry in each box is the payoff to A:

$$\begin{array}{cc} & b_1 \qquad\quad b_2 \\ \begin{array}{c} a_1 \\ a_2 \end{array} \left[\begin{array}{cc} -5, -5 & 10, -10 \\ -10, \ 10 & 5, \ \ 5 \end{array} \right] \end{array}$$

Matrix 10

What should A do under the circumstances? If he could only be sure that B will stand his ground, he would too, he thinks at first. Or would he? If B does not confess, why shouldn't he, A, confess and go scot free?

"In fact," A reasons, "no matter *what* B does, I am better off confessing. If he does confess, I would be a chump not to and take the whole rap (—10). If he doesn't confess, I stand to gain by confessing, since if I do, I won't have to take that other rap. Either way you look at it, I am better off if I sing."

The trouble with this cold calculation of self-interest is that B may reason the same way. If he does, both end up with —5 (somewhat commuted severe sentence), whereas if they trusted each other's integrity (as it is understood in the underworld), they would end up with +5 each (only a mild sentence for a misdemeanor). Of course, if they could talk to each other, they could make a deal. But they are held incommunicado; so what should they do?

Some workers in game theory insist that game theory does not prescribe to anyone what to do (61, p. 63). Game theory is a mathematical discipline. It draws necessary conclusions from a set of given assumptions. The conclusion to be drawn from the sort of calculation of self-interest just described is "confess" (assuming that collusion is not possible). If the results of this conclusion are not the best possible results (in the sense that both prisoners would be better off if neither confessed), this is too bad. "There ought to be a law against such games." And there frequently is, as Luce and Raiffa point out.

But others will not swallow this disclaimer. Various arguments have been advanced purporting to show the inadequacy of the theory of non-zero-sum games. I will offer a critique which seems germane to me.

THE INADEQUACY OF INDIVIDUAL RATIONALITY

The theory of the zero-sum game was conceived on the basis of a natural definition of "rationality" and did prescribe a mode of action (at least implicitly). The rationale for this mode of action was two-fold. First, one did the best one could for oneself under the circumstances. Second, one imputed to the opponent the same sort of motivation, and the same sort of cognition. The result was the maximin solution.

If only one is willing to extend a similar rationale to certain non-zero-sum games (with collusion disallowed), one can obtain pairs of strategy choices which are more acceptable than the harsh conclusions drawn from essentially zero-sum game considerations.

Examine once again the Prisoner's Dilemma. Instead of taking as the basis of calculations the question "Where am I better off?" suppose each prisoner starts with the following basic assumption: "My partner is like me. Therefore he is likely to act like me. If I conclude that I should confess, he will probably also conclude the same. If I conclude that I should not confess, this is the way he probably thinks. In the first case, we both get —5; in the second case, we both get +5. This indicates that I personally benefit by not confessing."

I can almost hear a chorus of derision. I have let morality temper reason, I will be told. How can my assumption of what my opponent will do influence what he will actually do? By telepathy? Yet is this not what I am assuming when I argue that he will act as I do and therefore decide what I decide? This is clearly absurd, since it implies that if I switch my decision, so will he. But if there is no communication between us, how is this possible?

My reply is that we choose our underlying assumptions arbitrarily. Many such assumptions, as has repeatedly appeared in science, seem absurd. It is the consequences of the assumption which are put to the test. In this case, I am recommending a particular choice of assumptions and submit that if my recommendations are accepted, the consequences will be beneficial to both participants.

But, it will be objected, suppose my assumptions are accepted by one party but not by the other. Then he who follows my advice will be the sucker. Quite so. But the recommendations of playing the zero-sum game, like mine, are also directed at *both* players. Ah, the objection continues, but in that case, if only one party accepts the recommendation, *he* will be the one who stands to gain, or at least will not lose. That is why the recommendation is easy to take. Yes, I reply, but in my case, *both* players stand to gain if they accept my recommendations. Therefore, I maintain, my recommendation has at least as much force as the maximin recommendation of the zero-sum game. My recommendation is more difficult to accept, because our habits of thought (including definitions of rationality, etc.) are too deeply ingrained in terms of individuals and their individual interests abstracted from a more inclusive context. We have difficulty in making social values the fundamental starting point of our definition of rationality. But the failure to do so, as in the case when rationality is defined only in terms of self-interest, leads to the anomalous conclusion that two "irrational" individuals will do better than two "rational" ones!

Actually, the maximin recommendation is not made in a social vacuum either. It too is based on an assumption about the *other,* namely, the assumption of the other's rationality with respect to his own self-interest. Without this assumption, the maximin strategy is not nearly so attractive; it fails to cash in *completely* on the other's possible mistakes. If the co-operative strategy recommended in the Prisoner's Dilemma is faulty, it is faulty for a similar reason, namely in the case that the assumptions made about the other are not valid. In the zero-sum game, these are assumptions of conventional "rationality." In the non-zero-sum game of the kind considered, they are assumptions of the other's "good will." The good will is not the vague, perhaps intuitively acceptable but operationally undefinable notion of the moralist. It can be as rigorously defined as "rationality" is (implicitly) defined in game theory.[51]

If we start with social values, the reasoning is straightforward enough. Each player presumably examines the whole payoff matrix. The first question he asks is "When are we both best off?" The answer in our case is unique: at (a_2, b_2). Next, "What is necessary to come to this choice?" Answer: the assumption that whatever I will do, the other will, made by both parties. The conclusion is, "I am one of the parties; therefore I will make this assumption."

Is this rationale less "logical" than the self-interest reasoning cited above? To some it would seem less logical, but I suspect only because they persist in a certain (arbitrary) framework of thought.

The assumption of similarity is indeed the rationale which induces the individual citizen to vote. The argument that a single vote "makes no appreciable difference" is countered with "Yes, but if everyone thought so, the will of the collective would find no expression." This is the rationale behind any co-operative effort. It is conceivable that the (minimal) danger inherent in submitting to vaccination actually exceeds the (still more minimal) danger of remaining unvaccinated. But if *everyone* minimized the danger to himself alone, everyone would be subjected to the much greater danger of a smallpox epidemic. The Prisoner's Dilemma is a powerful example of a social situation in which the "sum" of the two individual interests adds up to a disadvantage to both. The reason this appears paradoxical, I suspect, is that we have been too long accustomed to the uncritical acceptance of the laissez faire principle, namely, that a totality of individuals seeking their respective self-interests by *shortsighted* calculations actually will move toward the realization of this self-interest by the operation of economic laws derived from the assumptions of a free competitive market economy.

AGAIN THE BALANCE OF TERROR

Let us examine the pertinence of these considerations to the position in which our two unfortunate countries, Jedesland and Andersland, find themselves. It is sometimes argued by some of the Jedeslanders that Jedesland should attack Andersland before the latter has the chance to do the same. Extrapolating somewhat a few years hence, suppose both have their missile-launchers zeroed in on each other's cities. The "necessity" to launch the attack first now seems imperative. There is, however, perhaps a speck of sanity left in those who control the final irrevocable act. Yet, as they become aware of the "necessity," they cannot but become convinced that *the other is probably coming to the same conclusion*. The perceived "necessity" is thus self-confirming. The more certain it seems, the more inescapable it becomes at an accelerating rate, ultimately ending in a mad rush on *both* sides to the launching platforms. Two scorpions in a bottle, to use Robert J. Oppenheimer's gloomy comparison.

There are cases where the "assumption of similarity" recommended here has no value. This is true, for example, in a game of matching pennies, conceived as a non-zero-sum game, that is, suppose both partners win if they match and lose otherwise. The assumption of similarity will in no way help them, because the one choice is in no way distinguished from the other. The assumption of similarity is of value only if these conditions hold:

1. Communication would be of benefit to both but is impossible.

2. There is a pair of strategy choices *in some way distinguished* so that each player can reasonably assume that the other will use this distinguishing feature as a cue. In the choice of a vacation site, where communication was disallowed, a pair was distinguished by its symmetrical position. In the

Prisoner's Dilemma, a pair was distinguished by reason of its uniqueness in giving the best total payoff.

The best payoff (this is essentially the Pareto point discussed in Chapter IV) plays a prominent part in games where communication (collusion) is allowed. Our contention here is that in some cases it can be made the basis of "rational" play, even when communication is not possible, provided rationality is properly defined.

CHAPTER XI

GAMES WITH COLLUSION

THE "DILEMMA" VANISHES from the Prisoner's Dilemma if the two can get together. In that case, since they can agree on a joint choice of strategy, there seems to be no question that the only course worthy of being called rational is (a_2, b_2), that is, for neither to confess. Still the general situation of this sort is not so simple as it appears from the elementary example. Let us take another instance shown in Matrix 11, without the built-in symmetry of the Prisoner's Dilemma:

$$
\begin{array}{cc}
 & \begin{array}{cc} b_1 & \quad\quad b_2 \end{array} \\
\begin{array}{c} a_1 \\ a_2 \end{array} & \left[\begin{array}{cc} 9,\quad 9 & 2,\quad 15 \\ 10,\,-10 & 0,\,-30 \end{array} \right]
\end{array}
$$

Matrix 11

It seems sensible to agree on (a_1, b_1), because there the joint payoff is the greatest. But suppose A insists that he must have 10, even though it means a loss of 10 for B (i.e., A insists that they agree on (a_2, b_1)). What can B do? Threaten A with b_2 if A insists on choosing a_2? But he stands to lose more than A does at (a_2, b_2). He would be cutting off his nose to spite his face. His bargaining position is not good.

Consider now B's potentiality for making demands. Suppose he insists on 15 and announces that he will play b_2. A's counterthreat of a_2 is effective, because while A stands to lose only 2, as they pass from (a_1, b_2) to (a_2, b_2), B stands to lose 45. Both A's threat and counterthreat have teeth in them, while

B's do not. Must they then settle on (a_2, b_1)? This does not seem satisfactory either. After all, if A insists on having his 10, they can still agree on (a_1, b_1) and get their total of 18, after which they can split the 18 so that A gets 10 and B gets 8—that is, they can do this if "utiles" can be transferred, and it is by no means certain that they always can be.

Such problems have been treated in game theory in a variety of ways. The important question underlying the various treatments is whether utility is transferable and conservative. If we equate utility to the actual amount of some commodity, say money, the answer is, of course, yes. In that case, deals can be made in which the agreement to play the best joint strategy is sealed by monetary transactions.

However, utility can be transferable without being conservative. That is, after being redistributed, the total amount of utility may not remain the same. As we have seen, the utility of money may by no means be the same as the amount of money. If A has $100 to his name, and B has $1,000,000, the chances are that B can induce A to do things for a consideration of $100 that A cannot induce B to do for the same consideration. Contrariwise, B's threat of depriving A of $100, we rather suspect, would ordinarily carry more weight than a similar threat on the part of A, even if the threats had equal probabilities of being carried out.

Recall that the utility, as it has been used in "classical" game theory,[52] has been defined on an interval scale only. In this sense, the comparison of interpersonal utilities (the accepted technical term) makes no sense. One cannot therefore even raise the question of whether A stands to lose more than B stands to gain. Yet we have been raising just such questions. The questions *acquire* sense if additional properties are assigned to utility, for example if it is assumed to be transferable or both transferable and conservative.

The assumption of a utility which is both transferable and

conservative is, of course, the strongest assumption. It is implicit in much of classical economics.[53] It is not reprehensible to make it, because every theoretical investigation rests on some arbitrary assumptions. But if it is made, it must be made explicitly. One of the great heuristic values of game theory, especially its development since 1944, is the impetus it has given to various equally reasonable assumptions which can be made about the nature of utility. The consequences of each set of assumptions must be made separately and clearly labeled as to the explicit assumptions from which they are derived. A theory is clear only if its conclusions are distinctly related to its postulates.

A BARGAINING PROBLEM WITH NONTRANSFERABLE UTILITY

In what follows we will examine a non-zero-sum game with an implied bargaining problem in which utility is not transferable. At one stage it will be necessary to compare utilities of the two players. Since interval scale utility is in principle noncomparable interpersonally, such a comparison must imply the imposition of some *standard* scale to which the utilities of both players will have to be reduced. The definition of such a standard scale is the heart of the bargaining solution. It amounts to a definition of equity, as we shall see.

In my choice of illustration, I cannot do better than borrow Braithwaite's charming fable about two amateur musicians, Luke and Matthew (12).

Luke likes to play classical music on the piano. Matthew loves to improvise hot jazz on a trumpet. The degree of enjoyment each derives from his hobby is seriously diminished in the presence of noise. Unfortunately, the two men live in adjoining nonsoundproof flats and have only one hour each evening to play—the same hour. How can they jointly arrange for dividing the practicing evenings so as not to interfere with each other's pleasure?

Ordinarily, the two men might come together and arrange

to play or to be silent on alternate evenings. But is this an "equitable" solution? Does it take into account the strengths of preferences of the two and the amount of pressure each can exert on the other in the bargaining situation? Certainly not every bargain results in an evenly split difference. If I offer $20,000 for a house, and the seller asks $25,000, whether we can agree on the price and what the price will be on which we agree depends on many things, most of them intangible. To mention some, it depends on how desperately I need the house and whether I can borrow enough money, on how quickly the owner wants to sell, on the availability of other houses on the market and of other potential buyers, and, by no means least, on the forcefulness with which the offer (or the price asked) can be made to appear final. If I bargain tightly, that is, add small amounts to my offer with obvious reluctance, this may turn out to my advantage (if the seller wants badly to sell and if he does not conclude that I am bluffing), or to my disadvantage otherwise. There are even subtler influences. If somehow I have encroached on the sensibility of the seller, he may set down a "final" price in such a way that he will not be at liberty to budge from it without loss of face.

At least some of these vaguely perceived circumstances must somehow be taken into account in a theory of bargaining. Game theory proposes to take them (partly) into account by first of all assigning utilities to all possible outcomes. In the case of the house sale, a pair of utilities could be assigned to each price of sale (one to the buyer, one to the seller) and also, of course, to the outcome "no sale." The resulting matrix will then reveal the potentialities of the bargaining situation. It will appear that each player has certain vantage points. The solution of a bargaining situation is expected to take these vantage points into account, to the extent that they are recognizable.

The case of Luke and Matthew should be similarly represented before we start our analysis. The utilities for the four possible situations (all combinations of "play" and "not play") must be indicated for each player. Now it is easy to assume that each player has a certain order of preferences for the four outcomes. In our example, Luke has the following order of preferences:

1. Luke plays while Matthew remains silent.
2. Matthew plays while Luke remains silent. (Luke rather likes Matthew's playing.)
3. Both are silent.
4. Both play. (Luke would rather spend a silent evening than play against interference.)

Matthew's preferences are as follows:

1. Matthew plays alone.
2. Luke plays alone.
3. Both play. (Being a jazz player, Matthew does not suffer as much from cacophony as Luke.)
4. Neither plays. (Matthew, the extrovert, hates silence.)

As was said, it is quite possible that these orders of preference are ascertainable. But this is not enough for game theory. The preferences must be assigned numbers. True, the numbers need not be uniquely assigned, but however they are assigned, the ratios of the differences in the utilities of each player must remain constant.

To determine a set of numbers to qualify as utilities is much more difficult than to ascertain the order of preferences. The latter can in most cases be ascertained by straightforward questions of the type "Which do you prefer?" But to get actual utility measures, we must ask "outlandish" questions, which we are not sure will be properly understood, let alone definitively answered. For example, to determine the relative "distances" between Luke's preferences, one could ask:

"Suppose you split the evenings on which you alone play and the silent evenings in a certain ratio. What should the ratio be so that you will be indifferent between that arrangement and the alternative of having Matthew play alone every evening?"

Not many people confronted with a question of this sort would be sure of just what was wanted of them. But we will not take this matter up at this point. The critique of such matters as well as of game theory in general will be taken up in the last chapter of Part II. Suppose then that the difficulties are overcome, and that numbers can be assigned to the preferences. In Braithwaite's example, Luke's preferences are weighted 7, 4, 2, and 1, respectively; Matthew's 10, 3, 2, and 1, respectively (Matrix 12):

$$
\begin{array}{cc}
& M_1 \quad\ M_2 \\
\begin{array}{c} L_1 \\ L_2 \end{array} &
\left[\begin{array}{cc} 1,\ 2 & 7, 3 \\ 4, 10 & 2, 1 \end{array} \right]
\end{array}
$$

Matrix 12. Subscript 1: play; subscript 2: not play

These numbers may be taken as *the* utilities. But any other sets will do which are derived from these sets by multiplying each number by the same factor or by adding an equal quantity to each or by both of these operations performed in either order. It is only the ratio of differences which must remain unaltered. To illustrate, suppose we multiply Luke's utility numbers by 3 and add 5 to the products. His utilities then become 8, 11, 17, and 26. But the ratio of the differences of the first two to that of the last two is still $\frac{3}{9} = \frac{1}{3}$, just as it is with the original numbers. The problem posed by Braithwaite is now the following. Any solution of the bargaining situation between Luke and Matthew should remain invariant no matter how the utility numbers are assigned, provided only that the difference ratios remain constant.

Note that we cannot very seriously treat Luke's and Matthew's utilities as transferable, let alone conservative, like money. To assume this would mean to believe that the loss of any specific pleasure, like music-making, can be compensated by something else. Although the market mentality does encourage such an assumption (everything has a price), the assumption is belied by anyone who refuses to be bribed to do anything or to refrain from doing anything. Surely, some of the people at least some of the time find themselves in situations where they don't care to be bought.

If it were not for the nontransferable character of music-making pleasure, a part of the solution of our problem would be obvious. If utilities could be added and if we took the "weights" for the utilities, it would be clear to Luke and to Matthew that *together* they stand to gain most in the outcome (a_2, b_1), namely if Matthew plays every night and Luke holds his peace forever. For equity's sake, Matthew would have to compensate Luke somehow. If the utility were transferable, he would just transfer some to Luke out of their common stock. But since these utilities are not transferable, Luke's loss cannot be made good. Therefore, the Pareto point (a_2, b_1) does not look nearly so attractive as it did on previous occasions.

Let us examine the payoff matrix (Matrix 12) more closely. We see that the interests of the two players are partly opposed and partly coincident. For example, each would prefer the other to play (if he is not playing himself), an attitude not typical of antagonistic rivalry. But each does prefer to play alone, so that considerable individual competitive self-interest is involved. If only these two aspects of the problem (the co-operative and the competitive) could be disentangled, we could possibly arrive at a solution. For we know how to treat situations in which the interests are strictly opposed. They are zero-sum games, leading to the maximin solution. On the other hand, situations in which the interests are coincident present no problem at all, provided communication is allowed, which it is in this case. (Luke and Matthew commute on the same train and keep discussing their problem in terms of perfect frankness and good will.) It is the intermediate "mixed" cases which are troublesome. If only the intermediate case could be resolved into two games, one completely co-operative, the other completely competitive, perhaps a solution could be arrived at after all. Such things do happen in real life. Alliances are formed to gain some common aim; then the falling out occurs and the fight for the spoils. Some game theoreticians propose a reversal of this usual order: fight for advantage first; then co-operate.

Let us look at the relative advantage of one player over the other in each outcome. We still assume that the utilities entered into the matrix in Matrix 12 are the *actual* numerical values of the utilities, that is, that the zero point and the unit of the common utility scale have been fixed. Now we can subtract the utilities from each other. Taking the differences, we arrive at a matrix, each of whose entries represents the relative advantage Luke has over Matthew in each of the four outcomes:

$$
\begin{array}{cc}
 & M_1 \quad M_2 \\
\begin{array}{c} L_1 \\ L_2 \end{array} &
\left[\begin{array}{cc} -1 & 4 \\ -6 & 1 \end{array} \right]
\end{array}
$$

Matrix 13

Of course, the corresponding relative advantage of Matthew over Luke is represented by the same matrix with all the signs reversed. Therefore, the matrix represents a zero-sum game with a saddle point at (L_1, M_1). The value of this game is -1 for Luke ($+1$ for Matthew). That is to say, in jockeying for *relative* advantage, Luke can see to it that Matthew gets no more than 1 unit of relative advantage over him, and Matthew can be sure of securing this much relative advantage over Luke. This happens if both of them play. Of course, it is by no means the best arrangement for either of them, since each would rather listen to the other than play in competition with him. But this is because we have not yet explored the *co-operative* aspect of the game. Here is where mixed strategies come in. The way in which the evenings will be apportioned

corresponds to different mixed strategies. The strategy pair
(L_1, M_1) is merely a point of departure, a vantage point which
each man can assure for himself at the start of negotiations. In
the language of diplomacy, this is the "basis of negotiation."
From here they can both improve their lot, each keeping, however, the same relative advantage which he obtained "fair and
square," in a manner of speaking, in the preliminary zero-sum
game.

To show how this joint "improvement" proceeds, we introduce a visual aid, a convenient diagrammatic representation
of two-person games. Since each entry in the matrix consists
of two numbers, every entry can be represented as a point in a
two-dimensional co-ordinate system. The two co-ordinates of
the point (the horizontal and the vertical) will be the respective
payoffs to the two players. The payoff matrix will appear as a
set of points on a diagram, such as is shown in Figure 9.

The mathematics of game theory now teaches us that if the
two players play all possible mixed strategies (collusion being
allowed), then by choosing a proper pair of mixtures they can
get a pair of (long-run) payoffs to correspond to any point
inside the quadrilateral or on its boundary. In particular, the
four corners of the quadrilateral correspond to the four pairs
of pure strategies in the game represented in Matrix 12.[54]

Now if Luke and Matthew are to stick to the result of the
zero-sum game, that is, keep their relative advantage with
respect to each other, they ought to choose strategies to lie on
the line at each of whose points the vertical co-ordinate exceeds
the horizontal by 1 unit. This is the straight line inclined 45°
to the horizontal and going through the point $(1, 2)$, shown
in Figure 9. Any pair of payoffs on this line can be realized by
an appropriate choice and co-ordination of two mixed strategies.
So it is a matter of choosing a point on this line, which will
prescribe the mixed strategies to realize the payoff which the
point represents. Which point should Luke and Matthew

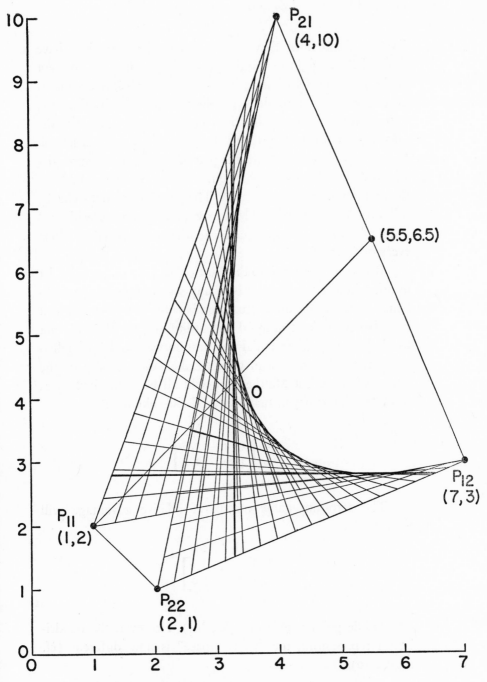

Figure 9. (After Braithwaite.) Graphical representation of the mixed-motive games between the two musicians. For explanation see text and Note 54.

choose? Remember they are now co-operating: they have finished their "fighting" and are now jointly making the best of the situation. Obviously, the point that lies as far up and as far to the right as possible is their best choice, subject, of course, to the constraints of the situation. This is the intersection of the dotted line with the "northeast" boundary of our quadrilateral. It remains only to determine the pair of mixed (joint) strategies which will realize this payoff point. The problem is solvable by the method of analytic geometry. The payoff turns out to be 5.5 utiles for Luke and 6.5 for Matthew, and the way to achieve it is to split the evenings equally, so that each practices alone every other evening.[55]

Before we inquire into the "justice" of this compromise, let us ask whether this answer is in any way unique to the problem. Recall that we used actual numbers for our utilities. But it must be always kept in mind that utility in game theory is not fixed absolutely. With equal justification we could have taken another set of numbers, in which Luke's utiles would be the same as before, but Matthew's would all be multiplied by 2. In that case, our payoff matrix would look like this:

$$
\begin{array}{c c c}
 & M_1 & M_2 \\
\begin{array}{c} L_1 \\ L_2 \end{array} &
\left[\begin{array}{c c} 1,\ 4 & 7,6 \\ 4,20 & 2,2 \end{array}\right]
\end{array}
$$

Matrix 14

The zero-sum game matrix of relative advantage will then be:

$$
\begin{array}{c c c}
 & M_1 & M_2 \\
\begin{array}{c} L_1 \\ L_2 \end{array} &
\left[\begin{array}{c c} -3 & 1 \\ -16 & 0 \end{array}\right]
\end{array}
$$

Matrix 15

The saddle point is again at (L_1, M_1). However, the quadrilateral representing the "payoff space" is now different (cf. Figure 10).

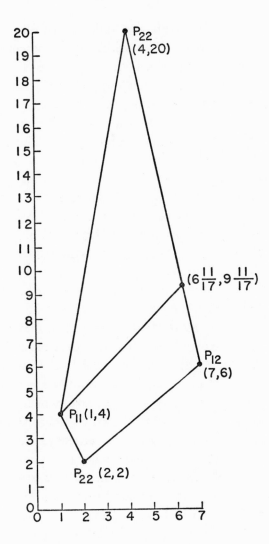

Figure 10

Starting with (L_1, M_1), as prescribed by the saddle point of the zero-sum game, we now arrive along the co-operative line at a different best solution, which gives $6^{11}/_{17}$ utiles to Luke and $9^{11}/_{17}$ to Matthew. The time split is now 15 out of 17 evenings to Luke and only 2 out of 17 to Matthew.[56]

Starting with two different choices of utility scale, we have arrived at two widely different compromises. This, of course will not do: both compromises cannot be equally just. We now see the crux of our problem. To arrive at a compromise which is somehow unique, we must agree on the zero point and the unit of utility for each man. Once this is done, the relative advantage matrix becomes unique. The zero-sum game can then be solved, and the starting point on the unique payoff diagram determined. The joint maximization point (the compromise) will then also be unique.

The principle by which such a common utility scale is established is the principle of arbitration. Braithwaite's principle of arbitration depends on a "symmetry argument," which we shall now present.

We note first that there is a certain strategy mixture, which Luke can employ to guarantee himself a certain level of utility, *no matter what* Matthew does. You may verify that this mixture is to play L_1 one-fourth of the time and L_2 three-fourths of the time. Although the actual level of utility will depend on the units in which Luke's utilities are measured and on the zero point, the *strategy mixture,* which guarantees the minimum, will always be the same. Braithwaite calls this strategy mixture Luke's *prudential* strategy: Luke is prudent if he guarantees for himself what he can get under *any* circumstances. Naturally, Matthew, too, has such a prudential strategy. You may verify that it amounts to playing M_1 one-fifth of the time and M_2 four-fifths of the time.[57]

Besides these prudential strategies, each has a *contraprudential* strategy, which has the following property: if the other plays his prudential strategy, the contraprudential strategy guarantees that the other gets *no more* than his guaranteed minimum. (In zero-sum games, the prudential and the contraprudential strategies coincide.) The contraprudential strategy, then, is the power each has over the other to keep the other down to his minimum. If now Matthew sticks to his prudential strategy, and Luke plays his contraprudential strategy, Luke will gain utility over and above his guaranteed minimum. The amount of gain will depend on the units with which Luke's utility is measured. The same holds for Matthew.

Braithwaite now proposes the following definition of equity: *Let the units with which the utilities of each player are measured be such that they gain equal amounts when each passes from his prudential to his contraprudential strategy, while the other sticks to his prudential strategy.* Let, in other words, the units of utility reflect the bargaining power of each player.

Using this criterion, we find that if the original utilities of Matthew (Matrix 12) are multiplied by ⅘, "equity" will be established.[58] We then proceed exactly as before, solving the new zero-sum game, now given by Matrix 16:

$$
\begin{array}{cc}
 & \begin{array}{cc} M_1 & M_2 \end{array} \\
\begin{array}{c} L_1 \\ L_2 \end{array} & \left[\begin{array}{cc} -3/5 & 23/5 \\ -4 & 2/5 \end{array}\right]
\end{array}
$$

Matrix 16

and carrying the co-operative solution along the 45° line starting at the saddle point $(1, 8/5)$ to the northeast boundary. It will now intersect that boundary at the point $(223/43, 311/43)$. To insure this distribution of utilities, Luke will have 17 out of 43 evenings reserved for his classical music, and Matthew will have 26 out of 43 evenings for his jazz. According to Braithwaite's definition of equity, this is an equitable compromise.

H. Raiffa (81) has proposed a somewhat different scheme. His definition of equity is the following. Call each player's lowest payoff o, and his highest payoff 1. Subdivide the interval from o to 1 into steps, whose lengths are proportional to the given utility intervals. Then solve the resulting zero-sum game, and carry out the co-operative solution. According to Raiffa, then, the payoff matrix for Luke and Matthew should be:

$$
\begin{array}{cc}
 & M_1 \qquad\qquad M_2 \\
\begin{array}{c} L_1 \\ L_2 \end{array}
\left[
\begin{array}{cc}
(0, 1/9) & (1, 2/9) \\
(1/2, 1) & (1/6, 0)
\end{array}
\right]
\end{array}
$$

Matrix 17

The zero-sum game gives Matthew an advantage of ⅑ over Luke. The final solution in this case turns out to be 17 out of 46 evenings for Luke, and 29 out of 46 for Matthew. Raiffa's solution is slightly more favorable to Matthew than is Braithwaite's.

There is no way to decide *a priori* whose definition of "equity" is more "equitable," Braithwaite's or Raiffa's. Certainly other equally plausible definitions can be offered. The value of these exercises is not to find out what "equity really means" but rather to explore the various *precise* meanings which can be *given* to the vague term "equity" and to follow the consequences of these meanings to wherever they may lead us. The essence of fair compromise is not in this formula or that but in the willingness of both parties to commit themselves in advance to abide by the consequences of *some* formula, which seems fair to them *independently of the particular situation in which they may find themselves.*

CHAPTER XII

COALITIONS

WE HAVE SEEN that if the two players in a non-zero-sum game can make an agreement and can make it stick, they can both do better than if they play against each other. If we assume that the winnings are paid by a "house," we can include the house as a third player in the game. This player has no strategy choice, but he does participate in the payoffs. In fact, his payoff is always the negative of the sum of the other two payoffs. Thus, if we include the house, we have a three-person zero-sum game.

Any N-person game whether zero-sum or not can always be pictured as a zero-sum game by adding a fictitious $(N + 1)$-th player, whose winnings (or losses) equal the summed losses (or winnings) of all the others. Since the $(N + 1)$-th player makes no moves, his inclusion makes no difference in the original game's strategic structure; but it is advantageous to include him, because his presence lets us treat every game as a zero-sum game. Zero-sum games are easier to treat from a unified point of view than non-zero-sum games.[59]

Here it may occur to ask why the difficulties of the non-zero-sum game were at all emphasized if they can be circumvented by adding another player. Note, however, that adding a player to a two-person game turns it into a three-person game, which is complicated by the possibility of forming coalitions. In the case of the Prisoner's Dilemma, if we assume that a coalition of the two players against the house will inadvertently form, the difficulty raised by the non-zero-sum game disappears. But, as we have seen, it is by no means certain that such a coalition will form, especially in the absence of communication. Even when communication is allowed, it is not generally obvious which of the many coalitions possible in an N-person game will, in fact, form. We see, therefore, that theoretical interest shifts, as soon as we pass to the N-person game, to the question of coalition formation and its effect on the outcomes of the game.

Let there now be N players, and we may assume that the game is zero-sum, because if it is not, we can always make it so by adding another (dummy) player. Let all conceivable coalitions be possible. There are 2^N of them. Let us also suppose that once a coalition of any k players is formed, the remaining $N - k$ players will form a countercoalition. It is to their advantage to do so, because collectively a set of players will do no worse if they form a coalition of the whole set than if they do not. A coalition means pooling together and co-ordinating the available strategies. The members of a coalition can always play their strategies the same way as they would have played them independently and so can do as well collectively as individually. But they may be able to co-ordinate their strategies to their *collective* advantage. Obviously, by the collective payoff of a coalition we mean the sum of the payoffs to its members.[60]

If a coalition and a countercoalition form, a two-"person" zero-sum game results in which the two coalitions are the two players. Then the theory of two-person zero-sum games applies, and there is nothing to say about the outcomes which has not already been said.

The important questions of N-person game theory (with coalitions allowed) concern, therefore, the process of coalition formation itself. In particular, one might ask:

1. Of all the 2^{N-1} possible ways of splitting the N players into two opposition coalitions,[61] which ones will actually form or at least are likely to form?

2. How will the collective payoff of a coalition be apportioned among its members?

Von Neumann's approach to these questions (125) begins as follows. Each of the 2^N coalitions, considered as a player in a two-person zero-sum game, "commands" a certain payoff. This is the maximin payoff which the coalition can insure *collectively* for itself and also which it cannot hope to make larger, because the countercoalition can insure the complementary amount. Remember that this maximin is called the value of the game to the player in question. To each coalition, therefore, there is assigned a certain value. This assignment of values to coalitions is called the characteristic function of the N-person game. In other words, the characteristic function is a table, on one side of which are listed all the 2^N coalitions and on the other the corresponding values.[62]

In answering the question which coalition will form, one might be tempted to answer, "The one that commands the largest payoff." But two difficulties immediately arise.

1. What happens when several coalitions command the same payoff?

2. If we assume that the coalition which commands the largest payoff will automatically form, then we also assume that the coalition which commands the *smallest* payoff (actually the largest negative payoff) will also form, for that is the countercoalition. While the spontaneous formation of the first coalition seems in accordance with common sense, the spontaneous formation of the second coalition seems against common sense.

It may be argued that the second coalition will not form "spontaneously" but only as a response (actually the best response) to the formation of the first coalition. But why should the first coalition form "spontaneously"? Will not the players not included in the strongest coalition try to prevent its formation, since they stand to lose most if it is formed?

We see that in the initial jockeying which leads to the

formation of coalitions influences can indeed be exerted for and against specific coalitions, namely in the form of promises of greater shares of the payoffs to players whose addition makes a coalition stronger.

These inducements may well operate in situations where several coalitions command the same payoff. Those "left out" may well exert pressure to break one of the coalitions up in order to form another in which they are included. The total payoff to the new coalition may be the same as to the old, but some *individuals* may stand to gain in one of them at the expense of others.

As we shall see in a moment, an analysis of possible jockeying maneuvers leads to extremely unsatisfactory but instructive conclusions.

DIVIDING A PRIZE BY MAJORITY VOTE

Consider the simplest possible three-person game in which coalitions make sense.[63] Three men are told to divide a dollar between them, the division to be determined by majority vote.[64] Since any two have majority vote, they can freeze the third man out. The characteristic function of the game is given in Table 6.

Table 6

The characteristic function of the Divide-the-Dollar Game.

Coalition	Value
A	0
B	0
C	0
{A, B}	$1
{A, C}	$1
{B, C}	$1
{A, B, C}	$1

Each single player forms a minority and therefore commands nothing. Each pair is a majority and therefore commands the payoff of $1.

For the "grand coalition" {A, B, C} to form makes little sense, because the three players together command no more than two players, and they will have to split the collective payoff three ways instead of two. Therefore, we assume that a coalition of two will form. But which two? Assuming the personalities, kinship ties, and what not to exert no influence (there is no room for such matters in game theory), we can sidestep the problem of identifying the particular winning pair and say simply that *some* pair will form a coalition. This does not say as much as the identification of the pair would say, but it does say *something*. But let us now see what may happen if such a coalition does form.

Suppose the pair is {A, B}. Suppose moreover that the coalition is tentative. Negotiations can still go on. At this point A and B have decided to freeze C out and to split the dollar between them. Player C may now approach B with the following proposition.

"A is splitting 50-50 with you, is he? How would you like to get 60¢ if you go with me instead of with A? I stand to lose everything otherwise. I might as well settle for 40¢."

Player B may now reason (silently) as follows:

"If he will settle for 40¢, will he settle for 30¢? Why shouldn't he if he stands to lose everything otherwise? But wait. If I ask 70¢ what is to prevent him from approaching A with his 60-40 offer? If A accepts, I am sunk. So I better take his offer while the taking is good."

So a different, still tentative coalition forms, namely {B, C}, who agree to split 60-40. Now A approaches B and says:

"Well, you played it smart. Now *I* am frozen out. So I'll tell you what. I will give you 70¢ if you come back in with me."

Player B is really riding the crest now. He goes back to A and now expects 70¢ of the dollar. But now C approaches A and says:

"Aren't we *both* the suckers now? You started in with B at 50-50. Now look at you going along for 30¢. Why don't *we* two join against that operator and freeze *him* out? We can split 50-50, fair and square."

Since both A and C stand to gain by this switch, the coalition {A, C} now forms at 50-50. But now B, who has had the worst of it, approaches A once more, hat in hand. . . .

We are trapped in the same sort of circular reasoning that gave us trouble in the zero-sum game without a saddle point. However, it will be recalled that an escape from that situation was provided by the notion of mixed strategy, which re-established the maximin equilibrium of the zero-sum game, even when there was no saddle point. So far no such elegant loophole was found out of the present difficulty of shifting coalitions.

THE MEANING OF "RATIONALITY" QUESTIONED AGAIN

We will examine three different attempts to establish a semblance of order in the theory of the N-person game with coalitions allowed. First, however, let us look at the nature of the difficulty.

Game theory purports to treat the logic of strategy. We have strong intuitive feelings that if there are alternative actions then a rational man ought to be able to decide which alternative he should choose. If each alternative leads *certainly* to a known outcome, then the preference for some outcomes over others determines the choice of alternatives. No logical difficulty arises there. If each alternative may lead to one of several outcomes, then the choice is not quite so obvious. But if the probabilities of the outcomes are known, the rational man can still construct a policy: if he assigns a numerical mathematical expectation of utility associated with each alternative and chooses the alternative with the greatest mathematical expectation. Even if the actual probabilities of the outcomes are not known, the rational man can *assign* a probability to each alternative. He may be wrong, but this is the best he can do. He can still claim rationality relative to his system of beliefs.

The last two situations are associated with gambles (choice under risk or uncertainty).[65] When the decision-maker faces a rational opponent, he can still make a choice (the maximin strategy) which can be defended on strong rational grounds: the outcome of the maximin strategy is the best that he can realistically hope for.

We have further seen that in some two-person non-zero-sum games, the maximin strategy can no longer be defended on the ground that it leads to the best outcome that can be realistically hoped for. But if collusion of the two players is allowed, the best co-ordinated strategy can still be indicated.

Once we have passed to the three-person game, even the simplest one just described, none of the methods listed seemingly applies. For suppose, as we have supposed at the start, that A and B are in tentative coalition against C. If C now approaches B with his 60-40 proposition, what should B do if he is rational?

To accept might mean to invite disaster (recall that we ended our story with B frozen out). Not to accept seems no better, for what is to prevent jilted C from approaching A? Did not Stalin make a pact with Hitler presumably because the Allies would not accede to the conditions he placed on the collective security pact with them (the deployment of Soviet ground troops in Poland)?

VON NEUMANN'S "SOLUTION" OF THE N-PERSON GAME

John von Neumann (126), in developing with Oskar Morgenstern the theory of the N-person game, approached the subject as a problem of mathematics. His "solution" may not appear as a "solution" at all to someone who views the N-person game as an abstraction from real life. In this context, the problem appears to be that of determining which coalition will actually form under given circumstances or, at least, which class of coalitions is more likely to form than others. In real life we know that coalitions do form, and they do form presumably because of strategic considerations. They also last for *some* time, presumably as long as the strategic considerations which insure their stability are in force. The real life problem, then (e.g., the problem which the political scientist faces), is to relate the events of political life to strategic considerations. But we have seen that even in our simplest coalition game we have not been able to find strategic considerations which would lend any stability to any coalition and its concomitant financial arrangement!

The mathematician, however, is not bothered by this. His task is to discover relationships dictated by mathematical considerations. The translation of these relations into assertions about human behavior is a separate job. We must point out, therefore, that the purely mathematical "solution" concept proposed by von Neumann and Morgenstern, untranslated into social reality, will appear most unsatisfactory to even the most abstract-oriented social scientist. It is, however, instructive to follow von Neumann's theory of "solutions," because it has provided a starting point for other somewhat more realistic treatments of the N-person game, which we shall take up later.

First, von Neumann and Morgenstern define an *imputation*. An imputation is a particular split of the total payoff among the N players in which everyone does at least as well as he would have done if he entered no coalition. For example, the split (50, 50, 0) among the three players is an imputation. Here C does no better than if he were alone, but no worse, while A and B do better.

Next, they define what is meant by one imputation *dominating* another. Say I_1 and I_2 are two imputations. If in some subset of the players all prefer I_2 to I_1,[66] and if they are able by forming a coalition to enforce I_2, then I_2 dominates I_1. For example, if $I_1 = (50, 50, 0)$ and $I_2 = (60, 0, 40)$, then I_2 dominates I_1, because both A and C clearly prefer I_2 to I_1 and are able to enforce it by forming a coalition. On the other hand, if $I_3 = (0, 50, 50)$, then I_3 dominates I_2, because B and C prefer I_3 and are able to enforce it by forming a coalition.

Next, a solution of an N-person game is defined as a *set* of imputations with the following two properties.

1. No matter which imputation we choose *outside* the set, we can find an imputation *inside* the set which dominates it.

2. No imputation within the set dominates any other imputation within the set.

We now show that the set of the three imputations

$$I = (50, 50, 0)$$
$$J = (50, 0, 50)$$
$$K = (0, 50, 50)$$

is a solution according to the above definition.

To prove this, note that in every imputation no entry may be negative, since otherwise the affected player could do better if he joined no coalition, contrary to the definition of an imputation. Now if two of the entries are 50, then the third must be 0; so such an imputation would be either I or J or K. But we are looking for others. Among the others, therefore, no *two* entries can be more than 50, because this would make the third negative. The only other possibility is for at least two of the entries to be less than 50. If these are the first two, then the imputation is dominated by I; if the first and last, it is dominated by J; if the last two, it is dominated by K. We have proved that every other imputation is dominated by one of the imputations in the set {I, J, K}; that is, we have satisfied the first condition of the definition.

We also see that none of the three dominates any other within the set, since no *two* players have a reason to prefer any one to any other.

So far the theory appears to be shaping up. The three imputations I, J, and K seem to offer some sort of stability in the sense that any departure from one of them to an imputation outside the set (as in the case of bribery cited above) is likely to instigate a return to the set because of dominance of some imputation in the set over the outside imputation. Moreover, *within* the set there is no reason to move from one imputation to another, since a preference of *two* players is needed to effect a change. One might then reasonably expect that once one of the imputations is arrived at, it will stick or at least all bribery or bargaining adventures are bound to lead back to one of the imputations in the set.

However, when we look closer, we see that to consider the set {I, J, K} as *the* solution of our three-person game is an illusion. For consider another set of imputations, much larger than the set {I, J, K}, namely the set of *all* imputations in which C gets 10¢. In other words, whenever A and B divide 90¢ between them in any way whatsoever and give C 10¢, this is an imputation of the set we are now considering. This immense set of imputations is also a "solution" in the sense defined by von Neumann and Morgenstern. Within the set, no imputation can dominate another, because C, getting 10¢ in every case, will remain indifferent to change, while A and B cannot *both* prefer one imputation to another within the set, because if one gets a bigger share of the 90¢, the other must get a lesser share. Thus, the second of our conditions is satisfied. Consider now an imputation outside the set. If C gets more than 10¢, A and B will prefer some imputation in the original set, since they get more collectively in all of them, and so each will get more in *some* of them, because all possible splits have been included.

If C gets less than 10¢, he is sure to join either A or B to force the return to one of the original set.

Far from having narrowed down the "solution" of this game to a set of three imputations, we see now that (if money can be infinitely divided) an infinite number of them can also constitute a solution. Moreover, the 10¢ could have equally well been given to A or to B, and in each case we would have had another "solution." Nor must the "consolation" prize be restricted to 10¢. Any positive amount less than 50¢ given to one of the players will do equally well.

In fact, it is shown that in the simple game considered, *every* imputation is included in *some* solution, and so our hope of finding a *restricted* set of imputations which would constitute the solution of the game has evaporated, not to speak of the original (not unreasonable) hope of pinning down a single imputation which we could call *the* solution of the game.

Whatever von Neumann might have thought of the implication of this result for possible applications of game theory to the study of actual coalition formations in real-life games of strategy (for example, politics), he was not disappointed in the *mathematical* implications of the result. He defined a formal "solution" of a mathematical problem, and "solved" several games in this sense. An infinity of solutions is a common occurrence in mathematics. The simple trigonometric equation, $\sin x = 0$, also has an infinity of solutions: $x = 0°, 180°, 360°, 540°, \ldots$ etc., ad infinitum. Far from being distressing, this mathematical fact is central to our understanding of so-called periodic functions.[67]

One should keep in mind that although every imputation of our three-person game is shown to be *in* a solution, it is not true that "every imputation is a solution." The solutions are *classes* of imputations, and although there is an infinity of such classes, and every one of them except the set {I, J, K} contains an infinity of imputations, nevertheless the solution concept does divide the imputations into classes in a certain prescribed way; so the solutions are not trivial mathematically. The mathematician von Neumann could therefore take off from there to more general and more difficult problems, for example, the determination of all the solutions of any given game or class of games. This is quite in the tradition of the brilliant history of mathematics. For example, at a given time in the development of mathematics, the solution of *all* quadratic equations was found; then of all cubic and quartic equations. Then came the futile struggle to solve all equations of the fifth degree with a single formula; then the ingenious proof, based on the researches of Galois and Abel, that no such formula could be given if it was to contain only the operations of arithmetic (the four operations) and root extractions (such are the formulae for the solutions of all equations of lower degree). About the same time appeared the proof by Gauss that formula or no formula, every algebraic equation had to have a root which might be a real or a complex number; and this made it easy to show that if there was one root there had to be as many as the degree of the equation.

Such are the problems of mathematics. Von Neumann took the challenge of game theory in this spirit. His job as a mathematician was to pose problems and prove theorems. The problem which he considered as the most important (again as a mathematician, not as a theoretical social scientist) was the following: to prove that every N-person game has at least one solution or else to show a game that does not. In other words, von Neumann hoped to prove the game-theoretical analogue of the Fundamental Theorem of Algebra. It was not granted to von Neumann to accomplish this.

What possible importance such a proof might have for game theory as a conceptual framework of social science, particularly as a theory of strategic conflict, is impossible to imagine. Such a connection, even if it existed, might be so farfetched as to escape understanding. But the connection between, say, the Fundamental Theorem of Algebra and the problems of applied mathematics is equally remote. Yet it can be argued that the theorem clarifies mathematical thinking and that clear mathematical thinking without reference to *particular* problems is indispensable if mathematics is to be a powerful intellectual tool.

In this light, von Neumann's preoccupation with the problems of pure mathematics emerging from game theory must be understood. I hope the reader will extend his charity to forgive this digression from our main theme.

VON NEUMANN'S AND MORGENSTERN'S SOLUTIONS AS "SOCIAL NORMS"

Von Neumann and Morgenstern, the theoretical social scientists, did try to interpret the social-scientific meaning of the solution concept (126, pp. 41–44). In their thinking, a particular solution, say of our three-person game, reflects a "social norm." Take the class of imputations in which C gets 10¢. All of them collectively form a solution. This solution, translated into a prescription, reads: C must get his 10¢; then A and B must decide how to split the 90¢. The solution does not prescribe how much A and B are to get separately, but it does prescribe how C is to be treated. In all the imputations of this solution, C is treated the same way. The dominance relations suggest that any departure from this rule may well result in a return to some (other) imputation within the solution, where C again gets 10¢. Moreover, the change from one imputation to another within this solution cannot be effected. These "rules" resemble the norms of social behavior.

Consider now the solution {I, J, K}. Here the situation is different. No player is guaranteed a fixed amount. Departures from the solution again tend to lead back to it but with a reshuffling of the payoffs. The social norm corresponding to this solution is: two players freeze the third one out and divide the dollar equally. *Any* one may be frozen out, but the two "conspirators" must share equally. Note: in all the other solutions the man with the constant payoff was specified. In the solution where someone is frozen out, the odd man is not specified.

Which social norm will operate cannot be determined by game theory in its present stage. Since every imputation is in some solution, to say that a particular observed imputation reflects the operation of a social norm is vacuous: it cannot be refuted. But the solution concept does suggest (though it does not prove) that the negotiations proceeding in any such three-person game will always gravitate toward either of these situations:

1. One *particular* player will always be offered a fixed amount less than 50¢.

2. Two players will freeze the third out and split evenly.

This prediction would be violated if no tendency were observed toward the one or the other settlement. Despite its weak conclusions, therefore, von Neumann's solution theory is not devoid of (normative) predictive content.

THE STRONG SOLUTION

We will now examine two other attempts to make the theory of the N-person game more "realistic." The first attempt was motivated by a desire to restrict the classes of imputations which would qualify as "solutions," so as to remove the embarrassing result that in the simple three-person game every imputation is in some solution.

The *strong solution,* proposed by Vickrey,[68] is defined as follows. A strong solution is a class of imputations with the same properties as a von Neumann solution but with the further qualification that any departure from the solution and subsequent return to it is *necessarily* accompanied by damage to one of the players who had helped engineer the departure. We have seen that this is just what happened to B, when he was tempted by C's offer to defect from his alliance with A.

It turns out that the only strong solution of our three-person game is the set of imputations {I, J, K}. This restricted result is logically more satisfactory than the one obtained by von Neumann and Morgenstern. It prescribes a much narrower range of behavior to the players. Even though the logic is not tight, the prescription of rational coalition bargaining is now as follows for our three-person games:

"If you are one of the lucky ones who gets 50¢, do not accept any offers from the player frozen out. For as soon as you get more than 50¢, you become vulnerable to a conspiracy of the two other players against you."

It must be admitted that this sounds like good advice.

Although the "strong solution" of the simple three-person game is clear cut, the extension of the same idea to arbitrary N-person games is difficult. The discussion of the developments resulting from this theory would carry us too far afield; so we must drop the subject here.[69]

LUCE'S THEORY OF STABILITY

Another modification of the N-person theory was introduced by R. D. Luce (59). This investigator considers not a set of imputations, which is the central concept of both previous approaches, but certain pairs of sets. Each pair is a particular breakup of the N players into coalitions (not necessarily two) and an associated imputation. Luce then considers this question: Given a coalition pattern and an imputation to go with it, to which coalition patterns and associated imputations is the game likely to move?

In principle there is no reason why the game should not move from one imputation to another that dominates it, accompanied by an appropriate reshuffling in the coalitions. In practice, however, such changes in coalition patterns are likely to be the results of certain negotiations, in which individuals are induced to leave or to join coalitions. If negotiations are conducted on an individual basis, these changes of coalition patterns are likely to proceed by small steps involving, say, only one or two individuals at a time.

Accordingly, Luce considers rules of coalition formation which restrict the changes in coalition structure to such small changes. The restrictions seem to be reflections of what is ordinarily observed and can perhaps be called "social inertia" or "social friction." In other words, alliances tend to persist; if changes occur, they involve only small numbers of turncoats or defectors, formation of only small splinter groups from scratch, etc.

When such restrictions are imposed, some of the coalition partitions with their associated imputations turn out to be "stable"; others "unstable." A stable pair is one in which there is no inducement to change to one of the *permissible* pairs (i.e., to those pairs, to which the rules restrict the possible changes from the given pair). The mathematical problem posed and solved for many types of games was to determine all the stable pairs of a game. The solutions have turned out to be much more "natural" than the all-too-general von Neumann and Morgenstern solutions.

POWER

One other recent development of the N-person game theory will be mentioned because of its possible relevance to political science.

L. S. Shapley considered the following question (107): When negotiations are conducted leading to formation of coalitions, how can the bargaining strength of each player be assessed? Presumably, some players are sought as members of coalitions more than others. Why? In our simple three-person game, there was no reason to suppose that the winning over of any of the players was more desirable than the winning over of another. In that game every one of the three players held the balance of power. By joining with another, any one could swing the decision. In games with more players and with more complex rules, this is, of course, not necessarily the case. The problem, therefore, arises to calculate the *power* which each player possesses in the bargaining process.

For some simple kinds of situations, this power index can be readily calculated. It is commonly agreed, for example, that the president of the United States formally commands one-sixth of the power of the whole Congress in matters of passing legislation: the difference between the simple majority needed to pass or defeat legislation and the two-thirds majority needed to override the president's veto. This measure of the president's (formal) legislative power results also from Shapley's index under the assumption that everyone may vote as he pleases.

The method can be applied also to situations where there are restrictions on voting behavior of legislators, for example, party discipline, caucuses, etc. Luce and Rogow (62) have investigated the results of applying the Shapley index to the distribution of power in the United States tri-cameral legislature (House, Senate, and president) under the assumption that certain legislators always vote with their party and others are always free to defect. The results depend on the proportion of the die-hards and the mugwumps, on whether the president's party is in the majority or in the minority, and on whether the president himself is a die-hard or a mugwump. One interesting conclusion is the following: the president's power is greatest when his own party controls about 55 per cent of Congress.

The result is not an unreasonable conclusion. It can be immediately seen that the president has no legislative power at all if his party is monolithic and in overwhelming majority, for then his approval or disapproval of legislation makes no difference. Nor has he any power if the opposing party is in complete control. His power derives from his ability to hold some *balance* of power. What is added to the common sense knowledge is a method of computing power quantitatively.

It has already been stressed but will bear more stressing that no result of a formal theory is binding on reality. Therefore, no conclusions dealing with the logic of strategy in coalition formation, with the distribution of power, etc., as these conclusions are derived in game theory, have any *a priori* value in giving us an understanding of how people actually behave in such situations. But these conclusions are useful points of departure for making hypotheses about how people behave. The hypotheses serve to focus the investigator's attention on what may be important determinants of behavior. Once the hypotheses are put to a test, whatever the outcome, a *systematic* investigation has begun.

In the next chapter we will look at some results of experiments which were inspired by the various formulations of game theory. Even the experiments do not tell us much about human behavior in the "wild" state. The laboratory is at best only a very artificial simulation of life. But the transition from a paper and pencil theory to questions about human behavior, even in the make-believe world of contrived laboratory situations, is a step forward in the investigation of strategic conflict.

CHAPTER XIII

EXPERIMENTS IN STRATEGIC CONFLICT

EARLY WORKERS in experimental psychology studied mostly those aspects of behavior in which physically measurable variables could be correlated, for example the magnitude of an overt response with the intensity of the imposed stimulus—that is to say, early experimental psychology was largely an extension of physiology. The first typically "psychological" events to be studied with precision were those involving relatively simple mental processes, such as rote learning, etc.

The growth of psychology as an experimental science proceeds not only in the direction of refining observations and measurements but also, more significantly, in the direction of extending the range of events that *can* be systematically observed and of variables that can be measured. Thus, gestalt psychology has brought within the range of experiment some of the "higher" mental activities, such as perception and integration.

Recently, this range has been further extended to such matters as the degree of subjective belief (as in experiments dealing with risky decisions) and values assigned to events (as in attempts to determine personal utility scales). There have also been attempts to design methods of investigation for objective assessment of personality. Now game theory is beginning to provide a natural theoretical framework for extending the range of experiment to interpersonal and social relations. Such traditionally multimeaning terms as conflict and co-operation, trust and suspicion, power of bargaining, balance of bargaining advantage, and equity (all social-psychological and even ethical concepts) either find rigorous operational definition or else emerge as *residual* theoretical constructs to complement the inconclusiveness of normative theory, something which frequently occurs in game-theoretical investigations.

So long as the theory remains normative, these residual constructs appear as unavoidable "props"—*ad hoc* explanations of why people do not behave as the normative theory prescribes or, on the contrary, why they *do* behave consistently when the theory deduces extremely ambiguous "solutions." But as soon as we pass to a theory based on experimental investigation, the residual constructs "spring to life" to be identified in the actual norms of behavior.

In a given population sample one can expect that some will resort to "tacit communication" when such is called for; some will not. In a mixed motive game, some will behave co-operatively, some competitively. In a coalition game, coalitions *will* form and will persist; winnings will be divided in ascertainable ways, even though classical game theory has very little to say *specifically* about such situations. Thus, we may expect to learn something about behavior in situations of strategic conflict which is outside of the scope of game theory in the present state. Nevertheless, game theory is distinctly suggestive for interpreting and systematizing the results. Let us therefore look at the results of some experiments inspired by game theory.

CO-ORDINATION OF STRATEGIES BY "TELEPATHY"

The completely co-operative game with communication between the co-operators allowed is, we have seen, trivial from the point of view of game theory, because it reduces to a one-person game ("against nature"). Such a game has two direct opposites, namely the completely competitive game (zero-sum) and the completely co-operative game *without* communication.

We have seen that rationality can be precisely defined in the context of the zero-sum game and that the definition does no violence to the meaning of rationality in common usage. Therefore, from experimental data on the zero-sum game we can draw conclusions about how the actual behavior of people departs from rationality in a completely competitive situation. Once certain generalizations have been made, we can try to construct theories about factors other than rational considerations which may underlie the motivation for such departures. We will, however, by-pass this kind of situation in favor of the other, namely that of the co-operative game without communication.

Some such simple games were investigated by T. C. Schelling (104). He concentrates on examining the extent to which tacit agreements between co-operators is possible. Obviously, such tacit agreements depend on cultural factors, as the following examples illustrate.

1. *Two people unable to communicate are asked to name "heads" or "tails." If they both name the same, they both win; otherwise they both lose.*

Schelling reports that 36 out of 42 people named "heads." Evidently, people *think* that heads is more likely to be named than tails. Or, more precisely, *they think that others think* that heads is more likely to be named. It therefore makes no difference whether *in fact* heads is more likely to be named (e.g., in tossing a coin to make a decision). If one *thinks that others think so,* then clearly heads is the rational choice.

The impressive majority (36 out of 42) would make for an even more impressive result if it were shown that the proportion of people calling "heads" in coin-tossing decisions is considerably less than 6/7. To my knowledge, however, such a control experiment was not run.

2. *Circle one of the numbers listed in the line below. You win if you all succeed in circling the same number.*

7, 100, 13, 261, 99, 555

Here "7" received the greatest number of votes with "100" a close second, and "13" in third place. I feel it would have been better if the culturally prominent numbers, 7, 100, and 13, were not placed in the beginning of the list. One does not know, for example, without a control study, whether the frequency of naming "7" is related to its position or to its cultural prominence.

3. *You are to meet somebody in New York City. You have not been instructed where to meet.*

An absolute majority named the information booth of Grand Central Station. As Schelling points out, the results may have been biased by the fact that the sample of subjects was taken from New Haven, Connecticut. But this strengthens rather than weakens the argument about the role of cultural prominence in making the choice.

4. *Name an amount of money. If you all name the same amount you can have as much as you have named.*

Out of 41 people, 12 named one million dollars. All other amounts except three were powers of ten. Of the other three, one was $64, and one $64,000. The cultural prominence makes itself felt in the million dollars as being the conventional symbol of wealth in the United States and in the $64 and $64,000 as equally prominent symbols of "reward for guessing." [70]

5. *You and your partner are each to divide $100 into two piles. If both of you divide in the same way, you both get $100; otherwise neither of you gets anything.* (Communication is, of course, disallowed, as in all these games.)

Here 36 out of 41 split 50-50. (It is rather surprising that the majority was not even greater.)

None of the above games involved a conflict of interest.

But they can be easily modified to include partial conflict and so to make them mixed motive games. For example, if the last game is modified so as to give each man the portion of the $100 which he has named for himself, conflict is introduced. But the co-operative aspect can also be kept by stipulating that if the sum of the amounts named exceeds $100, neither will get anything. In this case, too, Schelling reports, 36 out of 40 subjects named $50 for themselves.

The heads and tails game becomes a mixed motive game if the winnings are not equal. In Schelling's example, player A gets $3 and player B gets $2 if both name heads. If both name tails, A gets $2, and B gets $3. If they disagree, each gets nothing. Here A's superior position is tacitly recognized by 16 out of 22 A's and by 15 out of 22 B's, who all named heads.

An interesting question immediately looms. How great must the difference in the payoffs be to make the "tacit agreement" unattractive for the player at the shorter end so as to induce him to gamble on tails? Moreover, would not the player in the advantageous position feel that this inducement must be strong if the differential is high, and so might he not yield and name tails also so as to avoid the futile disagreement? In other words, is it possible some advantage accrues to the underdog if he is sufficiently under?

One more example deserves mention because of its possible relevance to serious conflict.

6. *A map of an area is shown divided into two unequal parts by a river. Each player is a commander of a military force. The forces are initially on the opposite sides of the river. Each commander is told to occupy as large an area as he can without coming into conflict with the opposing force.*

In spite of the fact that the area contiguous to Commander X's original position was smaller than that contiguous to Commander Y's, and in spite of the fact that other features could have served as boundaries (e.g., roads), 14 out of 22 X's and 14 out of 23 Y's chose the (unique) river to delineate their area of occupation.

Schelling concludes that in situations where collaboration is advantageous, even where conflict of interest is also present but where direct bargaining is impossible, tacit agreements will take place, provided the two parties can seize on some prominent, preferably unique feature of the situation, which each has reason to believe the other will also seize upon. Also, significantly, the impossibility of explicit bargaining precludes *quantitative* compromises, typical results of haggling.

A direct quotation will convey the nature of Schelling's argument:

> Gas was not used in World War II. The agreement, though not without antecedents, was largely a tacit one. It is interesting to speculate on whether any alternative agreement concerning poison gas could have been arrived at without formal communication (or, even, for that matter, with communication). 'Some gas' raises complicated questions of how much, where, under what circumstances: 'no gas' is simple and unambiguous. Gas only on military personnel; gas used only by defending forces; gas only when carried by vehicle or projectile; no gas without warning—a variety of limits is conceivable; some may make sense, and many might have been more impartial to the outcome of the war. But there is a simplicity to 'no gas' that makes it almost uniquely a focus of agreement when each side can only conjecture at what rules the other side would propose and when failure at co-ordination on the first try may spoil the chances for acquiescence in any limits at all. (104, p. 33.)

RESULTS ON THE PRISONER'S DILEMMA

Extensive experiments on the mixed motive game shown in Matrix 18 are reported by M. Deutsch (23):

$$\begin{bmatrix} 9, \ \ 9 & -10, \ \ 10 \\ 10, -10 & -9, -9 \end{bmatrix}$$

Matrix 18

This payoff matrix presents less temptation to choose the non-co-operative alternative than the matrix we have used to illustrate this game (cf. Matrix 10), but the logic of strategy is exactly the same.

Deutsch's experiments were performed under four different communication conditions and three different "orientations" suggested to the subjects before the game began—12 conditions in all. The communication conditions were as follows.

1. *No communication.* The game began without prior communication between the players. The strategies were chosen independently and in secret.

2. *Communication.* Before the game began, the players were able to communicate to each other by writing notes.

3. *Reversible decision.* Here there was no prior communication, but after the choices had been made and announced, each player could change his choice any number of times. If no change in choice was made during 30 seconds, the choices stood.

4. *Nonsimultaneous decision.* Without prior communication, one subject made his choice first, which was announced to the second subject before he made his choice.

The three orientations were as follows.

1. Co-operative: the importance of *joint* maximization was stressed.

2. Individualistic: each player was told to look out for *himself.*

3. Competitive: each player was made to feel that he played *against* the other.

The results of this experiment are shown in Table 7.

First let us look at the effects of the communication conditions, holding the orientation constant at the "individualistic" level. Note that the per cent of *individuals* who chose co-operatively increases from 35.9 per cent to 70.6 per cent as communication is introduced. However the per cent of co-operative *pairs* in the latter condition is only 58.8. In other words, some individuals' trust following preplay communication was not justified.

Table 7

The Prisoner's Dilemma Game played under various conditions and following different preliminary orientations given to the players (after M. Deutsch).

	N	Individuals who chose co-operatively (%)	Pairs in which both chose co-operatively (%)
No Communication:			
Co-operative	46	89.1	82.6
Individualistic	76	35.9	12.8
Competitive	32	12.5	6.3
Communication:			
Co-operative	32	96.9	93.8
Individualistic	34	70.6	58.8
Competitive	48	29.2	16.7
Reversibility:			
Co-operative	74	94.6	94.6
Individualistic	70	77.1	77.1
Competitive	62	36.1	36.1
Nonsimultaneous:			
Co-operative	46	78.3	73.9
Individualistic	48	20.8	4.2
Competitive	30	16.7	6.7

With reversible decisions, the percentage of co-operative individuals is the highest and the percentage of pairs who chose co-operatively is the same. In this condition each individual can *initiate* a co-operative solution by an actual trusting act, and he also has the opportunity to *withdraw* his offer if it is not reciprocated. Moreover, a double cross can be followed by immediate punishment. Thus the co-operative solution can be stabilized. It is nevertheless noteworthy that 23 per cent of the individuals and pairs failed to achieve co-operation even in these circumstances.[71]

Under the condition of nonsimultaneous choice, if the first player makes a "trusting" choice, he is at the mercy of the second, and he knows it. It is therefore not surprising that under this condition the percentage of individuals who chose co-operatively is lowest. We note also that most of these, who trusted their opponents, were taken advantage of. Only 4.2 per cent of the *pairs* chose co-operation.

Next we note the large differences in the frequency of co-operative solutions under the different orientations. As expected, the co-operative orientation leads to the greatest frequency of co-operative choices and the competitive orientation to the smallest frequency. These results, however, are, in my opinion, not nearly as impressive as the others. It is well known that subjects in psychological experiments follow instructions. The "orientations" may well have been interpreted as instructions; in other words, the subjects did essentially what the experimenter told them to do. A much stronger result would have been obtained if significant differences in the frequency of co-operation were observed in connection with conditions extraneous to the game itself. Such an experiment is also reported by Deutsch (23, pp. 277–78). Before the game begins, the players are asked to take an "intelligence test" in the same room with a third person, who, unknown to the subjects, is an accomplice of the experimenter and is instructed to behave in a "conspicuously obnoxious and irritating manner." The two experimental subjects then play Prisoner's Dilemma without instructions and without communication under each of the following three conditions.

1. The third ("obnoxious") person is present as an observer.

2. The third person predicts the choices. If he predicts correctly, he collects whatever the players lose.

3. The third person is absent.

Deutsch states that the tendency to make "trusting," that is, co-operative choices is greatest under condition (2) and least under condition (3), although he does not report the actual data.

It would seem, then, that it is possible to influence the tendency to co-operate by extraneous circumstances and the door is open to the investigation of these circumstances. Another approach would be to determine the tendency to co-operate in different population samples: subjects chosen from different cultures, nationalities, age groups, sexes (including matching players of the same and of opposite sex), etc.

EXPERIMENTAL STUDY OF COALITIONS

In a simple three-person coalition game, different "weights" can be assigned to the three players. A coalition is a combination of weights. The outcome of the game is simply a payoff (always the same) awarded to the coalition whose combined weight is greater than that of the third player. The object of the experiment reported by Vinacke and Arkoff (123) was to see what coalitions would form under what circumstances and also to see how the winnings would be divided among the members of the winning coalition.

There were six weight assignments among the three players A, B, and C, as shown in Table 8.

Table 8

(After Vinacke and Arkoff.)

Players	A B C	A B C	A B C	A B C	A B C	A B C
Weights	1, 1, 1	3, 2, 2	1, 2, 2	3, 1, 1	4, 3, 2	4, 2, 1
Conditions	I	II	III	IV	V	VI

It is evident that under conditions IV and VI, no winning coalition can be formed against the strongest player. In II and in V only one such coalition is possible. In III there are two stronger players, who may either combine or compete for the weaker one. In I, the game is entirely symmetrical. Table 9 shows the number of coalitions formed among the various pairs out of 90 groups. The results are approximately as expected. Predominantly the weak combine against the strong. Where a coalition is useless, the tendency is not to form one. Nevertheless the exceptions are notable. The strongest player sometimes *is* included in a coalition. In III, the two strong players sometimes *do* combine against the weaker one, etc.

Table 9

(After Vinacke and Arkoff.)

| | *Weights* | | | | | |
	I	II	III	IV	V	VI
Allies	(1, 1, 1)	(3, 2, 2)	(1, 2, 2)	(3, 1, 1)	(4, 3, 2)	(4, 2, 1)
AB	33	13	24	11	9	9
AC	17	12	40	10	20	13
BC	30	64	15	7	59	8
Total	80	89	79	28	88	30
None	10	1	11	62	2	60

The division of winnings (per cent of instances) under the six conditions is shown in Table 10.

Table 10

(After Vinacke and Arkoff.)

Division ratio	I	II	III	IV	V	VI
50/50	60	70	39	39	47	23
30/70–49/51	31	24	38	11	44	30
1/99–29/71	9	7	23	50	9	47

Again the over-all expectations are corroborated. Symmetry (I) encourages even division. Discrepancy of weight (IV, VI) encourages uneven division. The author maintains that these results are contrary to the conclusions of game theory, according to which the weak player who is as necessary to a coalition as a strong player should command equal bargaining power. It is not apparent to me that classical game theory leads to this conclusion. Rather, in von Neumann and Morgenstern's treatment, bargaining considerations are usually by-passed, while in later developments different postulates on the nature of bargaining lead to different conclusions.

It seems necessary to distinguish normative from descriptive approaches to strategic conflict. As we have seen, beyond the theory of the zero-sum two-person game and the rather vague notion of "solution" in von Neumann's sense, it is almost impossible to extend the *normative* theory of games, because the criteria of rationality become confused by the clash between individual and group norms and because "equilibria" are either nonexistent or not very relevant to the interests of the players. On the contrary, an empirical (descriptive) approach to bargaining situations (including that of coalition formation) seems full of promise. For example, we can ask straightforward questions of this sort. Given a three-person game with the players A, B, and C receiving weights x, y, z, respectively, what is the frequency distribution of coalitions AB, AC, and BC respectively? Given coalition AB with weights x and y, what is the frequency distribution of the way the winnings are split between them, and so on for other coalitions? Can a general (probabilistic) law be *observed* (not derived) which will assign this frequency distribution to all possible triples (x, y, z)? Having observed such a law, can we derive it from a set of reasonable postulates which possibly govern bargaining behavior? If different population samples show different distributions, can these differences be attributed to different norms of behavior (as reflected in the postulates)?

All these questions are related to theory construction based on experimental evidence. It cannot be emphasized too strongly that classical game theory is *not* based on experimental evidence. It represents an attempt to build a normative theory on a foundation of *strategic logic*. We have also seen how such a foundation becomes difficult or impossible to erect without invoking specific norms of behavior. These norms are not logical but arbitrary and can be exceedingly varied. From this point on, therefore, there can be no single game theory but only a great variety of such theories, each based on different norms. Here the experimental scientist should naturally take over to explore the norms actually operating in human affairs.

CHAPTER XIV

CRITIQUES OF GAME THEORY

AS HAS BEEN POINTED OUT, game theory was conceived by mathematicians (9, 10, 125), and since the publication of the fundamental treatise (126), has been developed almost exclusively by mathematicians. The theory can be viewed as a self-contained branch of pure mathematics—a system of theorems built up from a set of postulates. All purely mathematical theories are of this sort and, as such, are practically immune to criticism. The theorems are logical consequences of the postulates. They can be "wrong" only if errors have crept into the deductions. Therefore, when the validity of the theorems, solutions etc., has been checked, nothing remains to be said in criticism, except possibly about the intrinsic depth or elegance of the theory.

However, as soon as the theory is proposed as pertinent to some aspects of the real world, for example, as a basis for constructing models of human behavior in conflict situations, a substantial evaluation (as distinguished from a formal check of logical validity) is in order. To be sure, a critical evaluation is pertinent to the extent that it examines matters related to what the theory actually purports to do. It is hardly proper to criticize a theory for not having accomplished what it has not started out to accomplish.

I think a categorical disavowal of *descriptive* content is implicit in the entire game-theoretical approach. Game theory is definitely normative in spirit and method. Its goal is a *prescription* of how a rational player should behave in a given game situation when the preferences of this player and of all the other players are given in utility units.

A critique of game theory, therefore, should be directed at the way it has coped with this problem. Now we have seen how the "prescripts to the rational player" frequently become ambiguous, as soon as the realm of the two-person constant-sum game is abandoned; and we have examined the nature of some of these ambiguities. A detailed study of these matters is the natural task of a critique of game theory. The findings all seem to converge on a single theme: the shortcomings of game theory, even as a normative theory, can be traced to the exclusion of certain psychological concepts from its axiomatic base. Without such concepts, its normative conclusions either remain vague or are beset with paradoxes. We have seen, for example, that in certain two-person non-zero-sum games, the extension of a maximin solution leads to an outcome disadvantageous to both players, while other prescriptions, without additional assumptions, lack the categorical conclusiveness of the maximin solution. We have also seen that the N-person game theory is in general unable to prescribe to any player whom he should try to entice into a coalition and how much he should offer as enticement. Thus, the theory cannot predict what will happen if everyone "does his best."

T. C. Schelling (105) has offered a critique of game theory in which he undertakes to trace the specific sources of the difficulties and to propose a reorientation along distinctly psychological lines.

SCHELLING'S CRITIQUE OF GAME THEORY

The cornerstone of Schelling's argument is that game theory, in passing from zero-sum to non-zero-sum games, has nevertheless retained the basic framework of thought into which the zero-sum game has been cast. The fundamental concept of the zero-sum game has been of little value in non-zero-sum games. Here problems other than delineations of security levels arise, and to deal with these problems one needs, according to Schelling, concepts of another kind. We will list the principal ones.

1. *The concept of tacit communication.* We have already seen in Chapter XIII how tacit communication operates in co-operative games without explicit communication and even in mixed motive games, where tacit communication becomes tacit bargaining.

2. *The concept of commitment.* A commitment is an act performed presumably during the preplay communication (if such takes place) which makes it impossible for one of the players to choose some of the strategies. To take the simplest example, consider the game shown in Matrix 9. If the man can contrive a situation in which it becomes absolutely impossible for him to choose either a_2 or a_3, he can thereby force the woman to choose b_1. The act of burning the bridge behind is a commitment of this sort. The committed player becomes *immune* to bargaining. Thus dramatic announcements of "last offers" are commitments.

3. *The concept of threat and promise.* These are essentially *conditional commitments,* that is, commitments of what the threatening or promising player must do *if* the other acts or fails to act in a certain way. Often there is no motivation for the first player actually to carry out the threat or the promise in itself. The benefit accruing from either is in its potential to evoke or prevent some act of the other player.

The bulk of Schelling's essay is an elucidation and elaboration of these ideas supported by numerous enlightening examples.

COMMENTS ON SCHELLING'S CRITIQUE

The two central ideas are evidently the role of communication and commitment in strategic conflict and the relationship between communication and commitment. If we examine commitment alone, either in its direct form as overt acts, or in the indirect form as threats or promises, *which are believed,* we see that these concepts add nothing to the existing body of game theory. For a commitment, a threat, or a promise (which is believed) is essentially a switch from one game to another. In fact, when a game is given in normal form, that is, as a matrix of strategies, then if one speaks of "making a move" by choosing a strategy, one has essentially created a new game in *extensive* form. Consider the following simplification of the game represented by Matrix 9, or the Battle of the Sexes (as Luce and Raiffa have called the game typified by Matrix 19):

$$
\begin{array}{c c}
 & \begin{matrix} b_1 & \quad b_2 \end{matrix} \\
\begin{matrix} a_1 \\ a_2 \end{matrix} &
\left[\begin{matrix} 2,1 & 0,0 \\ 0,0 & 1,2 \end{matrix} \right]
\end{array}
$$

Matrix 19

The purpose of reducing a game to normal form is to present it in a way which permits only a single decision on the part of each player and moreover to exhibit these decisions as made *simultaneously and independently.* If the choices are to be made consecutively, we have two different games, depending on who chooses first. In extensive form, these two games look as shown in Figures 11 and 12.

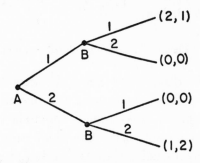

Figure 11. If strategy choices are made sequentially as moves in a game, the game represented by Matrix 19 becomes another game shown in extensive form. Here A moves first. The payoffs are to A and B, respectively.

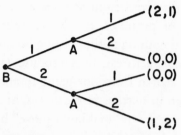

Figure 12. Here B moves first. The payoffs are to A and B, respectively.

Reduced once again to normal form, the two games are now shown in Matrices 20 and 21:

	b_1 choose 1	b_2 choose 2	b_3 do what A does	b_4 do the opposite of what A does
a_1: choose 1	(2, 1)	(0, 0)	(2, 1)	(0, 0)
a_2: choose 2	(0, 0)	(1, 2)	(1, 2)	(0, 0)

Matrix 20
The game shown in Figure 11 reduced to normal form.

	b_1 choose 1	b_2 choose 2
a_1: choose 1	(2, 1)	(0, 0)
a_2: choose 2	(0, 0)	(1, 2)
a_3: do what B does	(2, 1)	(1, 2)
a_4: do the opposite of what B does	(0, 0)	(0, 0)

Matrix 21
The game shown in Figure 12 reduced to normal form.

Note that in each game the second player now has *four* strategies. It is now assumed that one of *these* four and one of the first player's two strategies are to be chosen simultaneously. Thus, to consider what happens if strategies are chosen consecutively instead of simultaneously (a form of commitment by the first player) is really to consider a different game, *which can also be cast into normal form,* where the strategies are chosen simultaneously and independently.

All commitments, whether conditional or unconditional, lead to a similar analysis. A commitment, a threat, or a promise, *if believed,* amounts to an elimination by one of the players of some choices open to him. This creates a different game. Therefore, it is not a shortcoming of game theory that it has failed to consider the role of commitments, threats, or promises *which are believed.*

Similar considerations apply to the anomalous "solution" of the Prisoner's Dilemma in the absence of communication. The entries in the payoff matrix are utilities to the players. When we say that the outcome (a_1, b_1) of Matrix 10 is a poor one *compared* to (a_2, b_2), we may be tacitly assuming an additional negative utility associated with (a_1, b_1), which reflects the players' regret about what *might* have been, that is, about the loss of (a_2, b_2) which they might have achieved if they trusted each other. If we make the negative payoffs at (a_1, b_1) sufficiently large so as to include this "regret," say $(-11, -11)$, strategy 2 ceases to be unconditionally preferable to strategy 1 for both players, and the inevitability of (a_1, b_1) does not follow.

In short, many paradoxes of game theory can be resolved by simply substituting one game for another.

However, game theory, as originally formulated, does ignore the *problem* of communication and the role of communicative acts as strategic maneuvers in those instances in which one player is trying to convince another that he is playing a different game. For example, information concerning the utility values of the outcomes is essentially information about the structure of the game. Such information can be true or false, can be convincing or unconvincing, etc. Typically, effective communication is simply taken for granted in the original formulation of game theory. The rules are assumed to be perfectly understood by all; payoffs to other players are correctly imputed; agreements are kept, etc.; or, on the contrary, the possibility of communication is excluded, as in the treatment of games where collusion is disallowed.

Bargaining is, of course, communication. Problems of bargaining have been essentially by-passed in the early formulation of game theory (126, p. 616). Recent attempts to extend the scope of game-theoretical concepts to include a theory of bargaining must be seen as motivated by a desire to transcend the limitations just mentioned. The approaches of Braithwaite and Raiffa, examined in Chapter XI, belong to those attempts. We have seen that to a certain extent standards of bargaining can be set up, and these standards make possible the extension of the results of classical game theory. For example, in the case of some two-person non-zero-sum games, a bargain can be struck in accordance with some standard of equitable distribution, based on the strategic positions of the players, even where utility is nontransferable.

Bargaining associated with coalition formation raises similar problems. It is assumed in game theory that agreements entered into will be kept. But the pregame jockeying, in which coalitions are formed is by its nature a series of *tentative* agreements. If one demands that any coalitions tentatively established must stay put, this is tantamount to restricting bargaining to the extent of by-passing the crucial problem of coalition formation. If, on the other hand, tentative coalitions are allowed, then threats to leave coalitions must be allowed as "moves" in the bargaining game. How to make a *convincing* threat; how to elicit the alternative to nonacceptance of a promise (which alternative the promise-maker does not wish to disclose)—these become the crucial strategic problems. They are problems which involve communication skill, especially the skill of convincing others and of eliciting information from others.

To repeat, what is essentially missing from game theory proper is a rigorous analysis of situations where communicative acts are moves of the game, *and where effective communication may change the game*. For example, the choice of believing or not believing can be a move in the game, and the game may change according to which choice is made.[72]

To be sure, this is not always the case. In poker, for example, to fold or to call the opponent's bluff can be interpreted as a choice "to believe or not to believe." This is certainly a formal move of the game, and no conceptual difficulty arises there. Bluffing in poker is a communication about the state of affairs at a particular node in the game tree. Not being a game of perfect information, poker does not allow a player to know exactly where in the game tree he finds himself on a particular move. Whether he believes or disbelieves, he is still playing the same game. But there are other cases, of which we shall examine a sample, where believing or not changes the game itself, that is, its strategic possibilities and its outcomes. Here the very axiomatic base of game theory is shaken, and a reconstruction of the foundations is required to re-establish the possibility of rigorous treatment.

Schelling's critique is largely centered on these matters. To these we may add another serious weakness of formal game theory, as a basis for a normative theory of human behavior in conflict situations, namely, the implausibility of the assumption that human beings can assign an interval utility scale to any set of outcomes. Recall that such an assignment involves an estimate of a "cutting point" where a gamble involving two events is neither more nor less preferable than the certainty of a third event of intermediate utility value.

Quite aside from the complexity of this notion, we must recognize that the proposal of an *explicit* gamble usually brings serious disturbances into the estimates of desirability of outcomes. Risks cannot be avoided, but our attitudes toward them depend strongly on whether they are explicitly stated or not and on whether they are imposed by nature or by men. To take an example, a vaccine which promises to reduce the mortality due to some disease by a fixed amount but which introduces a mortality risk of its own would probably be opposed even if the latter were a small fraction of the former. The mortality risk of a vaccine must indeed be vanishingly small to justify the exchange of a much larger "natural" mortality for "man-induced" mortality.

At any rate, the psychology of gambles is an extremely complicated one. Today, it remains largely unexplored except in contrived laboratory situations. Since modern utility theory, without which game theory is powerless, is firmly welded in its applications to the psychology of risk, the hope of extensive application of game theory in human affairs remains limited.

We will illustrate the conceptual and practical difficulties of game theory by applying its techniques to a particularly human situation. The example may seem ludicrous, but the reader is urged to take it seriously, in order to appreciate the gap between "rationality," as it is conventionally understood, and another type of wisdom, with which we shall be largely concerned in Part III.

TRUST AND JEALOUSY

Imagine Othello and Desdemona as the players. Imagine that Othello has not jumped to the conclusion of Desdemona's guilt but has asked her point blank, "Did you or did you not give yourself to Cassio?"

Desdemona can now answer "Yes" or "No," and Othello may either believe her or disbelieve. Othello does not know, but Desdemona knows that she is innocent. Desdemona's strategies, therefore, appear to her as follows:

1. Falsely admit guilt.
2. Deny guilt.

Desdemona's motivation for a false confession is the faint hope that Othello may ultimately forgive her if she shows penitence *in case he is convinced of her guilt anyway*. That is to say, if the game is in normal form, Othello has already chosen his strategy of these two:

1. Believe Desdemona guilty.
2. Believe her innocent.

His choice in this formulation does not depend on Desdemona's answer to his question. At least so it appears to Desdemona, who has cast the situation into a 2 × 2 game. She may, of course, assume a different game, in which Othello's belief depends on her answer. For example, Othello may have four strategies.

1. Believe Desdemona guilty, whatever she says.
2. Believe Desdemona innocent, whatever she says.
3. Believe Desdemona, whatever she says.
4. Disbelieve Desdemona, whatever she says.

This game could also be analyzed. But we shall examine the simplest 2 × 2 game. In this game, Desdemona's preferences are clearly in the following order:

1. Deny guilt and be believed.
2. Falsely confess and discover that Othello is convinced of her innocence. (The happy ending is somewhat marred by her lack of faith in Othello's faith in her.)
3. Falsely confess guilt and be believed (hoping for eventual forgiveness for something she did not do).
4. Deny guilt and not be believed (the actual outcome of the tragedy).

Let us assume that interval scale utilities can be assigned to these outcomes by Desdemona: 100, 50, —50, and —100, respectively. She must also impute preferences to Othello. She cannot do otherwise than to ascribe the same order of preference to him. It appears to Desdemona, therefore, that she is playing a completely co-operative game with her husband. The decision is obvious: both she and Othello must choose strategy 2, to get the highest possible payoff (100, 100) and live happily after.

Let us now consider the situation from Othello's point of view.

The real Othello is convinced of Desdemona's guilt. But we will see what Othello should do as a "rational player." He will imagine the game as beginning considerably earlier, namely during his absence. It appears to him that Desdemona's strategies were:

1. To deceive him.
2. To remain true.

Combining with his own two strategies, mentioned above, we have the following outcomes in the order of Othello's preference:

1. Desdemona has remained true, and he believes her innocent—100.
2. Desdemona has deceived him, but he was not gullible—0.
3. Desdemona has deceived him, and he was gullible— —75.
4. Desdemona was innocent, but he did not believe her— —100.

Here we suppose that murdering his innocent wife was a more terrible outcome for Othello than wearing horns. A reversal of utilities of outcomes 3 and 4 is equally plausible, but we shall carry through with the present analysis.

Now Othello must assign utilities to Desdemona. It is reasonable for him to assume the following order:

1. She deceived her husband and was not found out—100.
2. She resisted temptation, and her innocence was believed—50.
3. She deceived her husband and was found out— —50.
4. She was unjustly punished— —100.

Othello's game matrix must therefore be:

Othello

	Believes Desdemona guilty	Believes Desdemona innocent
Desdemona		
Deceives	$-50,\quad 0$	$100, -75$
Remains true	$-100, -100$	$50,\quad 100$

Matrix 22

Examining Desdemona's payoff matrix, Othello discovers that she is playing a game with a saddle point. From her (selfishly calculating) point of view, it is better to deceive Othello if he believes her guilty ($-50 > -100$) and also if he believes her innocent ($100 > 50$). Therefore Othello is strongly tempted to impute guilt to Desdemona.

Note that if Othello's payoffs in $(1, 2)$ and $(2, 1)$ are interchanged, that is, if Othello prefers murdering innocent Desdemona to wearing horns, the above result is in no way affected.

Now Othello's payoff matrix has no saddle point. If this were a zero-sum game, it would make sense for him to calculate a maximin strategy, which would be to play strategy 1 and strategy 2 with probability ratio 7:4. In this way, he could guarantee himself an expected payoff of about -27 utiles. But this would be prudent only if the game were zero-sum. In that case, Desdemona would have no saddle point either and would be motivated to play her maximin mixture. But Desdemona does have a saddle point at $(1, 1)$. Her advantage is clear cut (according to conventional "rationality" and according to Othello's view of her utility payoffs). *Whatever* Othello does, she is better off with strategy 1 (Othello thinks). Therefore, she should play strategy 1 (Othello reasons), even if she knows he is going to play a mixed strategy. But if she does, there is no point in mixing strategies: Othello should clearly play his strategy 1!

Let us now consider the possibility of collusion. Why

should not the two get together and play (2, 2), where the total payoff is greatest? For Othello to agree to this, he must believe in Desdemona's innocence, for that is what playing strategy 2 means for him. But if he believes Desdemona, he may as well believe her version of the game, where there is not even a problem of what strategy to choose!

We see, then, that here the problem of choosing a strategy is intertwined with the problem of choice to believe or not to believe. The same decision must be made on two different levels, deciding on a strategy and deciding which game is in fact being played. This leads to confusion. To decide whether to "believe" or "not to believe" Desdemona as a choice of strategy, Othello must have a payoff matrix to examine. But to decide whether *to believe* or *not to believe* Desdemona as a person (not as an opponent in a game), Othello should be guided by entirely different considerations. He might reason thus:

"If Desdemona is to be believed, I am playing one game. If not, I am playing another. In both games, Desdemona's strategy is clear cut. In the first game, she should definitely play strategy 2; in the second, she should play strategy 1. If I act as if I am playing the second game, and if the probability of the first game is p, my expected payoff is $p(-100) + (1-p)(0)$ $= -100p$. If I act as if I am playing the first game, I expect $p(100) + (1-p)(-75) = 175p - 75$. Now what must p be to justify my playing my own game instead of Desdemona's? The condition is $-100p > 175p - 75$ or $-275p > -75$ or $p < 0.37$. Now can I assume that the chance that Desdemona's game is in fact what I am playing is less than 37 per cent? How much weight do I assign to her character as I thought it to be? Should I take my racial origin into account, which would assign a higher probability to the second game? Or would she on that account be, on the contrary, even less inclined to deceive me? Does the fact that she married a Moor indicate an unusual loyalty? How much credence should I give to Iago? To the fact that Cassio already has a mistress?"

All this sounds like a problem of a decision under uncertainty. But there is an additional complication. Even if Othello is convinced that he is playing the second game (Matrix 22), he cannot be absolutely sure that Desdemona will play strategy 1. For suppose Desdemona decides to play the co-operative strategy 2, trusting that Othello will do the same. If this were a symmetrical Prisoner's Dilemma, this should not worry Othello. The cynic in Prisoner's Dilemma does best if the other is trusting. But Matrix 22 is a version of the Prisoner's Dilemma only for Desdemona, not for Othello. *The worst possible outcome for Othello in his own version of the game is to distrust a trusting Desdemona!* Othello's dilemma is more baffling than the prisoner's.

Formidable as these difficulties are, we have not even touched on the problem of assigning interval scale utilities to outcomes. To do this, we must expect Othello to answer questions of this sort: "Would I rather have Desdemona deceive me and know it or gamble that with probability 30 per cent she has remained faithful and I have believed her and with probability 70 per cent she has deceived me and I did nothing about it? If the latter, what is my preference if the split between the two latter alternatives is 40–60?"

Furthermore, we must bear in mind that we have resisted every temptation to consider games more complicated than with two players, each with two strategies. If Othello had been an enthusiastic game theorist, he might well have sketched a game with four players (plus Chance) shown in Figure 13.

An examination of that game tree shows that Othello has 16 strategies. Iago is his only source of information. Othello can distinguish only two situations: Iago reports of Desdemona's unfaithfulness, and Iago reports nothing. In each case, he can either do nothing or initiate the subgame G, which he plays with Desdemona and in which he has four strategies. He therefore has $4^2 = 16$ strategies in all. Chance has only one move, two strategies, and, of course, no payoffs. Cassio has also only one move and two strategies. His payoffs, however, are many and varied, and Othello must take them carefully into account in order to make the best estimate of Cassio's move. For Iago and Desdemona, this is a game of perfect information (but not for Othello!). The reader may verify that Iago has 64 strategies, and Desdemona has 16,384. There are, however, only 55 distinct outcomes of the game, 4 outcomes at each of the 11 subgames G and 11 outcomes where Othello does nothing.[73] At each of these 55 end points, payoffs must be imputed to the four active players. Also the relative probabilities of Chance's two choices must be assigned.

Moreover, Othello should consider the possibility of collusion. For instance, there may be collusion between Iago and Desdemona, in case Desdemona has deceived Othello and Iago blackmails her and keeps his promise to keep quiet in return for Desdemona's favors.

Perhaps enough has been said about the practical difficulties of applying game theory in human affairs.[74] Yet I think it would be a grave mistake to dismiss the theory on that account as being inconsequential, "an empty mathematical exercise," as has been done repeatedly with many mathematical theories, some of which have since become firmly established in applied science.

Disappointment with a theory is inevitable if direct and practical results are expected immediately. Direct and immediate results are rarely fruits of the most important theories. To take an example, wave mechanics is extremely difficult to apply to the most familiar waves, namely the waves on the surface of bodies of water. And so wave mechanics is of little consequence in sailing ships, where one might naïvely think it had

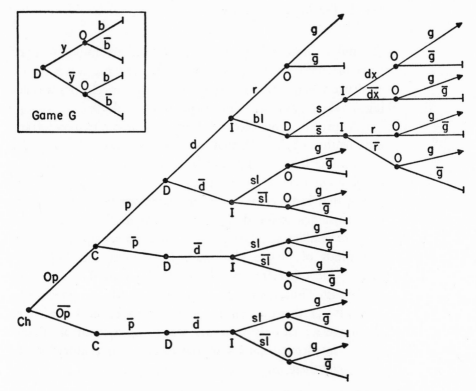

Figure 13. A game tree, as it might be imagined by a "rational" Othello.

The Players

Ch.: Chance	I.: Iago
C.: Cassio	O.: Othello
D.: Desdemona	

The Moves

Op.: Chance gives Cassio an opportunity to attempt to seduce Desdemona.

p: Cassio attempts to seduce Desdemona

d: Desdemona deceives Othello

r: Iago reports Desdemona's infidelity to Othello

bl: Iago blackmails guilty Desdemona

sl: Iago slanders innocent Desdemona

s: Desdemona succumbs to Iago

dx: Iago doublecrosses Desdemona (reports anyway)

g: Othello initiates game G (see inset)

The barred letters are negations of the moves listed above: $\bar{d}$, Desdemona does not deceive Othello, etc.

the most direct relevance. The tremendous importance of wave mechanics is in its use as a tool for studying waves whose existence was not even suspected when wave mechanics was being developed as a branch of mathematical physics.

At present game theory has, in my opinion, two important uses, neither of them related to games nor to conflict *directly*. First, game theory stimulates us to think *about* conflict in a novel way. Second, game theory leads to some genuine impasses, that is, to situations where its axiomatic base is shown to be insufficient for dealing even theoretically with certain types of conflict situations. These impasses set up tensions in the minds of people who care. They must therefore look around for other frameworks into which conflict situations can be cast. Thus, the impact is made on our thinking processes themselves, rather than on the actual content of our knowledge. In an age which only yesterday was being accused of "living on the intellectual capital of the seventeenth century" (129, pp. 55–56) these impacts are a hopeful sign.

PART III
THE ETHICS OF DEBATE

Judge not, and ye shall not be judged.—*LUKE*

AN APOLOGY

BEFORE WE GO ON, I must mention two difficulties I had to face when writing this book. The first was how to explain in ordinary language the results of mathematical investigations, with which Parts I and II were primarily concerned. The second was how to give the reader to understand the different senses in which the arguments here developed can lay claim to validity.

The first task is only an outgrowth of the general problem which has become urgent in our times. The scientific edifice is reaching for the skies, and the language of science is getting farther and farther away from ordinary language. To overcome the difficulties of explanation is a challenge to anyone who is seriously involved in disseminating knowledge or understanding, and even a partial success in this direction is rewarding, as every teacher knows. To meet this challenge, I have had to assume practically no technical mathematical knowledge in the reader, at the risk of boring the mathematically literate. On the other hand, a certain maturity of formal reasoning had to be taken for granted in order to do anything beyond scratching the surface of the mathematical theories of conflict. In these circumstances, the impression of a double standard is unavoidable. This is the stylistic price exacted for an attempt to broaden the base of understanding for theoretical science, and I have paid it.

My second task, however, is of a different kind. When I come to speak of debates in Part III, I will not be able to lay claim to any area of special competence. The ideas are borrowed, as I said, from certain sectors of psychotherapy and cultural anthropology, where my knowledge is anything but firsthand and is not tempered by systematic or professional experience, except by that of teaching, where similar ideas are relevant. Yet this is just where my convictions are strongest, and where the conclusions are most controversial. In Part III, I shall not be able to refrain from preaching, even though I am aware that the support for the ideas I shall be preaching stems primarily from intuitive convictions. It is small consolation to realize that most preaching is of this sort. In other words, in Part III, I must abandon my role as a popularizer of science and become a propagandist.

I have been a propagandist before, and I am not reticent about assuming this role. But what I have previously advocated, for example, the adoption of a scientific attitude in the evaluation of values, was a natural appendage to the exposition of the scientific outlook. Thus, until now, even in my role as propagandist, I did not abandon my task of explaining science, its aims and its methods. In the present case, however, when I pass from exposition to exhortation, I shall not have the orientation of the "scientific attitude" to lean on. The theme will be "empathetic understanding," and I still shrink from the sentimental overtones of this word.

There is nothing in either logical or empirical analysis (the semantics of science) which indicates how one is to come by an "empathetic understanding," of an opposing or an outlandish point of view. More can be learned in this respect from the humanities or simply from worldly experience than from any application of "method." It seems "empathetic understanding," like the disciplines from which the notion stems (psychotherapy and cultural anthropology), belongs properly in the arts rather than in the sciences. Nevertheless, attempts will be made to spell out in terms as close as can be found to the terms of scientific analysis, just what the problem of "empathetic understanding" involves. In some instances, an analogous notion in science and in logic will be offered, for example, the notion of the "domain of validity." The model of fruitful debate will be built around that notion, and it will be argued, in effect, that an important task in a debate is to delineate the domain of validity for each of the opposing stands. "Empathetic understanding" then will emerge as a recognition that practically every conviction has a certain "domain of validity."

In spite of such attempts to connect the ethics of debate with certain insights characteristic of the scientific attitude, it should be emphasized that the foundations on which Part III rests are not scientific. The plea for "empathetic understanding" will itself be based on the hope that the "empathetic understanding" of the reader can be enlisted.

CHAPTER XV

TO LEARN IS TO SELECT;
TO SEE IS TO SELECT

IN THE CLASSICAL DEMONSTRATION of primitive learning, an animal is faced with a choice of two alternatives. The choice of one alternative is rewarded; the other is punished. Typically, the choices of alternatives at first appear random. As learning progresses, the rewarded alternative is chosen more and more frequently, until eventually it is chosen exclusively.

The mechanism of conditioning, originally discovered in physiological context, makes possible a simple explanation of such learning without resorting to speculations about what the animal "feels." In fact, it has become a simple matter to construct a mechanism which will do what the laboratory rat does. The mechanism then becomes a *model* of a learning organism. If we are willing to assume (and there is good justification for doing so) that the operation of the nervous system of the animal is in *some* ways analogous to the operation of the "learning" mechanism, we can partly understand the former in terms of the latter. Let us, therefore, see how the learning mechanism works.

LEARNING AS A TRANSITION FROM CHANCE TO CHOICE

To simulate the initial seemingly random choices of the animal, some chance device is built into the mechanism. This device channels the mechanism's responses now this way now that way, by opening and closing relays or by increasing and decreasing resistances in a random fashion. In addition, there is a feedback circuit, through which the *outcome* of the one or the other choice affects either the chance device or the connections in such a way that each "success" makes the repetition of the associated response more likely and each failure makes the repetition of the associated response more unlikely. Accordingly, a bias is established favoring the correct response. The resulting greater frequency of correct responses increases the bias still further, until the correct response is fixed.

According to the theory of learning based on neural conditioning, some such events occur in the nervous system. There are some known neural mechanisms to account for these events. For example, randomness of response can be attributed to the "fluctuations of thresholds," that is, the variation in the resistance which must be overcome to channel the responses. These fluctuations, stemming from many sources (metabolic processes, presence of irrelevant stimuli, etc.), can be assumed to be random. The *systematic* increments or decrements of the *average* thresholds at the connections leading to the two alternatives can also be accounted for by known neurophysiological mechanisms. And so the analytical explanation of learning enjoys a certain amount of credence. This credence is augmented by the fact that simple and reasonable quantitative assumptions about this learning model lead to good quantitative predictions of learning curves (say the cumulative number of errors plotted against trials under various conditions of the experiment).[75]

Our confidence in this mechanistic theory of learning is somewhat shaken when we turn our attention within ourselves and take stock of our consciousness of similar situations. When *we* are faced with a choice of two alternatives, we try one. If it leads to an undesired result, we try another. If one of the two is "correct," it takes at most two trials to determine which one it is. There is no "learning curve" and no random fluctuations to account for. What we feel introspectively is something we call "recognition," the ability to identify the alternatives, and something we call "reasoning," the association of acts with consequences.

However, it is not hard to name situations where we are no better off than the laboratory animal. If a rote learning task is complex, say learning to associate many alternatives with many outcomes without systematic connection between the associations, our performance will show gradual improvement rather than a spontaneous insight. We may still be able to follow the process introspectively. For example, in a memorization task, we can attribute our successes to "remembering" and our failures to "forgetting." But even this introspective knowledge disappears as we contemplate our learning of a complex muscular skill. There we cannot give an account of what happens as we improve, say in learning to type or to skate or to play the flute.

Nor can a child give an account of what happens as he learns to speak. It seems plausible to extend the selective theory of learning to these processes. The acquisition of speech is particularly suggestive. It is commonly agreed that the human infant begins to produce sounds at random. There are no differences in the samples of sounds produced by infants born into the several language communities. We are almost forced to the conclusion that the sounds of the language eventually to be spoken by the child are "selected for," to put it in the language of organic evolution.

The use of the evolutionary term is not entirely figurative. If it were possible to identify units in the entire repertoire of responses in a given situation, the repeated occurrences of these unit responses could well be viewed as the propagation of a "population." If overt responses are sequences of such unit responses, we can view the "competition" among such sequences as a selective process formally entirely analogous to the selective process which assembles the units of heredity called genes into larger units called chromosomes. These complexes of genes, according to current genetic theory, determine to a large extent the life history of the organism in whose cells they are contained.[76]

What we see as an "entity," say a cat, can be viewed in another way as a vast aggregate of entities (genes, chromosomes, cells, tissues, anatomical structures), whose particular configuration is a result of the evolutionary selective process. Similarly, what we perceive as a coherent act, say the skilled performance of a musical composition or an executed ballet figure or a pronounced word, can be viewed as an aggregate of minute units, such as muscular contractions or, looking still deeper, discharges of nerve cells, selected and ordered into proper sequences among innumerable possible ones.

This view is in harmony with the behaviorist orientation in psychology. It seems strange that the so-called *Gestalt* school of psychology should at one time have found it necessary to develop its principles in opposition to those of the behaviorist school. The main objection of the Gestaltists, as I understand it, was that the behaviorist scheme did not take into account the organizational function of the nervous system. Thus, according to the Gestaltists, our perception of a geometrical figure *as a whole,* evidenced by our ability to recognize the figure regardless of its position, orientation, or size, invalidates a crucial assumption of behaviorism, namely, that external stimuli determine responses. But if only one admits that what we introspectively feel as "recognition" is also the result of responses (although, of course, not necessarily overt ones), then the same conceptual scheme in which learned skilled acts are viewed as results of a selective process can be extended to perception, recognition, concept formation, etc. Just as the *pronunciation* of a word is a skilled act, so the *recognition* of a word or of a pattern (including the corrections unconsciously introduced to iron out distortions or to fill in missing parts) is a skilled act.

252 | The Ethics of Debate

Nor do all skilled acts need to be learned by any specific individual. Some are clearly inborn, as are all the complicated "skilled acts" of metabolism, visceral activity, etc. Also, some overt seemingly purposeful acts of animals are unmistakably inborn and are subsumed under "instincts." It can be pointed out, however, that when learning is viewed as a selective process, instinctive acts (including perceptual ones) can also be considered as "learned," except that the selective process in the case of instinctive acts must be seen as operating on many generations of individuals instead of on many repetitions of a situation in which the individual finds himself (109).

Therefore, both the overt responses and those inner responses which, we can assume, govern perception and recognition are basically results of selection. Of all the impinging stimuli, some are filtered through a given channel, others are blocked, just as in a half-tone picture, some small areas are inked and some are not. The pattern of responses (or inked areas) emerges as an organized act (or a perception or a picture).

"SEEING" AS SELECTION

The reason the world around us "makes sense" is that we accept some stimuli and exclude others; we also accept the *linking* of certain groups of stimuli and exclude the linking of others. It is difficult to recognize a camouflaged geometrical figure, because extraneous stimuli compete for being included in the "picture," and so the proper linkages necessary to see the camouflaged figure may not occur. *Once we have seen* the camouflaged figure, however, we have selected the proper linkages and have facilitated their repeated selection. We will then continue to see the figure without difficulty.

This principle can be dramatically demonstrated in the ambivalent picture shown on page 253, a standard example in many psychology textbooks. If you see the picture for the first

Permission of Dr. E. G. Boring.

time, you almost certainly see either a young woman elegantly dressed with the back of her head turned to you, or an old, surly-looking woman in profile. If you see one of them, you will think it unlikely that the other is there too. But once you have seen both (i.e., once you have learned to link the stimuli induced in your nervous system by the ink marks, one way *or* another), you can see either woman at will. If you make an effort, you may even be able to see both at once.

To see both at once is not easy, however: the images compete for recognition. Usually, one or the other is suppressed. In some experiments on perception it is shown that the suppression of images can go to great lengths and may even bring out an active illusion. In one type of experiment, the subject is shown a frame in the shape of a window. The actual shape of the frame is trapezoidal, but from a distance it tends to be perceived as rectangular. The "apparent" trapezoidal shape is attributed by the subject to the foreshortening of perspective. In other words, the frame is "seen" as a *rectangular* window inclined at an angle to the plane perpendicular to the subject's line of vision.

If now the frame is made to rotate, it is "seen" as oscillating instead of rotating, because the misinterpretation of the angles must persist. If an object is attached to the frame, the *object* is seen to revolve about the axis of rotation of the frame. But now a difficulty occurs. The object cannot revolve while the frame oscillates unless the object passes *through* the frame. To resolve the difficulty, either of two "conclusions" must be made:

1. It is admitted that the frame rotates, and this can be "seen" only if the frame is perceived to be trapezoidal, not rectangular.

2. It is admitted that the solid object passes through the solid frame.

The one or the other conclusion will not be made verbally, of course, because no one is arguing the issue. It will be made "perceptually," that is, either the object will be "seen" passing through the solid frame or the frame will be "seen" as trapezoidal. Although the latter is actually the case, and although verbally most people would sooner deny conclusion 2 than conclusion 1, nevertheless almost everyone "sees" the object passing through the solid window frame. They do not "believe" what they "see," but they "see" it. Evidently, the tacit conviction that "windows are rectangular" is too strong to be overcome by contrary evidence.

So far we have been discussing demonstrable properties of perception. Two conclusions seem warranted:

1. Perception is a selective process, where not only stimuli are selected but also the way these stimuli are linked to form perceptive wholes.

2. There is resistance to change in the perceptive pattern.

We have also given what seem to us plausible explanations of these phenomena. If perception is viewed as a sequence of (inner) responses, then a pattern perceived is a pattern learned.

If learning can be viewed as a selective process, so can perception, possibly involving similar mechanisms of selection, that is, the facilitation of certain neural linkages and the inhibition of others. Moreover, since the formation of selected patterns is generally a gradual process (as is most learning), change of perception involves a relearning. The lag associated with relearning manifests itself as a resistance to changes in perception.[77]

THE "OUTLOOK" AS A PERCEPTIVE SYSTEM

Now we leave the relatively safe inferences, well backed by experiment and strict deduction, and embark upon speculations of a different sort, speculations which derive their support much more from intuitive feelings of their "rightness" than from objective evidence. I shall make two hypotheses, upon which my entire argument to follow will rest.

The first hypothesis extends the notion of perception pattern from geometrical figures, identifiable objects, units of speech, etc. to a much broader class of configurations. We shall assume that such things as ideologies, ethical systems, religious and political convictions, complexes of attitudes, are also perceptual systems and that they arise through the process of selective learning, as the simpler patterns do.[78]

The second hypothesis states that in addition to the ordinary inertia responsible for the resistance that perceptual patterns offer to modification, those larger patterns, which we shall call "world images" or "outlooks" usually offer additional resistance to being changed, stemming from certain emotional commitments.

To put it crudely and very figuratively, a man holds onto his world image not only because it takes effort to change it, but also because he *needs* his particular image or else because he is afraid to look at other images.

Now these hypotheses are not scientific hypotheses, because they cannot be translated into clearly verifiable statements about operationally definable terms. For example, the words "needs" and "is afraid" in the last paragraph are not used in an operationally definable sense. The behaviorist may point out that operational definitions might be made of such terms. For example, he might define "is afraid" in terms of increased heart beat, tremor, etc. But we are not using the words this way. We are using them in the old-fashioned way: "he is afraid" refers to a certain inner state of the other, which you can recognize if you recall the times *you* were afraid. We go even further afield from verifiable context in our use of the words "needs" and "is afraid." We assume with Freud and others that a man may have needs and fears of which he himself is not aware. Therefore, in the case of such unconscious needs and fears, even the definition by appeal to introspection is not possible. Nevertheless, we believe that the concepts of unconscious needs and fears are useful concepts, and we shall use them in spite of their dubious legitimacy in scientific discourse. As we have said, in our apology, we shall have to abandon rigorous argument in this last part of this book.

The resistance of world images to change because of need or fear is a commonplace hypothesis in psychiatry. It is sometimes assumed, for example, that the schizophrenic, although he seems "maladjusted" from our point of view, has actually succumbed to his disease as an "adjustment." He has seized a new world image, in which tensions that had become unbearable have been relieved. Once he has been "rewarded" by the release of tensions for organizing his world image in a peculiar way, he holds on to it. He resists any attempts to force him into an organization of his world image from which he had fled. He may be suffering from his disease from our point of view, but according to the hypothesis he needs the disease to escape even greater pain.

It is often assumed that the hypochondriac "needs" his imaginary symptoms. They bolster his needs to be dependent on others. Similarly, it is often assumed that the overly jealous spouse needs his suspicions. They offer rationalizations for his own appetite for infidelity or for his aggressive impulses against his partner.

Sometimes events are selected to dominate the focus of attention, because they are interpreted as evidence of something that is dreaded. A person with a neurotic dread of cancer recognizes cancer symptoms in himself daily. Some would argue that this is evidence of his unconscious *wish* for the disease, but we need not go so far in our hypothesis. There is no reason why something dreaded cannot command the organization of perception as well as something wished for. It is quite normal to be on the alert for signals that portend danger. An exaggeration of this normal biologically useful inclination to direct attention to signs of danger may well degenerate into neurotic or psychotic organizations of experience.

Whatever may be the merits of these hypotheses, they are implicit not only in psychiatry but also in much of great world literature which has reflected man's intuitive self-knowledge.

Where Sancho Panza sees windmills, Don Quixote sees wicked giants.

When the Connecticut Yankee sees slaves whipped, he sees the misery of the human condition; but his sixth-century companions see the virtuosity with which the whip is wielded.

As Isolda in the second act of *Tristan* is preparing to signal to her lover, her maid implores her to wait until the horns of the departing huntsmen are no longer heard. When the maid listens, the horns sound faintly in the orchestra, but when Isolda listens, only the tremolo of strings (like the rustling of leaves) is heard.

We see the same principles operating in the cleavages that constantly divide our populations on social issues. Those who see a miscarriage of justice in some *cause célèbre* emphasize all the evidence which supports the innocence of the accused. Those who see the defendant and his supporters as a threat to their perception of social order will emphasize the evidence which points to guilt and will ignore what is not consistent with it.

Thus, without falsifying a single fact, entirely contradictory descriptions can and are given of persons, situations, social orders, etc., by selecting (often unconsciously) only the features which support preconceived notions.

Controversial issues tend to be polarized not only because commitments have been made but also because certain perceptions are actively excluded from consciousness if they do not fit the chosen world image.

CHAPTER XVI

THE BLINDNESS OF
INVOLVEMENT

IF THE ANALOGY between the perception of organized patterns
and the organization of a world image is valid, we may assume
that a world image resists change or disorganization by "cen-
soring" stimuli incompatible with it. The operation of prejudice
based on stereotypic conceptions of members of an outgroup is
well known. The carriers of extreme prejudice are notoriously
impervious to some stimuli and exquisitely sensitive to others.
The world image of a paranoiac seems like an ingenious selection of a web of linkages among events, all chosen for the
corroboration they give to the basic organization of the image.

It is not possible to call every instance of selective perception pathological, because all organized perception is selective.
Nor can we even call every instance of "bizarre" selection pathological, unless we are willing to subsume every manifestation of
genius under mental disease. For the essence of genius is sensitivity to farfetched connections, an ability to perceive hidden
analogies, a tendency to juxtapose what does not ordinarily
seem to belong together but can be seen to do so upon being
juxtaposed.

The distinction between Darwin and Sherlock Holmes is
more in their specific preoccupations than in the workings of
their minds. From Sherlock Holmes, who dealt presumably
with the real world, to Stalin, who dealt partly with the real
world and partly with a world of his own making, to the mental
patient who sees the world as a giant conspiracy against himself

and manifests unusual perceptiveness in making observations consistent with his fantasy and amazing ingenuity in interpreting them, is only a sequence of steps.

Involvement has been a constant source of inspiration for depicting the drama of human existence. Medea, Macbeth, Don Quixote, and Faust are all irreversibly committed to their respective world images, and the blindness of their commitments is the essence of their tragedies.

Let us take a few examples from fiction and from recent history in order to see in greater detail the state of mind which represents complete involvement, for this is the state of mind that usually must be dealt with when a serious debate is joined. Instead of taking great universal figures now, who represent "aspects of man," drawn on immense canvases, we will take examples closer to home, where the involvements are more relevant to the specific problems of our own age.

THE MAD BUILDER

Our first example is from *The Bridge on the River Kwai* (film version).

The hero, it will be recalled, is a British regular army captain, who together with his company is taken prisoner by the Japanese. Being a stickler for protocol, he refuses to allow his officers to do manual labor. The Japanese commander sets out to break the spirit of the British. A struggle of wills ensues, in which the Japanese colonel holds the trumps of physical force over the British, but the British captain has the edge, because *he* controls the prisoners, whose labor the colonel needs to fulfill his assignment—the construction of a railroad bridge in the depth of the Burmese jungle.

It turns out that the British have not only the necessary labor force but also the engineering skill, which the Japanese lack. The colonel capitulates. The British captain is released from the corrugated iron prison (the "hot box") and the officers freed from manual labor. In return, the British captain undertakes the construction of the Bridge.

Now the drama begins. The captain's victory over his captor will be complete only if the Bridge is a masterpiece of engineering, built in record time. For his victory consists of wreaking the revenge of humiliation on the Japanese commander. Naturally, the goal must be rationalized, because, after all, it amounts to collaboration with the enemy. But rationalizations are never lacking, once involvement takes grip. It is necessary, the captain argues, for the prisoners of war to "remain soldiers." Hence they must have a clearly discernible goal to work toward. Moreover, the demonstration of ingenuity and energy by the British will, he argues, be a serious blow to Japanese morale.

There is also a third figure, an American prisoner, who escapes soon after the British arrive. To the American the war is what it appeared to most of us, civilians, both in and out of uniform: a nasty business to get over so as to be able to return to the blessings of American abundance. The American is not even averse to goldbricking, when he can get away with it, and he can do so for a while in the country club atmosphere of the British headquarters in Ceylon, which he reaches after a perilous flight through the jungle. But the American too becomes "involved." The British inveigle him into leading a demolition party back into the jungle through which he had miraculously escaped to blow up the Bridge, which the British captain is building for the Japanese.

The wrecking crew arrives on the night before the ribbon cutting. The wires are strung and the detonators ready. They are waiting only for the train with the Japanese brass to arrive at the Bridge so as to put on "a good show."

The dramatic climax comes in the unfolding of the nature of the captain's involvement. He and the colonel stand side by side on the Bridge, waiting for the great moment when the first train will pass over it. Suddenly we realize that this is a triumphal moment only for the British captain. The Japanese colonel has already completed his preparations for hara-kiri. He has been humiliated by the British, who succeeded where he had failed.

Now the British captain sees the wires leading from the Bridge to shore. He turns to the Japanese colonel, nominally his enemy, but now his only ally. He points to the wires and quietly motions the colonel to follow. They come on the demolition squad and the American. *These* are now the captain's enemies. The saboteurs attempt to explain: "It's all right, captain . . . We're British soldiers . . . We've come to blow up the bridge . . ."

"*Blow up my Bridge!*" is all the captain can say, as he grapples with them. There is a bloody struggle, and the captain, mortally wounded, falls on the detonator, just as the train rushes onto the exploding Bridge. The surviving British get to see the "good show."

The whole force of the drama resides in the suddenness of our realization that the captain is insane; that he must have been insane all along, as we identified with him through his formidable *tour de force* of courage and will power. The captain is the essence of manhood, as we usually understand manhood; and at the same time he is stark mad. If "pity and fear" induced in the audience are the ingredients of tragedy, as Aristotle would have it, then *The Bridge* is a tragedy. With astonishing suddenness, the captain turns from a heroic into a pitiful figure. The fear, too, is quite real. It stems from the fuzziness of the line which separates "manhood" from insanity.

THE FIGHT FOR "JUSTICE"

Another good example can be found in the recent popular novel, *Anatomy of a Murder* (122).

The considerable literary value of this book is in the faithfulness and the vividness with which the author pictures a competitive involvement rationalized as a noble fight for justice. There is no denying that the philosophy of American jurisprudence, as that of many other aspects of American life, is cut from the same cloth as our business philosophy. The essence of the latter is an unreserved acceptance of competition as the way of life and the zest of life. Business is a game,[79] in which the prizes go to the bold, the shrewd, and the lucky. Ethics is equated to "fairness." To be fair is to stick meticulously to the rules of the game. The authority of government is delegated authority, mainly the authority of an arbitrator. Thus, the most appropriate role of the government is that of an umpire, who enforces the rules and settles disputes between the competitors.

A court of justice too is an arena where the game is played. The opposing attorneys are the contestants. The stakes may be the life or the liberty of the defendant. The judge is an umpire. An American plays the game "hard,"—he asks for no favors and gives none, but he plays "fair," that is, he does not cheat.

Now traditionally a court of justice was a place where justice was supposed to be administered. Somehow the notion of justice has to be squared with the notion of the competitive game. This is not easy, since a basic contradiction is apparent. A competitive game, by its very nature, cannot indicate justice on one side or the other. By definition, the opponents in a "fair game" are *a priori* both entitled to win. The fact that only one wins is an *a posteriori* indication of where the *might* lay. Justice, however, again by definition, belongs on one side or another *a priori,* hence independently of the outcome, unless one insists that "right is might" (*sic*). But such an insistence would open one to a charge of naïveté, something from which the American male shrinks. The American image of manhood combines fairness with toughness and with world-wise knowledge, which borders on cynicism. Hence the dilemma. Justice is on one side only. But one must fight for one's *own* side. More-over, one must fight as hard as one can, using all the tricks of the trade, as long as the rules are obeyed. But what if justice is on the other side?

The cynic will dismiss this question. His job is to defend *his* side. He considers himself a professional mercenary soldier. But the hero of *Anatomy of a Murder* is not a cynic, in spite of a quasi-cynical mask he must wear as a virile American. He is not a cynic, and he must defend a killer, because it is his job. Moreover, the defense must be not a plea for mercy but a bid for an acquittal. He must therefore convince himself (himself, as well as others, because he is not a cynic) that the killing was an act of blind passion, committed under temporary insanity. The defendant, who *is* a cynic,[80] helps the defense attorney weave the web of delusion in which everyone becomes en-tangled, including the reader. The awakening, engineered by the acquitted defendant's sadistic prank played on his rescuer, comes with brutal suddenness and in a flash reveals the nature of the drama.

MEN AND WAR

Our next three examples are taken from recent history.

I

There was intense excitement about the landings in France, which every one knew were in progress at the moment. Nevertheless I devoted ten minutes to the campaign in Italy and in paying my tribute to the Allied Armies there. After thus keeping them on tenterhooks for a little while, I said:

I have also to announce to the House that during the night and early hours of this morning the first of a series of landings in force upon the European continent has taken place. In this case the liberat-ing assault fell upon the coast of France. An immense armada of upwards of 4000 ships, together with several thousand smaller craft crossed the Channel. Massed airborne landings have been successfully effected behind enemy lines, and landings on the beaches are proceeding at various points at the present time. The fire of the shore batteries has been largely quelled. The obstacles that were constructed in the sea have not proved so difficult as was apprehended. The Anglo-American Allies are sustained by about 11,000 first-line aircraft, which can be drawn upon as may be needed for the purposes of the battle . . . Reports are coming in in rapid succession. So far the commanders who are engaged report that everything is proceeding according to plan. And what a plan! The vast operation is undoubtedly the most complicated and difficult that has ever taken place.

2

And then came a damp, cold night in Flanders, through which we marched in silence, and when the day began to emerge from the mists, suddenly an iron greeting came whizzing at us over our heads, and with a sharp report sent the little pellets flying between our ranks, ripping up the wet ground; but even before the little cloud passed, from two hundred throats the first hurrah rose to meet the first messenger of death. Then a crackling and a roaring, a singing and a howling began, and with feverish eyes each one of us was drawn, faster and faster, until suddenly past turnip fields and hedges the fight began, the fight of man against man. And from the distance the strains of a song reached our ears, coming closer and closer, leaping from company to company, and just as Death plunged a busy hand into our ranks, the song reached us too, and we passed it along: *Deutschland, Deutschland ueber Alles ueber Alles in der Welt.*

Four days later we came back. Even our step had changed. Seventeen-year-old boys now looked like men.

3

The struggle for existence is, in the life of Nature, the basis of all healthy development. All existing things show themselves to be the result of contesting forces. So in the life of man the struggle is not merely the destructive but the life-giving principle. 'To supplant or to be supplanted is the essence of life,' says Goethe, and the strong life gains the upper hand. The law of the stronger holds good everywhere. Those forms survive which are able to procure themselves the most favorable conditions of life, and to assert themselves in the universal economy of Nature. The weaker succumb. This struggle is regulated and restrained by the unconscious sway of biological laws and by the interplay of opposite forces. In the plant world and in the animal world this process is worked out in unconscious tragedy. In the human race, it is consciously carried out, and regulated by social ordinances. The man of strong will and strong intellect tries by every means to assert himself, the ambitious strive to rise, and in this effort the individual is far from being guided merely by the consciousness of right. The life-work and the life-struggle of many men are determined, doubtless, by unselfish and ideal motives, but to a far greater extent the less noble passions—craving for possessions, enjoyment and honor, envy and the thirst for revenge—determine men's actions. Still more often, perhaps, it is the need to live which brings down even natures of higher mold into the universal struggle for existence and enjoyment . . .

Frederick the Great recognized the ennobling effect of war. 'War,' he said, 'opens the most fruitful field to all virtues, for at every moment constancy, pity, magnanimity, heroism, and mercy, shine forth in it; every moment offers an opportunity to exercise one of these virtues.

'At the moment when the State cries out that its very life is at stake, social selfishness must cease and party hatred be hushed. The individual must forget his egoism, and feel that he is a member of the whole body. He should recognize how his own life is nothing worth in comparison with the welfare of the community. War is elevating, because the individual disappears before the great conception of the State. The devotion of the members of a community to each other is nowhere so splendidly conspicuous as in war . . . What a perversion of morality to wish to abolish heroism among men.'

The first of these three passages is Churchill's (17, pp. 5–6). The situation he describes is still fresh in the memory of many of us, and many of us will have no difficulty reliving the moments when we may have felt the elation that Churchill appears to have felt. There was a colossal "job" to do, which offered an unsurpassed challenge. ("And what a plan!") "Everything" seemed to depend on the fulfillment of a task assigned by destiny. Success meant for some the preservation of everything they held dear; to others the opening of new vistas for humanity. Failure meant a prospect of hopeless slavery, an "order" under which it was unthinkable that one could go on living. The pursuit of the task meant suffering and death for millions, but the acceptance of suffering and death was for many of us a tragic necessity which lent even more dignity to the great undertaking which lay before all men of good will. In short, it was commonplace to think "historically," abstracting from the ordeals of the individuals involved.

The second passage is Hitler's (43, pp. 164–65). His mood, too, was once the mood of millions, but it is harder to capture. No task is clear. The violence of war does not appear here as a "necessary evil" (the way it was made to appear by Western statesmen in World War II), but rather an exhilarating experience. Hitler, the soldier, in his preoccupation, is closer to the actuality of war than Churchill, the Prime Minister. Hitler sees it under greater resolving power, as it were, in terms of actual sights and sounds, not in terms of maps, logistics, and "war aims." (Later, Hitler too is to think in "global" terms, but he does not do so in the passage cited.) The physical danger, the threat of pain and annihilation are closer, but the attitude toward war is, like Churchill's, distinctly positive. But where Churchill's elation is over the moral challenge as a total effort, Hitler's enthusiasm is over the physical joys of the battle itself.

The third passage is from a book by General Friedrich von Bernhardi (5, pp. 18–19; 27–28). To this man, war is both necessary and good. War is not only an exhilarating experience for the individual, a school of moral education; it is also Nature's instrument for the improvement of the race. War is a good to be heartily accepted, not merely tolerated. War does not unleash hatred alone but also, in fact primarily, enhances the noblest qualities of man.

Note that the three passages could be easily paraphrased so as to substitute sex for war. Then the three attitudes depicted would appear so: Hitler's would express the joy of passionate sexual union without a thought of what sex means in the scheme of nature; Churchill's attitude would be that of a woman who has been taught to regard sex as sinful, but who knows her duty as a future mother and therefore in surrendering feels the serenity that comes with yielding to the inevitable; Bernhardi's would be the "mature" modern view, the view which enlightened psychotherapy tries to inculcate into men and women: sex is a great creative power, psychologically as well as in the scheme of nature; the full development of the mature personality goes hand in hand with the blossoming of sexual activity as a creative nurturing activity instead of a narcissistic or a rapacious one.

The analogy drawn between war and sex may appear shocking. But such analogies are taken seriously in depth psychology. It is often maintained, for example, that those who invest their involvement in the struggle for power and who derive their deepest satisfactions from destruction and domination are those who have been denied the opportunity to develop a mature sexuality.[81] Still it is instructive to see the creative urge even in the distorting mirror of sadism. It is also instructive to see how we tend to accept the "inevitable" not without satisfaction, when it is properly rationalized. There is no denying that war is a deeply satisfying experience for many more than care to admit it in the present climate of opinion.

Read on in Churchill's memoirs and you will find an enthusiastic description of his first visit to the theater of operations, where he relates with boyish delight how Admiral Vian consented to his proposal "to have a plug at them," that is, to fire a salvo from their destroyer in the general direction of the Germans.

"I slept soundly on the four-hour voyage to Portsmouth," Churchill concludes. "Altogether it had been a most interesting and enjoyable day." (17, p. 13)

For all the disgust that his crass militarism arouses in the "man of good will" of today, Bernhardi, too, has something instructive to say. Let the activity he describes be not war but some pioneering enterprise, say a giant undertaking of public works, or the colonization of Antarctica, or space exploration, and Bernhardi's sentiments will become irreproachable in the eyes of many.

We note also that the "best" aspects of Communism still command the respect of many "men of good will." By the "best" aspects I mean the drama of industrialization, of collective effort, of devotion to a common cause, the rejection of "petty" self-seeking values, a Spartan indifference to comfort—all these command sympathetic understanding of many millions not merely through inciting slogans but through a thoroughly humanitarian appeal.

Involvement in a gigantic collective effort has always engulfed men's devotion. Characteristically, this involvement often destroys the image of the individual and his specifically individual needs: the need for individual survival, for response, for unique experience, for love. Often the destruction of this image is carried out deliberately. The uniform, for example, is a device that belies the differentiation between individuals. The elaborate ritual of military calisthenics (close order drill, etc.) was once rationalized as contributing to battle efficiency. Today such a rationalization is manifestly absurd, and so the true purpose of these exercises is frankly recognized: to negate the individual will. Callousness is a necessary by-product of involvement with organized activity, especially in a directing capacity.

PREOCCUPATION WITH THE SMALL WORLD

War has also brought out the opposite focus of preoccupation: the conviction that the individual consciousness *is* the cosmos. The concomitant dismissal of the values of suprapersonal organization as evil or sham is a recurrent theme of practically all great war novels. Sometimes it seems that these novels carry the message that only women and children are sane, that is, those who see most clearly and relate themselves most spontaneously to the immediate. These beings may be nurturing or demanding, self-effacing or hedonistic, but they are never threatening: they wield no power and have no appetite for manipulating large masses of humanity.

Profound thinkers have believed this, the foremost among them Leo Tolstoy. But he and others like him, the St. Francises, the Lao-tzes, the Socrateses, they too were blind with their involvement. Their involvement was with virtue, and virtue to them meant doing good *here* and *now* to whoever happens to be around. This is possible only if one renounces participation in any planned, organized, communal activity, motivated by a future goal, because it is possible to see the "here and now" clearly only if the field of vision is sufficiently small and properly focused. Under these circumstances there are no goals which can be reached *instrumentally*. There can be no goals that require passing over intermediate steps, for it is such goals that provide rationalizations to those who do evil in the name of good. Lenin called Tolstoy's ethics "The sermon of the *yurodivyi*" ("saintly idiot").

PREOCCUPATION WITH CRAFTSMANSHIP

Most of the glory-debunking authors lack an understanding of the nature of perhaps the strongest of adult involvements—the involvement of the expert. The expert is one who successfully orders or manipulates a portion of the world which he understands. And there are few satisfactions which surpass the satisfaction of mastery and understanding. All too frequently, of course, these satisfactions are spiked with sadism, but often the line between sadism and craftsmanship is hard to draw. Certainly, we do not think of sadism in connection with the satisfactions provided by a mastery over the inanimate world or over abstract problems. Often the mastery over men is so far removed from men that the satisfactions it provides cannot be distinguished from satisfactions we admire unreservedly.

The magnitude of the problem facing a Churchill or a Khrushchev or, for that matter, a financial tycoon, a first-class racketeer, or a public-relations virtuoso quite compares with the magnitude of the problems facing an outstanding physicist, an architect, a brain surgeon, or a devoted teacher of handicapped children. Facing such problems is one of the most genuine satisfactions of adulthood. Paradoxically, the goals for which many of the activists we have mentioned strive, particularly those of the power-wielders, are often infantile goals; but the implementation of the goals requires soundness of judgment, insights, mastery of techniques, and perseverance—all marks of human maturity.

The most serious accusation against the moral tone prevailing in the United States can be traced to the almost universal acceptance by Americans of involvement with techniques. Nowhere, except possibly in the Soviet Union, is "know-how" more ardently admired. The usual superficial accusation against United States morality is that of money-mindedness. I doubt whether we are more "money-minded" than Europeans. True, measurement of "worth" in terms of money is commonplace and uncouthly frank in American folk culture, but what is really worshipped is know-how. It so happens that the know-hows most admired are also those most generously remunerated, but it is nevertheless the know-how which is really worshipped, not the money. Inherited wealth does not command nearly as much popular respect as wealth amassed by ingenuity, by clever manipulation, and by shrewd exploitation of popular fancy.

It is the worship of technique, not of money that eclipses the moral sense in the United States, to the extent that the morality of "public relations" and of demagogic advertising is seldom questioned in the popular mind. Technique takes skill and the acquisition of skills is associated with the higher aims of life. Therefore, the public-relations man can be proud of his promoting ability even though he has helped to call public attention away from a shady deal; the advertiser can be proud of having "put a product over" even though he has not the slightest personal interest in the product itself. Such activities are seldom linked with dishonesty; they are linked with expert service, loyalty to the client, and know-how.

I am sure that something like this feeling of pride lurked in the professional assassins of the Italian Renaissance. It is present in the soldier of fortune, who hires himself out indifferently to one side or another in a war or a rebellion for the thrills of coping with dangerous situations. It must motivate the spy, because it is hardly thinkable that the average spy's modest remuneration is commensurate with the risks he takes.

In short, the interest in an activity, its challenge, the feeling of mastery it imparts to its successful practitioners usually far outweigh both the acquisitive impulses and the moral considerations associated with it. Preoccupation with craftsmanship dulls moral sensitivity, just as preoccupation with large-scale affairs dulls empathy.

To summarize, the blindness of involvement is blindness to other contexts, the impossibility of shifting the focus of vision. Since we *must* select, we must be blind to what we have left out.

CHAPTER XVII

WAYS OF PERSUASION

THE OBJECT OF DEBATE, as we have defined debate, is to modify the image of the other. Here we must emphasize the distinction between debate and argument. If I try to convince or unconvince someone by marshaling facts or by calling attention to chains of logical consequences, I am making an argument. The success of the argument depends on whether the facts will be examined and whether the chain of logical consequences will be checked. Thus, a dispute between two scientists concerning the status of a theory is an argument, not a debate, as long as facts are taken into account and consequences are weighed. A dispute about directly verifiable facts is most certainly not a debate; nor is a dispute about the validity of a theorem.

A debate, by our definition, is not resolvable by "rational" procedures. It results from a clash of incompatible or partly incompatible images. The main effort in a debate is to induce the opponent to adopt another image. How realistic is this effort? Certainly it is not wholly unrealistic, since conversions are matters of record.

If we admit "partial conversion," that is, a modification rather than an abandonment of the opponent's image as a goal of debate, then fruitful debate seems even more within the realm of possibility. We are thus led to examine ways in which an image can be modified, in spite of the resistance which images typically offer to efforts to modify them.

It seems to me there are three methods of modifying images

(or patterns of response), namely brainwashing, explaining the image away, and removing threats associated with alternative images. All these methods have been used in psychotherapy: they represent respectively the Pavlovian, the Freudian, and the Rogerian outlooks. Our thesis will be that only the last of these is promising as a principal method in debates between equals.

BRAINWASHING

The technique of brainwashing is based on the presumed effectiveness of conditioning in all aspects of human behavior. There are certainly forms of behavior where the efficacy of simple reward-punishment conditioning is unquestioned. Nor is there anything reprehensible about applying this technique in proper circumstances. For example, when you learn a complex muscular skill, say skating, you are actually brainwashing yourself, because you put yourself in a situation where correct patterns of response will be automatically rewarded and incorrect ones punished. Indeed, all *training,* as distinguished from education, rests squarely on the principle of brainwashing. The squeamish may object to the use of an odious label to denote morally irreproachable activity (like teaching someone a useful skill). But it is advisable to keep the term in spite of its bad connotation in order to keep in mind that all brainwashing, good and bad, shares this feature in common: patterns of responses are modified by a system of rewards and punishment. Moreover, it is advisable to keep this term to remind us that we cannot really be sure where to draw the line between good brainwashing and bad.

For example, electric shock, administered through the brain is, or has been until recently, standard procedure in psychotherapy. To the extent that the nervous system is manipulated even more drastically than in conditioning responses, electric shock can be considered as an extreme form of brainwashing.

We must admit that we are in no position to condemn this practice on that account alone.

It is sometimes argued that brainwashing is distinguished by a malevolent intent toward the victim. Such malevolent intent is not always easy to prove. Granting that much of the brainwashing administered, say, by the Chinese Communists on American prisoners was simply a form of torture, it is reasonable to suppose that at least some of the brainwashers considered the procedure therapeutic. This is understandable if we realize that Western ideology (or what the Communists take to be Western ideology) is viewed by many Communists as a form of insanity. Hence the abandonment of this ideology may appear to them as a form of cure.

If we dare to take George Bernard Shaw's *Saint Joan* seriously as a portrayal of the medieval attitude toward the heretic, we have in this play a vivid picture of "benevolent" brainwashing as it was practiced in Christendom. The inquisitor is portrayed as a man of impeccable integrity, selfless and devoted, moved by genuine love for his "patient," Joan of Arc (108, pp. 148–61). He brainwashes the Maid with the same determination and with the same good will that we impute to our military authorities who *de*-brainwashed the soldiers returning from Chinese prison camps.

Life imprisonment awaits Joan even if the brainwashing succeeds, but this appears to the inquisitor no more appalling than the forced confinement of a convalescent appears to the modern physician. And it cannot be otherwise if what we call "life" appears in the world outlook of the inquisitor as a relatively unimportant prelude to the "real" life in the hereafter.

Possibly what Meerloo (72) has called "the rape of the mind" (brainwashing as practiced by the Communists today) appears to some of its practitioners as a rehabilitation of a victim of delusion, just as similar procedures might have appeared to the inquisitors.

There are, of course, cases where the rehabilitation of the brainwashed is not the issue. If we are to believe Nathan Leites (55), who has combined the method of political analysis with that of depth psychology to explain the purges and the confessions of the Communist leaders, then the torments to which those victims were subjected were of purely vindictive nature. If the final extraction of confessions was regarded as a "cure," then the victims were cured only to be destroyed, much as in our society everything is done to save the life of a critically ill condemned murderer in order to electrocute him. In both cases, the "therapeutic" motivation is suspect.

The technique of brainwashing with therapeutic intent appears to be based on the same principle which is thought to underlie psychological aberration as an escape from an unbearable situation. The cure is supposed to work in reverse of the original aberration. One makes the holding on to the "wrong" image unbearable, until, in desperation, another image is grasped. The transition is immediately rewarded. The same principle is assumed in purely vindictive brainwashing.

For example, the NKVD inquisitor Gletkin in Koestler's novel, *Darkness at Noon,* a work of fiction but frighteningly convincing, uses a simple device controlled by a foot pedal to regulate the brightness of overhead lights. To his sleepless victim, Rubashov, grilled for hours at a time, increasing brightness (even to a slight degree) comes to represent punishment and decreasing brightness reward (47, p. 208; p. 240). Since the victim is not fully aware of the correlation between his responses and the behavior of the lights, he cannot be on guard against Gletkin's maneuvers. Thus he becomes *conditioned* to giving Gletkin the kinds of responses Gletkin wants, and these Gletkin immediately rewards by dimming the lights. When the responses become automatic, they "carry the perception with them," as it were. The "patient," not being aware of the real source of his responses and being compelled to have a rationale for them (such compulsions characterize intellectuals), *manufactures* the source in his own changed perceptions. In the language of Pavlovian psychology, this can be said more simply: just as the responses become conditioned to the questions, so the perceptions become conditioned to the responses. We see in Gletkin's technique a supposedly early example of subliminal conditioning, which has recently caused so much discussion in the United States, when pilot experiments in subliminal advertising of consumer goods were publicized.

In another example, the inquisitor (O'Brien in Orwell's *Nineteen Eighty-Four*) demonstrates the brainwashing technique to his "patient" by making him see five fingers when four are held out. The technique is cruder there. It consists simply of inflicting excruciating pain for the wrong *inner* response. Of course, it is easy to make the "patient" *say* "Five" by punishing the response "Four" sufficiently severely. But the object of the brainwashing is not achieved by such a change in the overt response. Brainwashing seeks to reach deeper. The object is to make the "patient" actually *see* five fingers when only four are shown. The assumption is that prolonged severe torture will eventually cause a change on the deeper level of perception (76, p. 255 ff.).

These examples are taken from fiction, and the "theory" behind them is admittedly speculative. However, the accounts of actual brainwashing techniques are approximately of similar content. Both the practitioners of brainwashing and those who condemn it seem to agree on how it works. But, of course, the discussion of the subject is obscured by the emotional charge it carries. In a neutral setting it ought to be possible to examine the underlying principles more closely. Experiments aimed at uncovering the mechanics of perception are especially revealing in this respect. Many of the so-called illusions seem to be induced by a strong need to have sense impressions organized into some sort of scheme, usually one preconceived on the basis of past experience. Impressions which do not fit into the scheme are, therefore, subjectively distorted so that perceptual harmony is achieved.[82]

Recommendations of therapeutic brainwashing are not uncommon even in our supposedly humane and patient-oriented medical practice. Voices are sometimes heard in favor of making some mental diseases or emotional disturbances so uncomfortable for the patient that he has to abandon the corresponding perceptions, just as he had "embraced" them, because they had facilitated escape from unbearable reality.

In summary, leaving the moral issue aside, brainwashing is another name for training. In simple training, patterns of responses or perception or, perhaps, world outlooks are modified by letting the selective process of the trainee's nervous system operate in such a way that responses in the direction of the desired patterns are rewarded and those away from it are punished. Again, ignoring the moral issues and examining only the effectiveness of this simple technique, we have ample evidence that it is effective in inducing simple skills (motor skills, speech, manners, etc.). Nor do we find anything objectionable in the practice of brainwashing on this level. On other levels, beginning with the inculcation of *attitudes* (as distinguished from overt acceptable behavior patterns) in children, serious questions arise concerning both the effectiveness and the moral justification of simple training techniques.

Finally, we must recognize a most fundamental limitation of brainwashing as a method of inducing important changes in the world image, which is a consequence of the very nature of the method. Brainwashing can be effective only if the party of the first part has complete control over the rewards and punishments meted out to the party of the second part. In malignant brainwashing (of prisoners, etc.) this condition is met. In other situations, this can occur if the trainee voluntarily places himself under the control of the trainer. At any rate, brainwashing presupposes an abrogation of the will, at least in part, of one of the parties. Therefore, this technique holds little promise as a method of changing the outlook of an opponent who cannot be brow-beaten or who does not himself submit to the process.

EXPLAINING THE IMAGE AWAY

Another approach to the problem of modifying or supplanting an image is by explaining it away, that is, by revealing its origins. This approach is at the core of psychoanalysis. There, the assumption is that neurotic urges stem from unresolved early conflicts and are symbolic transformations of those conflicts. The underlying meaning of the urges is hidden, because the conflicts had been repressed into the unconscious realm. The therapeutic idea is based on the assumption that once the roots of the neurotic urges are revealed to the conscious mind, the neurotic urges lose their compulsive character. In our language, an image collapses once it has been explained away.

Again, as in the case of brainwashing, no conclusive evidence has been marshaled either in support or in refutation of this view. But also, as in the case of brainwashing, the technique seems plausible, because it is manifestly demonstrable in simpler, more manageable situations, for instance in situations often encountered in teaching. The following examples from my own experience may serve as illustrations.

Once when teaching elementary physics, I was impressed with the resistance of mature intelligent students to some fundamental facts and concepts. For example, when a man falling in a parachute has reached constant velocity, the forces acting on him add up to zero. Beginners almost invariably resist this conclusion. "If there is no resultant force acting on a falling body," they ask, "why does it fall?" Proof by appeal to the fundamental equation of motion is of little avail. They "believe" the equation, but they *believe* their preconceptions.

Getting to the core of the matter usually helps. One must

point out *where the preconceptions come from*. They come from an inner conviction (based on direct experience!) that it takes a force to move a body. The force in the muscles is felt directly, but the opposing force, say of friction or air resistance (which must be equal and opposite if the body is moved with constant velocity) is not directly felt and therefore ignored. Hence the false notion that an unbalanced force is acting on a body moving with constant velocity.

Another idea difficult to put across was that underlying the operation of a Venturi tube. As the stream of air passes through the constriction in this device, the velocity of the flow increases, and the pressure decreases. The prevailing image resists these facts. Most students believe that pressure is greater in the narrower portions and the velocity of flow is smaller. When the probable origin of this notion is pointed out ("You are thinking of squeezing tooth paste and of traffic jams") the mental resistance usually collapses (85).

To summarize, the idea of explaining the image away is this: you point out to the "patient" that it is "natural" for him to have the mistaken idea, because here is how he happened to pick it up, and here is why he is hanging on to it.

PSYCHOANALYTIC FEATURES IN MARXIST DIALECTICS

There is a similar underlying idea in the Marxists' analysis of what they call the superstructure of a culture—its religion, art, political ideas, even science. The idea has been later considerably elaborated by Karl Mannheim (66) in what is termed the sociology of knowledge. Let us examine a sample of such analysis.

Consider the pre-Civil War clash of convictions on slavery in the United States. By and large, the prevailing opinion in the North was that slavery was morally wrong, and in the South that it was morally right. In the debate that raged in those days, both sides appealed to the highest moral authority in support of their respective points of view. (What made the question difficult to settle by appeal to authority was the ample availability in the Scriptures of evidence to support either side.) Such a clear-cut division of moral sentiments on geographical lines is most remarkable. It could not have happened by chance and must be explained.

Today most of us would accept the explanation that the different convictions derived from the existence of different institutions. Slavery was a fact in the South. It was woven into the very fabric of southern life. Therefore, a disturbance of slavery meant for southerners a profound change in their way of life. Under the supposition that man usually resists profound changes of established ways (except when established ways become unbearable), we see that the southern support of slavery was understandable.

But the Marxists wish to delve deeper. "This is all very well," they may say, "but why did the North want to bring about these changes in the South? The *northern* way of life was not threatened by slavery in the South?" Note that here the very question is raised which the South considered the main moral support of their position. Actually, the most eloquent appeal made by southern spokesmen was the appeal to "peaceful coexistence."

It seems, therefore, that the "established institutions" argument, while possibly sufficient to explain the southern attitude, is insufficient to explain the northern. From the Marxist point of view, it is possible to explain both attitudes.

Underlying the clash of conceptions of what is morally right, according to the Marxists, were the clashing economic interests of the ruling classes of the North and the South, respectively. In the South, the ruling class, that is, the owners of the large plantations, derived their incomes and therefore their power, by exploiting agricultural labor. In those days, agricultural labor required no skill and could best be controlled if the laborers were kept in complete ignorance. Slavery, therefore, filled the bill. In the North, however, a new ruling class was emerging—the industrialists, who controlled the means of production in manufacture. Now the increasing importance of machinery made slave labor unfit in factories. The industrial worker had to be at least somewhat literate. More than that, he had to be motivated in a way that a slave could not be. Finally, it was in the interest of the manufacturer to have a fluid labor force, a labor market, a reservoir, from which labor could be recruited and on which it could be dumped when not needed. The industrialist wanted no responsibility for the *person* of the worker. The slave owner had to assume that responsibility if only to keep the body and soul of his slave together, and this not necessarily on moral grounds but because he owned the *whole slave* and so felt that he would be neglecting his property if he did not feed him whether he worked or not. But the industrialist did not buy the whole worker; he bought only the worker's labor. "Freedom of contract" was an important concept in the industrialist's image of the productive process.

An ambition to extend the industrial system to the South would therefore be coupled with a conviction that slavery must be replaced by a free labor force. Since high-sounding ideals are easier to defend (to oneself as well as to others) than economic self-interest, it is easy to see how the real aim, freedom of contract, became translated quite sincerely into "freedom of person." [83]

Such is the Marxist explanation of an ideological conflict. The theory, later developed still further by Lenin, has a distinctly psychiatric flavor. One can trace two links to the later psychoanalytic orientation. One appears already in Marx's sociological theory. He argues that the economic arrangements based on exploitation are doomed by the increasing awareness of the character of the arrangement in the exploited class (70). He terms this awareness "class consciousness." In the absence of class consciousness, the exploited class could be kept in its place by an imposed value system, for instance that of religion or of nationalism. But once the mechanism of the arrangement becomes apparent, such value systems lose their grip on the exploited classes' image about what is "right" or what is possible. The class "finds itself," so to say, and thereby acquires the freedom and the power to dissolve the arrangement.

According to the psychoanalytic assumptions, too, we are not free to the extent that we do not know where our attitudes and compulsions came from. Once we discover how these attitudes and compulsions and even some of our convictions about the nature of reality[84] came about, that is, once the ontogeny of our personality has pushed through from the "unconscious" to the "conscious," we attain the freedom to change the image, to free ourselves from attachments of dependency, free to release creative energy, free to love.

But there is another link between Marxist analysis and psychotherapy, probably not to be found in Marx's writings but quite evident in Lenin's and in the attempts of Communists to win liberals, especially in the West to their point of view.

Lenin waged a struggle within his own party against moderate and gradualist tendencies. The liberal faction of the party felt that the transition of Russia to socialism should go via parliamentary democracy. They questioned the morality of the capture of power by violent means and of the dictatorship of the proletariat. Later, when the revolution was an accomplished fact, they raised embarrassing issues of civil rights; they questioned the justice administered by the "People's Tribunals"; they persisted in claiming freedom of speech; they condemned the forceful dissolution of the Constituent Assembly, to which the delegates had been elected in free elections; and they were repelled by the punitive excesses practiced by the Bolshevik faction. Lenin's answer was always the same. There is no Morality. There is only a class morality. What appears in the image as

Morality is simply a reflection of one's class morality. The liberals, being primarily intellectuals, did belong (by their social position) to the "bourgeoisie." Therefore, what they conceived as moral principles or the tenets of democracy or even ordinary human impulses were nothing more, according to Lenin, than rationalizations of the unconscious urge to preserve the economic system which used these principles as its trappings. Lenin was "explaining away" the image of libertarian democracy in the minds of Russian socialists by pointing to its supposed origins, just as a psychoanalyst tries to explain away a neurotic image by unearthing its roots, and just as a teacher of physics tries to remove a block to accepting a physical law by pointing out an illegitimate analogy internalized by the student.

Somewhere, Lenin writes of the dangers inherent in listening to great music. When he hears the *Appassionata* of Beethoven, Lenin confesses, he feels his revolutionary determination drifting away. He is inclined to "stroke the heads" (a Russian metaphor, meaning to empathize with) of the people who produced such magnificent works of art. But one must resist this temptation, Lenin concludes. One cannot stroke those people's heads, he says, because one must strike them *on* the head, for they are the class enemy (56). (I may mention in passing that the resemblance to Tolstoy's latter-day renunciation of art for seemingly entirely different reasons is striking.)

Explaining away is a debunking technique. It has been used by enthusiasts of psychoanalysis to "explain" the creativity of genius by laying bare the supposed infantile desires which have served to propel it. It has been used by anti-Communists on the Communists (clothed in Freudian terminology) as well as by the Communists on the anti-Communists (clothed in Marxist terminology). Refutation by explaining away is a favorite weapon in cocktail party debates. As every other device of persuasion, it has its own level of effectiveness and its definite limitations. The conditions prerequisite for its greatest effectiveness probably depend on a complete trust placed by the target of persuasion in the persuader. In some psychotherapeutic situations and in some pedagogic situations, these conditions may be approximated. They may have been approximated in Russia, where the need for strong and ruthless revolutionary leadership was keenly felt. But where such complete trust is absent, "explaining away" usually fails: it can always be countered by conjuring away the rival image by the same methods.

THE REMOVAL OF THREAT

The method of brainwashing, we have seen, is based on the assumption that the hold on the image will be loosened if it is punished severely enough. When this happens, the patient will grope for another image. The image to be grafted is then suggested, and when the patient "tries it on," as it were, it is immediately rewarded. Psychoanalysis proceeds in another way. It proposes to weaken the patient's need to hold on to the old image by revealing to the patient its underpinnings. The third method, sometimes called the permissive or nondirective, is based on the assumption that the stability of the persisting image is based on the patient's refusal even to look at other images, because they are threatening. If this is so, then the new image suggested by the brainwasher will not even be "tried on," and the result of psychoanalysis may be nothing but a traumatic experience of having one's world shattered without another to take its place.[85]

Actually, the psychoanalysts maintain that they too are basically concerned with the removal of threat, so that the differences between the permissive and the psychoanalytic approaches are not basic. They are differences in emphasis only. Presumably, the advantage of the permissive emphasis is that it guards against the perversion of the psychoanalytic method into an instrument of aggression. I will not undertake to defend this point as it regards the real psychoanalytic situation, but it is clear enough as it bears on debate. For in a debate, the psycho-analytic argument (or its equivalent) does often become a weapon of psychological aggression. Its implication is this: Certainly it is understandable how you feel. This is because you are deluded, and your delusions stem from such and such (unworthy) unconscious desires, which you rationalize thus and so. The argument may not be intended this way, but it is often perceived this way.

The practitioner of the permissive view says in effect, "I understand how you feel," and then proves that he does. No attempt is made to "sell" another image or even to shake the old one loose. The expectation is that simple proof of being understood makes the patient receptive to the impact of other views and feelings, because the threat which has prevented their examination has diminished. In other words, according to the permissive view, the rigidity of an image stems not so much from the satisfaction it provides as from the necessity of de-fense against other images, all of which are threatening.

The technique of permissive therapy has been explained and defended by its principal proponent Carl R. Rogers (98). He has also suggested applying similar techniques in conflict situations, particularly in debates (99).

As I see it, the removal of threat in a debate should involve three components.

1. *Conveying to the opponent that he has been heard and understood.*

This is the principal component of permissive psycho-therapy. The assumption is that the often novel experience of being heard and understood without being judged opens up for the patient potentialities of mobilizing his inner resources for reorganizing his image. In the debate situation, it would seem that the inclination to listen and to understand can be stimulated only by imparting the experience of being heard and understood.

2. *Delineating the region of validity of the opponent's stand.*

It is usual in debate to point out grounds for considering the position of the opponent *invalid*. It is argued, for example, that some or all of the premises assumed by the opponent do not hold. In the approach where the removal of threat is a major consideration, this procedure must be reversed. The logical implications remain formally the same: by delineating the conditions under which the opponent's point of view *is* valid, we imply the residual conditions, under which it is *not* valid. But the emphasis is on the former, not on the latter. Showing examples which support the opponent's point of view is a continuation of our message to him that he has been heard and understood.

3. *Inducing the assumption of similarity.*

Having shown the opponent that we *can* see his image and that we recognize the contexts in which this image is valid or inevitable, we must invite him to perform the same exercise with respect to us. This is the hardest task in the debate. No rules can be stated for carrying it out, because an explicit following of rules is self-defeating; it makes the invitation appear as a strategy and calls for a counterstrategy. Once the method of persuasion is seen as a stratagem, the whole situation falls into the pattern of game-like conflict, and we are back where we started: we have not transcended the limitations described in Part II.

Only a feeling for the nature of the empathetic approach to ideological struggle can be imparted and that only to a reader who is already somewhat attuned to this approach. The object is to induce the opponent to assume that you are like him; that if he feels that he deserves to be believed and trusted, then you can also be believed or trusted; that if he feels that he has been relieved by the removal of threat, then it is to his advantage to relieve you, in order that threats (and the inevitable limitations of outlook that go with them) do not interfere with the co-operative potentialities of the situation.

There are, of course, *examples* of such alleviation and resolution of conflicts, but the procedure by which such ends are accomplished do not lend themselves to systematic description or analysis. The most we can do is cite some examples or invent some of our own. In the end of this book, we shall try to do the latter.

CHAPTER XVIII

THE ASSURANCE OF UNDERSTANDING

THE CHIEF CONCERN of people who wish to modify the image of others is with ways and means to make themselves heard and understood and with techniques to make what they are saying sound convincing to others. The reciprocal task has been proposed as the foundation of ethical debate, namely, the task of stating the *opponent's* case as clearly and eloquently as possible (99). The purpose is to convey to the opponent the assurance that he has been understood, so as to reduce his anxiety on that account, and to induce him to listen.

The futility of most debates as means of modifying outlooks can be traced to the unwillingness or the inability of the opponents to listen to one another. If this failure to listen is the result of protective censorship, that is, an attempt to shut out stimuli which threaten to disrupt one's own image, then clearly the way to circumvent this censorship is to present *admissible* stimuli to the opponent. The assumption is that the statement of *his own* outlook will be admissible to the opponent, and that he will therefore listen to it. That the assumption is a reasonable one can be gathered by imagining the attention which would be commanded by a Russian delegate at an international conference if, before he stated his own case, he took pains to state, say, the case argued by the United States, *and if he persisted in the attempt until the United States delegate "capitulated,"* that is, had to agree: "Yes, you have now stated our case well."

To convey something of the flavor of the permissive approach, I will refer to a magazine article of some years ago (106), written by a lady born in Boston and bred at Wellesley, who had the job of coaching Jacob A. Malik, the Soviet delegate to the United Nations, in English. This was in the days when the Russians never smiled in public. The author described the intense earnestness with which Malik went about the business of improving his English, and also the total futility she experienced when she tried to convey to him something about the United States which did not fit into his prefabricated image.

Her last job was to coach the delegate in the speech he was to deliver on the radio in English. The speech was the usual mixture of clichés and invectives, and it must have taken some fortitude on the part of the lady to help Malik to deliver it "effectively." But she came through. At one point, after he said, "The Soviet Union threatens no one," in a particularly belligerent tone of voice, she started to say,

'If you really mean that . . .'
'What do you mean *if* I really mean it?' Malik interrupted . . .
'What I was trying to say was that it doesn't seem in the least as though you have peaceful intentions when you say that line. You sound as though you were just about to shoot someone. I'm only suggesting that you say it with less hostility.'

In spite of this bit of sarcasm, which we must forgive the lady, her conduct was entirely in the spirit of the principle of ethical debate. *She was concerned with the task of presenting the opponent's case well.* She helped him to do it.

Needless to say, this approach is based on an ulterior motive. I am sure, for example, that the American woman who took pains to teach the Russian to make an effective presentation of his speech realized that in her own small way she was contributing to an effort to make a dent in the Russians' mental armor. My guess is that she has probably contributed more toward that end than the combined outpourings of righteous indignation of all the Western delegates. To make a dent in the opponent's mental armor, you must make him listen, and something he is sure to listen to is his own case.

There is no guarantee that the opponent will continue to listen after you have presented his case and gone on to present your own. But there is at least hope, indeed on two counts. First, having had the experience of listening *and agreeing* (when his own case was being presented), the opponent may carry some of his responses over at least for a while to listening to another point of view. Second, he too has a job of presenting your case *to your satisfaction.* He will want to do it well, because getting an admission from you that he has succeeded is a minor victory in the debate. Listening to your case will make the job easier for him. He therefore has some motivation for listening. In the usual polemic he has none.

Conveying assurance of understanding to the opponent is the first step in the removal of threat.

CHAPTER XIX

THE REGION OF VALIDITY

ONCE THE OPPONENT is convinced that you have heard and understood his view, you may tell him under what conditions you think his view is justified.

It is hard to find a statement in ordinary language without *any* region of validity. There are, roughly speaking, no absolutely false assertions. If one tries hard enough, one can usually think of circumstances under which any given assertion might be true. Even mathematical statements, which most people consider to be absolutely exact, and therefore either absolutely true or absolutely false, have a certain penumbra of ambiguity as they are usually stated. This ambiguity is less characteristic of mathematical statements than of others, but it is there nevertheless, because certain qualifications are likely to be tacitly assumed in every statement. It would simply take too long to make a statement irreproachably unambiguous.

AMBIGUITY IN MATHEMATICS

Mathematical assertions will serve as the clearest examples of unavoidable ambiguity. Let us start with a simple one.

At least two different perpendiculars may be erected at any given point to a given line.

If you are used to thinking in terms of plane geometry, the statement appears manifestly false. But of course any corner of your room, where two walls and a ceiling meet, vindicates the statement. The statement is true in three- (or more) dimensional space.

Let us now take one that sounds more incredible.

The sum of two quantities may change in value if the quantities are added in reverse order.

This statement is false if by "quantity" we mean the class of things that elementary arithmetic and algebra deal with, that is, positive and negative whole numbers, fractions, irrational numbers like $\sqrt{2}$, and even so-called imaginary numbers like $\sqrt{-1}$. All these "quantities" and also expressions indicating operations on arbitrary quantities of this sort, such as $x^2 - 7\sqrt[3]{x}$, obey the "commutative law of addition." That is to say that the sum of any two is independent of the order in which they are added.

It is, however, possible to define "quantity," and "sum" in such a way that the commutative law will fail. What will now be said may seem outlandish to the nonmathematician, but I ask him to bear with me for a while.

Place a die used in dice, so that the ace shows on top. The die can now be rotated about each of three axes, two horizontal ones and a vertical one. Call the axes North-South, East-West, and Up-Down.

Consider now the rotations about the North-South axis. They can be in either of two directions. Call one of the directions positive, the other negative. For simplicity, consider only rotations of multiples of 90°; that is, tipping the die to an adjacent face is a unit of rotation. The North-South axis rotations can now be added and subtracted. Say that the clockwise rotations (as one faces north) are taken as positive and the counterclockwise as negative. These units of rotation can then be counted as the units of an "arithmetic." Within limits, these units behave just like ordinary whole numbers. For example,

$$1 + 1 = 2; 1 + 2 = 3; 2 - 1 = 1; 2 - 2 = 0; 1 - 3 = -2;$$

etc., just as in ordinary arithmetic of positive and negative numbers.

But there are also certain peculiarities. For example, four rotations in the same direction give the same result as no rotation. Therefore in this "arithmetic" only the whole numbers 1, 2, and 3, their negatives, and zero need be used. Moreover, the negative numbers can be dispensed with, because, considered as results of rotation, we can set $-2 = 2$; $-1 = 3$; $-3 = 1$. The "addition table" then becomes:

$$1 + 1 = 2; \ 2 + 1 = 3; \ 3 + 1 = 0; \ 2 + 2 = 0.$$

From this table, we can derive all the other sums, for example,

$$2 + 3 = 1; \ 3 + 3 = 2, \text{ etc.}$$

This arithmetic may seem strange, but recall that it is the same kind of arithmetic that you naturally use when reckoning time by the clock, except that here 4 instead of 12 serves as the zero.

The commutative law of addition has been preserved in our rotations about the North-South axis: $A + B$ still equals $B + A$. So the statement with which we started this discussion is still false in this context. But so far we have considered as our numbers only the rotations about a single axis. Let us now include all rotations in multiples of 90° and see whether we can construct an "arithmetic" from those. The numbers must now be labeled by appropriate subscripts. For example 2_N will mean a rotation of two units in the positive direction around the North-South axis; -3_E will mean a negative rotation of three units around the East-West axis; 1_U will mean a positive unit rotation around the Up-Down axis, etc.

Clearly the die may be brought from any orientation to any other orientation by an appropriate sequence of rotations. There are, of course, several combinations which can effect the same change of orientation, but we have the same situation in ordinary arithmetic, where we can "go" from one number to another in many different ways. For example, we can go from 5 to 14 by adding first five, then four; by adding first 11, then —2, etc. The sum of any two numbers, positive or negative is unique, but a given sum can be formed in many different ways. There is, therefore, no reason why the set of rotations about all three axes of our die cannot be considered as an "arithmetic" appropriate for describing the situation. In many ways it behaves like "ordinary" arithmetic, and the results of computations performed according to the rules of rotation arithmetic are perfectly consistent.

Now this arithmetic of rotations around all the three axes of the die has another peculiarity: the order in which the rotations are performed may make a difference in the result. To see this, consider the results of rotating by a positive unit around the North-South axis from our initial position shown in Figure 14, followed by a positive unit around the Up-Down axis. The rotations and the "sum," that is, the final result are shown in the figure.

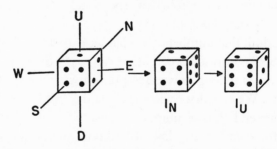

Figure 14. The sum of rotations 1_N and 1_U in that order.

When the rotations are performed in the reverse order, that is, when the numbers are added in reverse order, according to our arithmetic, we get a different result, as shown in Figure 15.

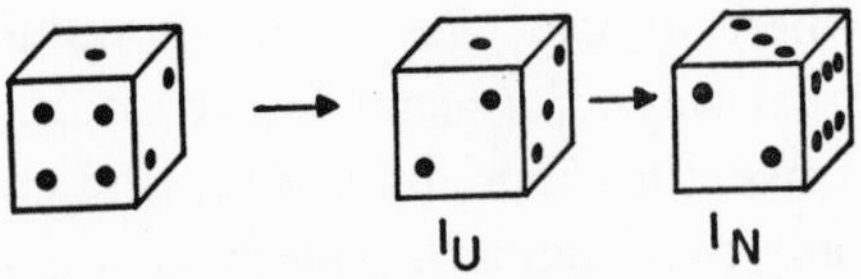

Figure 15. The sum of rotations 1_U and 1_N in that order.

Hence

$$1_N + 1_U \neq 1_U + 1_N \qquad (54)$$

When people unaccustomed to the ways of mathematics are confronted with such and similar examples, they are usually not overly impressed. The illustration does not seem relevant to the argument that $A + B$ may not always equal $B + A$.

"This may well happen with rotations," they may admit, "but it does not happen with *numbers*."

But what are numbers?

In seeking a definitive answer (people are accustomed to regard authoritative definitions as definitive answers to questions beginning with "What is . . ."), it is easy to get entangled in metaphysical speculations, from which there is no way out. The only way of staying in the realm of sense is to admit that numbers are what we choose to call numbers. "Number" is only a word, and we can apply this word to anything we please so long as we can agree on what we are going to apply it to. We can, if we wish, exclude the rotations of a cube from the general class of numbers, if we feel that numbers *should* obey the commutative law of addition. But then why stop with excluding the rotations? How about imaginary quantities like $\sqrt{-1}$? Should we not exclude these, because they do not obey a law we learned in first-year high-school algebra, namely, that the square of every number is a positive number? Until about the eighteenth century, mathematicians felt this way; that is why they christened expressions like $\sqrt{-1}$ "imaginary."

But then why stop with these? Should not fractions be excluded from the realm of numbers on the ground that every "number" should be either even or odd, but fractions are neither? Should not negative numbers be excluded on the ground that every number should have a physical aggregate as a referent, such as so many sheep or fingers or so much barley? Who ever saw —3 cows? An accountant can deal with "negative wealth," but is this not just a fiction, invented by accountants so that they can balance their books?

Yes, negative numbers were "invented" to make certain mathematical operations possible (such as subtracting larger numbers from smaller ones). Imaginary numbers were invented so that certain algebraic equations should be solvable. That is just the point. *All* of mathematics was invented. Mathematics is a language, not a set of facts about the external world. This language was invented in order to deal with quantities and operations in the abstract, that is, without dependence on pebbles, abacuses, measuring sticks, diagrams, and similar devices which are no more than extensions of our fingers, without which we could not reckon when we were children or preliterates. When the independence of mathematics from concrete realizations was recognized, mathematics came of age. The objects of modern mathematical discussion are neither numbers of oranges nor rotations of cubes, nor flights of projectiles, but certain contentless relations among entities and operations derived from undefined terms and unprovable assumptions. These entities and operations are sometimes "maps" of real quantities and relations, but the laws of mathematics are independent of the way any of the "real" quantities and relations behave. For the laws of mathematics were invented too. The only demand made on them is that of consistency in a given context. But in different contexts, different laws may operate. Therefore, any statement of mathematics is valid or invalid not because certain relations are true or not true in the real world, but because these statements are or are not consequences of certain definitions and assumptions, which we are free to choose.

The ambiguity of a mathematical statement results from a failure to specify with sufficient precision the exact context in which the statement is made. It follows that every statement of mathematics is ambiguous unless a set of underlying assumptions is revealed.

To recapitulate, let us look at a number of such ambiguous mathematical statements and resolve the ambiguity by *delineating their region of validity*.

1. $A + B = B + A$. This is true in all the familiar mathematical systems. It is true of whole numbers, fractions, algebraic expressions, and in many other contexts, as the notion of "addition" is extended to those contexts. For example, it is true in the context of the rotations of a cube if all the rotations are around a single axis. But it is false when the notion of addition is extended to other contexts, for example, to the rotations of a cube around all of its axes.

2. $9 + 7 = 4$; $9 + 7 = 14$. The first of these equations is true in "clock arithmetic." The second is true in duodecimal notation.[86]

3. *The square of every number is positive.* This is true in the algebra of real numbers, in which the concept of number has already been extended from whole number to fraction, to irrational. But once the concept of number is extended to imaginaries, the statement becomes false.

4. *The square of a positive number is greater than the number itself.* True for all positive numbers greater than 1 and only those.

5. *The sum of the three angles of a triangle equals 180°.* True in Euclidean geometry of the plane. False in non-Euclidean geometries and in spherical geometry.

6. *The square of a number is equal to twice that number.* This is true for 2 and for 0.

7. *The square of a number increased by 12 equals 7 times the number.* This is true of 3 and of 4.

Etc.

We have delineated the region of validity for every statement given. In mathematics one does this all the time. In particular, to solve an equation (a fundamental mathematical act) means essentially to find the region of validity (i.e., the values of the unknown) for which the equation becomes a true statement, an identity. Some equations have unique solutions, that is, they are "satisfied" by only one value of the unknown. Others have more than one solution (as our Example 7 above). Still others have an infinity of solutions. Some have no solution.[87] Let us see how this technique—the determination of the region of validity—can be extended to nonmathematical statements.

AMBIGUITY OF LANGUAGE

In textbooks on logic, statements like "feathers are light" are sometimes given as examples of a "true statement." The examples serve their purpose, namely, to show how "true statements" can be combined to derive other true statements. But it would be a grave mistake to accept "feathers are light" as a true statement without reservation. If by "feathers" one means the feathers of birds of moderate or small size, and if by "light" one means, say, weighing less than one ounce, then the statement is very probably true. But the statement is false with regard to ostrich feathers and with regard to all feathers if "light" means weighing less than a milligram. We can go on in the same vein.

Paper is thin. Yes, if this means thinner than cardboard; no if it means thinner than soap film.

The heathens are shameless. Yes, if by "shameless" is meant lack of reticence about nudity and if by "heathens" are meant people who have a lack of reticence about nudity. No, if by "shameless" is meant the absence of taboos, since all cultures have taboos, and most humans have similar emotional reactions to being discovered in the violation of their taboos.

Atoms are immutable. In a conventional chemical laboratory, yes. In a physical laboratory, no.

Scientific knowledge is reliable. Yes, if certain limits are placed on attainable reliability and if scientific knowledge is properly circumscribed. No, if theoretical speculations are included and if criteria of reliability are made stricter.

Democracy is a desirable form of government. Yes, if certain values are cherished; no, otherwise.

Note that none of the statements examined is a universal statement (in the form "All X are Y"). Such "all" statements are all too easy to refute, because a single counterexample refutes such a statement. But we are not concerned with formal refutations. The object in a debate is to change the opponent's image, not to prove his statements "wrong." The opposing views in a genuine debate stem not from different notions of what the facts are, nor even from different inferences drawn from facts. The opposing views stem largely from different criteria for *selecting what to see, what to be aware of.* Therefore, the object in a debate is to induce the opponent to admit stimuli which he had not admitted before, in short to enlarge his vision. To do this, some feel, it is best to show him not the limits outside of which he is wrong, but, on the contrary, the limits inside of which he is right. They are, of course, the same limits! But putting it one way is likely to emphasize the threat to the image, while putting it the other way is likely to dilute the threat.[88]

Especially, definitions are not to be quarreled about. "A hen is not a bird," says a Russian proverb. This is false according to the accepted classification of *Gallus domesticus* in the taxonomic scheme of biology. But the proverb is not a biological assertion. It is an expression of a certain attitude, namely, of not wishing to call anything a bird which does not fly with ease and does not lead a "free" life. It is a statement of what people prefer to associate with the word "bird." Since the associations of symbols with referents are arbitrary in any scheme, it often serves a constructive purpose to grant the opponent his particular associations.

As is probably apparent by now, the purpose of establishing a region of validity for every statement is two-fold. First, it serves to minimize threat by additional evidence of understanding. Being a co-operative act, the granting of a valid region for the opponent's stand postpones the posing of antagonistic positions. Something is done to minimize the explosions of *irrelevant* opposition, which makes so many debates futile from the start. Second, the delineation of the region of validity by implication points up the boundaries which separate the positions and thus provides the transition from the acknowledgment of the common area of agreement (without which debate is futile) to the frank recognition of the area of disagreement, related to specifically stated differing frames of reference. Indeed, this procedure draws attention away from the primitive level of verbal opposition to deeper levels where searching investigation is encouraged.

If one maintains that "Black is white," the first impression is that the speaker is a madman or a liar or intends to shock. The method of establishing a region of validity requires that we actually *search* for situations in which what was said is true. A rejoinder like "This is so, if one is interpreting a photographic negative" will carry the discussion farther than a categorical dismissal of the statement as "self-contradictory."

If someone maintains that "Freedom is slavery," perhaps he is trying to say that sometimes the absence of any restrictions on one's whims makes one a slave to those whims.

If someone maintains that "Love is hate," perhaps he is trying to put into common words some insights of depth psychology.

If someone maintains that "War is peace," perhaps he is

302 | *The Ethics of Debate*

emphasizing the well-known unifying effect of war on a nation waging it.

I have deliberately chosen the most preposterous "lies" which were depicted as slogans decorating the Ministry of Truth in the totalitarian state of Orwell's *Nineteen Eighty-Four,* to show that no matter how preposterous an assertion may be, one can always find ways of interpreting it, stretching definitions and digging up exceptions to make it true in a certain limited context. The idea, as pointed out, is to steer the debate away from polarities and toward the examination of contexts. If both parties do this (if one starts, the other may follow—imitation is a surprisingly widespread principle of human conduct), progress may be made toward the resolution of the issue.

THE SEMANTIC APPROACH

Stressing the arbitrary nature of definitions brings the point of view developed here close to that of the semanticists. To some extent, however, there is a divergence in that the semanticists often insist on the futility of most debates. The emphasis on the verifiability criterion of meaning makes many convictions "meaningless" in the operational sense, and all too frequently the semanticist's job is finished when he has shown an assertion to be operationally meaningless (1, 15, 134). Our point of view is that debates in which opposing positions are verbalized in operationally meaningless assertions will go on anyway, so we may as well try to do something about making such debates more meaningful and more constructive in spite of the lack of firm ground of verifiability behind the contending assertions. This is especially desirable in view of the great importance attached to the debate now raging between the two most heavily armed states in the world. We cannot afford to turn away with a sneer on the ground that both sides are talking mostly nonsense. Often the semanticist can do no more than point this out.

In spite of the divergence from the usual point of view of the semanticists, I find it necessary to dispel possible misconceptions regarding their position, to which mine has always been very close.

First, it is important to keep in mind what the semanticists do not say. They do not say that the way to resolve social conflict is to agree on "proper" definitions. A more serious misinterpretation of an outlook is hard to imagine, but it continues to be the most prevailing one. Semanticists cannot prescribe "proper" definitions nor believe in their conflict-resolving potential, because in the first place they believe there is no such thing as a "proper" definition (41, Ch. 4); and even if "agreed upon" is substituted for "proper," such a procedure is often worse than useless, in the opinion of the semanticists, because a definition often imparts a false conviction of knowing what a term stands for in the *other's* experience. The semanticists were among the first to point this out.

Another thing that the semanticists do not say, at least today, is that abstractions are meaningless. An impression of this sort might have been conveyed by one of the early popularizations of semantics (15), whose author might have been carried away somewhat by the idea that abstractions cannot be ascribed the same kind of reality that concrete objects enjoy. But most semanticists realize that so-called "concrete objects" are also abstractions which our senses make from still another "level of reality" (molecular structure), which, in turn, is only a gross manifestation of still another level described in quantum mechanics, where matter has none of the properties ordinarily ascribed to it (49, Ch. XXIV).

Therefore the concrete-abstract axis does not represent a clear-cut gradation, and it is naïve to interpret the "degree of reality" in terms of such supposed gradation.

Semanticists do say that there are different abstraction levels, and that this must be kept in mind in rational discourse.

It is erroneous to ascribe the *same kind* of existence to an institution as to the individuals that compose it; to concretize time-worn virtues, vices, and "isms" on the par with specific acts, etc. The levels of abstraction must be distinct; but not much can be said about their relative degrees of "reality."

What semanticists maintain most emphatically is that no necessary connection exists between things and their labels (41, 44, 49, 86). Furthermore, the class of things or events subsumed under the same label is an arbitrary result of the degree of discrimination developed in a given culture. The Patagonian gaucho, it is said, has 200 different names to distinguish colors of horses and only four different names for all plants.[89] The many names we now have for automobile types—sedan, convertible, station wagon, jeep, bus, truck—can be matched by as many names for horse-drawn vehicles of a century ago. But not many of our contemporaries will distinguish among a fiacre, a phaeton, a chaise, a droshky, a buggy, and a cabriolet.

Distinctions are man-made, say the semanticists. There is no "natural" level at which distinctions ought to be made. The level is determined by the needs of the language user and by resulting social usage. Therefore, arguments about what terms should be applied to what referents are not settled by "determining truth" but only by convention.[90] They are like arguments over the rules of a game. To be sure, these are usually settled by consulting authority, but only because there is a standing agreement to accept authority on the question of game rules; and, moreover, because the translation of the rules into concrete events is clear to the disputants. There still are no "real" rules of any game—only conventions. Change the conventions and you have changed the game. Whether you still want to call it by the same name (chess is still chess in spite of many changes) or by a variant of this name (stud poker, draw poker) or whether you want to rechristen the game is a matter of taste.

We will apply these semantic principles to the ethics of debate in the following way. If by changing definitions or properly delineating the area of validity, we can accept some of the opponent's assertions as true (whereas they had seemed false to us otherwise), let us do so. By doing so, we make it easier for him to do the same for us. If the issue of the debate evaporates on that account, then the debate was not really worth the effort.

Most serious debates are *not* simply about words; so we cannot, as a rule, expect the issues to disappear as a result of semantic analysis and improved communication. But this preliminary job of understanding must first be done to make sure that it is not only words we are concerned with, and if it is not, to get down to the real business.

CHAPTER XX

THE ASSUMPTION OF SIMILARITY

THERE REMAINS THE THIRD PHASE—to induce the opponent to make the assumption of similarity. I suppose the most promising way to induce the assumption of similarity in the other is to make it oneself. In common invective-evoking debates, one usually projects one's own shortcomings, aggressive urges, etc., on the other. What is proposed here is the reversal of this procedure: one seeks within oneself the clearly perceived shortcomings of the opponent. The opponent often seems stupid or rigid or dishonest or ruthless. It will serve us well to ask ourselves to what extent we resemble him. This is recommended not on moral grounds but as a measure to insure a greater success in our effort. To convince, we must be heard, and to be heard, we must be listened to; people listen most attentively to what they like to hear; they like to hear their own shortcomings projected on others, not others' shortcomings projected on them. Our ultimate purpose in raising questions about ourselves is to induce the opponent to raise similar questions about himself. We see ourselves as intelligent, honest, and considerate. It will often serve us well to imagine that the opponent possesses these qualities to *some* degree. Maybe he does not, but maybe this "delusion" of ours will induce a similar delusion in him about us.

I am, of course, discussing the psychological set conducive to conflict resolution. There is no question that such a set is necessary and often sufficient for resolving conflicts in a great variety of interpersonal and social situations. As you may have guessed, I am going to urge this approach (as has been repeatedly urged by many) to the most serious and crucial debate in history, the current ideological struggle between East and West. Some will dismiss the approach from the outset. They will argue that good will and mutual understanding, important as these may be in interpersonal and community relations, are either irrelevant or impossible in the relations among powerful sovereign states. They will point to the record of cynicism and ruthlessness which evidently guides the policy of the other side (whichever this may be) and will insist that only force or the threat of force or clever strategy will accomplish whatever is supposed to be accomplished. Others will argue that although there may be a time in the future when some moral considerations or mutual understanding will enter the relations among states, this is certainly not true today. Therefore, time must be bought until the climate improves, and so deterrents must be used to postpone the outbreak of violence as long as possible. Conciliatory policies which in any way jeopardize the effectiveness of deterrent threats are therefore held to be mistaken. Well-meaning as they may be, they are declared to be self-deceptive and therefore dangerous.

In view of what is actually taking place, the argument seems to carry force, the more so for the reason that those who are considered experts in international relations (that is, those who actually engage in diplomacy or determine foreign policy) think almost exclusively in terms of power play, strategy, and maneuver. Those who think in other terms (for example, in terms of depth psychology) are seldom, if ever, among the practitioners in international affairs and therefore cannot claim any professional knowledge of what is involved. But this is a cycle: international affairs are managed by the practitioners of power strategy; hence the experience which accumulates in these affairs is that of power strategy; hence other types of experience are held to be irrelevant; hence others than those who practice power strategy are kept out or themselves shy away from international politics. In the arena of this politics, power experts meet power experts, and the struggle continues to be cast in power-play maneuvers. It may very well be true, then, that skills other than strategic skills are irrelevant in international affairs, because the decision-makers cannot think in other than strategic terms. The whole situation may be a huge Prisoner's Dilemma, in which it is impossible for the players to do the mutually advantageous thing, because there is nothing in their experience that allows them to make the assumption of similarity, which might solve the dilemma to the advantage of both (cf. p. 177).

Therefore, the content of this chapter may be entirely futile as an attempt to exert even an infinitesimal influence on the course of international affairs. The non-zero-sum game, which results in a loss to both players (who reason as if they are playing a zero-sum game) may epitomize the tragedy of man in society. If so, there is no hope. There is only hope if the players of the power game are to some extent receptive to public pressure. This pressure is hard to estimate, because it is seldom given coherent expression, to be sure for different reasons in different societies. But if this pressure does make itself felt, the race toward mutual annihilation may be retarded and eventually stopped. It would seem, then, that much depends on contact between ordinary, not power-oriented people of the two worlds, the shortsighted people, people devoid of "vision," people concerned with survival and procreation, people who love their children more than ideas.

But the effects of such contacts would be quite limited, because they would not lead to coming to grips with the issues. Of course, the "common people," that is, those involved in the "small world," are likely to speak the same language. Of course they are peace-loving. But it is not the language of the "common people" that underlies the frightening images that each side nurtures of the other. These images are the products of "vision," imagination, theory, in short of the large view of the world. To be dealt with, they must be faced. The discovery that in the close-up view people are peaceful and friendly does not contradict anything in the global view, which pictures current history as a struggle for supremacy of two ways of life, a struggle that in effect blinds the decision-makers to the consequences of their actions in spite of the lip service paid to the necessity of avoiding the impending holocaust.

The so-called cultural exchange contacts, which have recently become common, are also of limited effectiveness. The decorum of good will tours, sport meets, artistic functions, and the like, demands a studious avoidance of the issues. One is tempted not to let anything interfere with the slender threads of nonpolitical accord. The welcome extended to visiting artists, scientists, and farmers is almost exaggerated, as if in a frantic effort to offset the ominous, festering, political and military hostility.

To come to grips with the issues, a debate must be joined, a debate carried on by people who are keenly aware of the issues but who are not inhibited from making the assumption of similarity on the grounds that such an assumption is evidence of professional incompetence. This excludes statesmen, soldiers, and diplomats. In other words, the debate must be a genuine debate, not a fight and not a game. And since neither party is either in the position of a captive being brainwashed or in that of an eager disciple, the debate must be a debate between equals. Persuasion must be tempered by self-appraisal.

What follows is a sample of what someone who genuinely believes in the values for which the Russian Revolution was fought might say to someone who cherishes traditional American values, and vice versa. In composing it, I have tried to apply the principle of ethical debate outlined in the preceding chapters—a difficult exercise, as Ruth Benedict once wisely pointed out.[91]

THE DEBATE

We had everything before us; we had nothing before us.—*DICKENS*

THE CASE FOR COLLECTIVISM

I WILL BEGIN by outlining the objections to Communism from the standpoint of a Western liberal and by stating, as well as I understand them, the values which the liberal believes he is defending when he gives support to his anti-Communist government in its struggle against the spread of Communism.

My remarks pertain most directly to the American audience, because the United States is the undisputed leader of the anti-Communist camp. And, as I said, they are directed specifically at the American liberal, since I shall be dealing with ideas, and those in the United States who are concerned with ideas are very largely of the liberal persuasion.

See if the historical analogy I am about to draw will make sense to you. One hundred years ago the United States lived through an ordeal, which Lincoln saw as a gigantic test: Could a nation dedicated to the ideal of equality of man survive? Your national existence, it seems, had become precarious, because the two halves of the nation subscribed to two incompatible ways of life. The North was "free," and the South was "slave." The real struggle came when you became aware there was a continent to conquer. The question was which way of life would be extended to the *new* lands, slave or free? Over this more than anything else, your historians agree, the Civil War was fought.

Now I wonder if you do not see a parallel in the present situation. Your half of the world appears to you as "free." Ours,

I suppose, appears to you as "slave." The "new lands" are populated by the great masses of the uncommitted, now rapidly crystallizing into nations, just as your new territories a century ago were crystallizing into states. Is it not for these new nations and their loyalties that we are contending? In a way they are to be the judges between us. We trust their instincts to choose the right way. Each of us wishes his own way to be vindicated by history. The way that prevails will be the more viable, therefore the right way.

You say there is more to this. You say that we, Communists, wish to impose our way on the whole world, including your world, by violence if necessary. Indeed we have said that we would, as the Christians and the Moslems, and many others have said and have tried to do before us. And this stated intention of ours is unbearable to you. Lately, we have emphasized that we have no intention of exporting Communism. We only intend to induce it by example. But you do not believe us. This point, therefore, is futile to discuss. And anyway, even if Communism were to spread without active intervention on our part, this too you would find unbearable. Therefore, not our intentions (of which we cannot convince you) but your aversion to Communism as such is the central issue.

You cherish something that you call liberty and the dignity of man, and you are convinced that we are intent upon crushing liberty and upon debasing man. These are truly terrible fears. But so long as liberty and dignity remain aloof abstractions, the fear of "losing" them can only be demoralizing. To defend liberty and dignity in any real sense, you must know specifically what you are defending.

I must say that Americans do make attempts to spell out the realities behind these principles. Two specific kinds of liberty are your concern. Different sectors of the American public place the main emphasis on the one or the other kind, but the nonsocialist majority of American liberals consider the two kinds inseparable.

The American businessman conceives liberty largely as the liberty to pursue his occupation as a businessman. That is not to say that he necessarily gives only lip service to other components of liberty, with which the nonbusinessman liberal is concerned. But the businessman does see "free enterprise" as the cornerstone of the edifice which he calls liberty. And free enterprise is the liberty of the businessman to pursue his calling. There is no denying that it is indeed a liberty, especially as conceived by Americans, because in America everyone is invited to participate in this calling, which is to say that everyone is invited to try to organize some section of the national economy, be it a very small one like a barbershop or a very large one like an automobile industry, according to his organizing ability, availability of capital or credit, and luck. The assumptions are that

1. The sum-total of such efforts adds up to a thriving national economy.

2. The noninterference by the government in the ideally freely competing system of such efforts prevents a centralization of power and so promotes the other components of liberty.

The nonbusinessman, particularly the intellectual liberal is more concerned with the freedom of conscience. He concentrates on defending the freedom of minority views, freedom of discussion of important issues, freedom of association, civil liberties, etc. He opposes official ideology, political dogma, bureaucracy. He is horrified by demagogy, by coercion, especially the coercion of regimentation. The preservation of the dignity of man is his special concern.

It happens, of course, that the champion of free enterprise ignores the main concern of the intellectual liberal, and not infrequently the left-wing liberal sharply criticizes the demands from the right for a totally unregulated economy. There are even socialists among the left-wing liberals. But all are united by an abhorrence of Communism, even if for different reasons. No doubt, both the Right and the anti-Communist Left have good grounds to fear the extension of Communism. The businessman sees Communism as a threat to his very existence. The humanitarian liberal associates Communism with coercion and cruelty. Both conjure up a picture of Communism in terms of slave-labor camps, liquidations, deportations, regimented media of communication, an arrogant bureaucracy, and utter cynicism, in short in terms of a social system in which the individual appears *only* as means in the pursuit of an end to serve a colossal superorganism, the state. Most anti-Communists see little difference between the Communist and the Fascist conceptions of the relationship between the individual and the state.

Moreover, the anti-Communists take note of the fervent belief of the Communists that the social order of tomorrow will certainly be Communist and therefore that the only criterion for evaluating an action as moral or immoral is whether the action helps or hinders what is inevitable, that is, the ultimate victory of Communism. This view of morality is especially repugnant to anti-Communists. To this view they ascribe also the conduct of foreign affairs by Communist states and the inevitability of an eventual interference by Communists in the internal affairs of non-Communist states.

There is much more unanimity among the anti-Communists on what they are against than on what they are for. Indeed, protests against the lack of a positive program are most sharply voiced by both the Left and the thinking portion of the Right in the United States.

To the extent that positive programs are envisaged, they all have this feature in common: the economic might of the United States is to be used in helping the uncommitted populations of the underdeveloped countries to develop an industrial potential. The hope is that if they are able to develop such potential within the framework of a noncoercive social system, they will become immune to Communist subversion (as you tend to label any development which happens to be in our direction).

The image, then, behind the positive program is largely the repetition in the underdeveloped countries of recent American history: industrialization without overt coercion by government agencies. According to this view, the underdeveloped countries will "develop," because the populations *want* to establish higher living standards. They will, moreover, develop noncoercively, because the same populations *do not* want to be coerced.

In summary, to the extent that a positive alternative is offered to the spread of Communism beyond the borders of the countries with Communist programs, it is a program of an individualistically oriented democracy, emphasizing, as we Communists do, industrial development and a rising standard of living, but relying on the sum-total of individual desires to improve one's lot rather than on a rigidly enforced plan of capital investment. The emphasis on individual liberty and so on is a consequence of this orientation.

Now we submit that when people live at subsistence level, they do not willingly divert a part of their income into capital investment, because it directly hurts them to do this. It is necessary to coerce them into doing this, if it is to be done at all. Under capitalism, this coercion was not imposed by law, because the surplus to be invested was *already* in the possession of those who could well afford to invest it. But in a socialist system, where no one has *title* to the surplus by virtue of private ownership of the means of production, the diversion of this surplus to capital investment must be accomplished by the exercise of state authority. The state, in fact, dictates how the national income is to be spent. In an economy of relative scarcity, this is the most important source of authority in society. This is why the socialist state appears so coercive: it must perform *openly* the coercive function which in a capitalist state (in an economy of relative scarcity) is performed *surreptitiously* by private control of capital. The exercise of one type of authority usually carries with it the necessity to exercise other types of auxiliary authority. The monolithic state is the inevitable result of the *first stage* of socialism, the stage of relative scarcity. The belief that this form of organization is the result of malice and connivance instead of being a historical necessity is what alienates the bourgeois liberal from Communism.

I believe I have given a fair picture of the basis of the liberal's distaste for the Communist program—its reliance on openly coercive methods and its potential for spreading into areas where the liberal would like to see his own values prevail, and, in the extreme view, its threat of imposing the coercive system upon societies where the liberal's values are presumably operating.

My next task is to indicate the conditions under which the liberal's view would have ample justification. The view is justified, to an extent, if the individual and his self-seeking activities are taken as the standard of value. This particular measuring stick is appropriate in a certain stage of social development. So long as that particular stage is not obsolete, so long as it still carries some potential for further progress, the liberal's view makes sense. Let us therefore examine the particular social matrix which delineates the region of validity of the liberal's view.

Just as you liberals believe that the individual human being must be given the opportunity to develop his potentialities, so we Communists believe that the human society as a whole must be given this opportunity, for it is not only the individual who grows, develops, and matures. The human society as a whole does this too. Moreover, only if the human society as a whole is allowed to develop its potentialities fully, can such an opportunity exist for the individual.

I know that the idea of a unidirectional cultural evolution is dismissed by many Western cultural anthropologists, who fix their attention upon "cultures" (plural) as units of development. Since the "cultures" ordinarily studied by the anthropologists are usually small and "exotic" (small cultures can be more completely described than large ones, and exotic ones are especially interesting to the scholar), it often appears to the Western anthropologist that no direction is discernible in social evolution. The small exotic cultures may have evolved in several different directions, and so no corroboration is found for the thesis of a general development, posited by the anthropologists and cultural historians of the past generations—a development through stages of civilization and social organization toward more complex and advanced forms, supported by richer material bases and enveloping larger co-operative units.

However, once we turn away from the special investigations of the anthropologist and view the large lines of human history, the unidirectional trend from primitive to complex forms, from parochial to national, to supranational organization, from small competing to large co-operating aggregates becomes obvious. Another thing is apparent. Historically, the evolution of social forms has been accompanied by intense social conflicts.

I shall not dwell on the theory of class struggle as a unifying idea of social history, because my audience will tend to dismiss arguments based on that theory. I shall, however, call attention to one aspect of Marxist theory which can be easily defended: the distinct class basis of individualistic ideology, the ideology which nurtures the liberal's hostility toward Communism.[92]

Three hundred years of European history following the voyages of discovery (roughly 1500–1800) were dominated by the emergence of a new class to positions of influence and power. We call it the bourgeoisie. In our writings the word "bourgeoisie" has been stained with a bad connotation. But in its original usage, "bourgeoisie" was simply the French name for the middle class. Actually, the bourgeoisie were the city dwellers, the active, practical people, the merchants, the professionals, the entrepreneurs. They were the people who more than any others viewed life in terms of result-producing *activity*. They were the people who had to deal with the ever-increasing complexities of human environment, often in an organizing capacity. The bourgeois's success, be he a trader or a captain of a ship or a lawyer or an inventor or the founder of a banking or industrial concern, depended on his shrewdness or skill or diligence. It was measured by *amounts accruing to him,* whether of money or of control over the activities of other people or of recognition or acclaim of his achievements.

The notion of a *career* and the concomitant notion of success is primarily a bourgeois notion. It reflects the optimistic outlook of the bourgeois: a man's destiny depends on what he makes of it. Moreover, the desirable life is one which ends with more, in terms of individual possessions, than it began with. We usually designate the ambition of accumulating capital as the primary bourgeois motivation. But this is an oversimplification. Any ambition centered about any kind of accumulation is a reflection of the bourgeois outlook with this important qualification, characteristic of bourgeois *democracy:* accumulation is declared to be everyone's privilege. In this way the ambition of the bourgeois is different from the ambition of the conqueror. The conqueror cannot tolerate rivals. The bourgeois, as he pursues his ambition, actually needs rivals. His standing among them indicates to him to what extent his ambitions are being realized. The achievements of the rivals provide leverage to his own achievements. Even the greater successes of others are often sources of inspiration rather than despair; they corroborate the bourgeois's rationale of the essential fairness of the competitive system and reassert for him the idea of the ever-present opportunity. (He too can achieve more if he tries or if he is lucky.)

The bourgeois outlook could not be as attractive as it is to so many if it were completely devoid of social value. It pictures society as a matrix in which the pursuit of personal gain is facilitated, encouraged, and rewarded. The notion of competition provides a rationale for the social worth of the pursuit. Since in competition, the efficient are rewarded and the inefficient eliminated, and since a large part of the bourgeois's activity is directed into productive channels (the bourgeois is not really the "parasite" that our myths picture him to be; he is typically a hard and often productive worker), it appears that the bourgeois's efforts, although primarily motivated by his own ambitions and appetites, indirectly contribute to the common good. Here, then, is an apparently admirable resolution of the dilemma, which juxtaposes in conflict the individual and the social "good."

This social arrangement is reflected in the bourgeois image of society, in which the ego is the "figure" and the society with its institutions the "ground." Accordingly, the values revolve around the worth of the individual. The individual is "born free." Only the necessity to safeguard this "natural freedom" from being arbitrarily encroached upon induces the individual to enter into social arrangements with others—"to secure these rights." The state is assigned a function of a neutral referee, who sees to it that the game is played according to the rules. Once this image is internalized, all limitations of individual freedom become at best necessary evils, at worst symptoms of despotism.

I have tried to specify the image in which all forms of social coercion are suspect. Those that have been long established, the "rules of the game," are tolerated, but new ones are dreaded. The dread is undeniable, because the absence of certain coercions appears to the individualist liberal as a hard-won gain in the struggle which the bourgeoisie itself has had to wage against the ruling class of an earlier epoch. It was the bourgeoisie that defeated absolutism in England and broke the might of the aristocracy and of the Church in France. It was the bourgeoisie that had staked its fortune along with its sacred honor on the independence of the United States. The gains of these struggles appear to the individualist liberal as the fruits of progress. He is constantly on guard against giving up these fruits. It is natural for him to imbue these spoils of victory with the deepest meaning of moral value.

The domain of validity of implacable opposition to Communism is coextensive with the domain of validity of this image. The opposition becomes less justified if we assume that this image of man in society, like so many other images, is a limited one. It has had a limited existence in human history, and it is likely that it will be replaced by other images which will also be outcomes of certain dramatic historical experiences.

We, Communists, believe that the most important historical experiences, which give rise to these persistent images, are social struggles. But it is not necessary to agree with this special point to recognize the transient character of all ideologies and their dependence on particular historical experiences.

We are trying to anticipate the image of man in society which will replace the image now current in the Western world. This forecast is the heart of Communist social theory. We note first that it was the nature of the productive process which emerged from the Industrial Revolution that determined the typical Western image: free individuals, naturally competing, but bound to co-operation by contractual arrangements. This image, realized in social arrangements, became the modern capitalist system. Conversely, continued acceptance of the capitalist system perpetuates the image. The two are inseparable. The shortcomings of the one are the pitfalls of the other.

I need not remind this audience of the price paid by the European masses for the introduction of industrial capitalism, of the social dislocations, of the unspeakable miseries which accompanied the early factory system. Bourgeois thinkers have done this. When *Das Kapital* was being written, the forecast of the eventual pauperization of entire populations, mobilized into the factory system, was not unreasonable on the basis of the evidence available. The present comparatively high standard of living and the rise of the white-collar class in Western industrialized countries have been the basis of assertions that Marxist theory has been refuted. But on a larger scale, this conclusion is not really warranted. On the world scale, we do have a teeming, pauperized, constantly increasing population, living on the verge of starvation: the victims of the colonial system, an extension of the capitalist system. We do have a tremendous concentration of wealth and power in the states that have fallen heir to the accumulation of capital largely based on colonial exploitation. No matter that *within* some Western countries, particularly in the United States, the "ruling class" cannot be as sharply identified as Marx or Lenin would have it identified. The world is still divided into haves and have-nots, into the rulers and the ruled.[93]

Admittedly, the Marxist prognosis of social revolution which was pictured as an organized seizure of political power by the working class, now seems oversimplified. While it was once possible to picture a social revolution as engineered by an armed citizenry gaining control of communication centers and arsenals (as actually happened in Paris in 1871 and in Petrograd in 1917), this model has ceased to make sense. The power of the haves is much more diffuse today. Not only is an organization for armed struggle of a "world proletariat" impractical, but there is also no possibility of implementing the results of such a struggle should it take place and be successful. It is romantic to imagine a world governed by "workers' committees" as it was once possible to imagine a nation so governed.

Nevertheless, the outlines of two hostile camps can be definitely discerned. The struggle has even been given a name —the Cold War.

Now if you see the Cold War as it is fought in the newspapers, then it does seem bizarre to interpret it as the "final" class struggle, once envisaged by Marx. I grant that in the newspaper accounts the United States and the U.S.S.R. resemble far more two empires struggling for world domination than the champions of exploitation and freedom, respectively (or vice versa), even though the propaganda machines of both countries cast the respective country in the role of a champion of the oppressed.

However, the *repercussions* of the Cold War, that is, the stirring of the impoverished masses of the world, does resemble the social revolution envisaged by Marx. There are obvious discrepancies. The oppressed are not the urban industrial proletariat of the classical theory. Nor are the oppressors clearly identifiable members of the owning entrepreneur class. The oversimplified theory of surplus value seems inadequate to explain the pattern of exploitation on the world scale. But we submit that the grand outline of social revolution is there. The basis of the revolution is undoubtedly industrialism, which has woven all of humanity into a network of interdependence. Industrialism is a collective enterprise. It therefore imposes on man a new image of man in society—man as co-operator.

Americans have declared the "pursuit of happiness" to be the chief preoccupation of free men. But the kinds of pursuits that are interpreted as "pursuit of happiness" in Western society have been limited to a very small portion of human history. Man has pursued happiness in many ways—through indulgence and asceticism, through conquest and martyrdom, through debauchery and chastity. The "career"—the channel along which the Western free individual pursues his happiness and from which his conceptions of social and political morality are derived—is a by-product of the early entrepreneur days of Western industrialism.

Already the image of the "career" is being modified, especially in American society. The entrepreneur has been replaced as a prototype by Organization Man. To be sure, the shift of value system is bemoaned. But it is nevertheless being internalized and will continue to be internalized (97, 132).

Now let us see why the image of the Organization Man is painful to behold to the Westerner. Both the Right and the Left turn away from this image with dismay, but for different reasons. Those of the Right see in Organization Man the abrogation of the old virtues of entrepreneur economy. Those of the Left do not lament the passing of the entrepreneur as the cultural ideal; but they do view with distaste the Corporation as the emerging focus of man's loyalty. For the Corporation is not a "lovable" unit of society from the point of view of humanitarian values. Viewed as a "living unit," the Corporation is seen as an extremely primitive organism. Much of its "behavior" is explained in terms of one or two motivating principles—to survive and to grow. It is impossible to empathize with an organism that stands in such primitive relations to its environment. A society composed of such units grossly violates the image of a "good society," which men of good will use as a standard for estimating the moral worth of institutions.

Now what Communism offers in a *moral* sense is an opportunity to satisfy man's longing to identify with large cooperative units and at the same time a way of preventing the emergence of large competing units, whose "psyches" consist entirely of appetite. Corporations and national states and isolated "cultures" are examples of such totally ego-centered units.

They may foster co-operation *within* themselves and thus may satisfy man's need to belong. But this is done at the expense of atomizing human society as a whole into ruthlessly competing units. When a man has identified himself with a larger social unit, he has transcended the frustration of contemplating his inevitable dissolution as an ego. But in identifying with a unit whose only "concern" is survival and growth amid competing units, man succeeds only in shifting the frustration to another level. Indeed, he is worse off than before. As an individual, he still could *relate* to other individuals in symbiotic relationships. He still could give and receive love. But the larger units of the bourgeois world—the corporations and the national states— these are incapable of such relationships; they are too primitive as organisms. Man is trapped with his human psyche as a part of a subhuman "ego" of the self-centered organization.

Communism seeks to organize man's social life so as to avoid this trap.

You will ask how? By designing social arrangements in harmony with the ever-increasing co-operative aspect of the productive process, because we believe the productive process to be the most important determinant of social arrangements.

You will point out the inadequacies in the social arrange- ments in the existing Communist states. We could, of course, trade blow for blow by seeking out equally prominent inade- quacies in the bourgeois social order. Also for each source of satisfaction in your system of "individual freedom" we can list *other* sources of satisfaction in our system designed to give each individual a feeling that he contributes to a common good. These satisfactions are not far-fetched. You will recognize them immediately if you examine carefully what happens to your "free individuals" in times of national crisis.

I submit that World War II, to take an example of such a crisis, was a deeply satisfying experience to the majority of Americans. Kept away from American soil, this war did not bring the destruction and dissolution of social life which it brought to other countries. Thus, the "positive" aspect of war psychology had its full impact. There is no denying that there *is* a positive aspect to war psychology. If wars were totally distasteful, there would be no wars.[94] The positive side of the war is in the feeling of belongingness which it engenders, the release of aggressive impulses it makes not only possible but commendable, in the opportunity it provides for loyalty and acts of heroism.

The price paid for these opportunities has always been exorbitant and has now become prohibitive. What we Communists are trying to do is to provide the same *kinds* of satisfactions to man in society but at a price commensurate with the benefits. Ours is not a war mentality, since we do not direct all the psychic energy of our people toward the hatred of an enemy. I know this statement will be disputed by reference to Communist theory with its emphasis on the class struggle. Yes, the theory, the outgrowth of our ideological roots, is belligerent. But in practice, in real life, our people are not incited to belligerence nearly to the extent that a preoccupation with Communist theory would indicate. Apply the standards of objectivity on which you Westerners pride yourselves. Look through our newspapers, the bulk of our propaganda. Make "word counts" and "content analyses" of our political speeches (at home, not in the international arena). See whether the weight of our colossal effort to direct human thoughts, energies, and commitments is in the direction of war or peace. Look at our popular entertainment, yes and at our toys and at the games of our children. Compare them with yours.

We do abstract one thing from war mentality: the grand total effort. But we direct it toward peaceful ends. You see the unwholesome products of this effort, what you call regimentation, thought control, authoritarianism, mass mentality. But all of these were present in your own war effort, and no one but the pacifists questioned the necessity of these means by which all large-scale effort is achieved.

There is nothing *inherently* bad or immoral about discipline. The moral question should be directed at the ends which are served by discipline. You make little distinction between Fascism and Communism, because you emphasize the similarity of means. We say ends should be considered first. The large "unit" with which the Fascist regimes sought to identify their masses was the national state or a "race," pursuing a rapacious career of conquest. Therein lies the viciousness of Fascism, not in the discipline imposed on its people. The discipline itself must have been a source of satisfaction, otherwise the people would not have accepted it as enthusiastically as they did. All discipline rests in the long run on a people's commitment to common ends. The regime which imposes discipline for its own sake or for the sake of unacceptable or unattainable ends digs its own grave, as the fate of all rapacious authoritarian regimes has shown.

I repeat there is nothing *inherently* bad or immoral about discipline. If you think there is, you should condemn symphony orchestras, in which each player actually surrenders his musical ego to the will of the conductor. You should condemn the emotional climate of the football team, where each player merges his very reflexes with those of the others for the greater efficiency of the team. You should condemn the Catholic Church and many other organized religions. Discipline is present in every phase of life and not only as a necessary evil—also as a source of satisfaction and inspiration. Why should satisfactions be limited to the gratification of impulses? Is it unreasonable to attribute to man the power of deriving satisfaction from exercising *control* over his impulses? Everyone recognizes power-seeking (control over others) as a motivating force. Why not control over oneself?

The opposition to Communism boils down to this: Communism seeks to impose discipline on the productive process. (All other discipline is derivative.) This frightens in the first place those whose identification is with the psychology of the entrepreneur, who thrived when there were no restrictions on this process. In the early years of Communist rule in the U.S.S.R., this fear was the real motivation in the attempts to suppress the first Communist state by military intervention. In its struggle to survive, the Communist state became an "authoritarian" state, demanding, as all states do in wartime, unquestioned obedience in practically all phases of life, since all phases of life were conceived as mobilized in the battle for survival. This historically inevitable development frightened away the Western liberal too, who, even if he did not identify with the entrepreneur, had nevertheless internalized the derivative values.

It would be too much to expect the liberal to rethink the issues involved. He has been the unfortunate victim in the world class struggle. He cannot identify with the unabashed champions of unfettered "free enterprise," because he sees too well how his own individualist ideals are trampled upon when it comes to a showdown, when "free enterprise" has to defend itself against any encroachments in the interest of the common good. Nor need I dwell on what free enterprise in full bloom (as in the United States) has done to the sensitivities of the intellectual liberal with its creations, Salesmanship Unlimited and the Organization Man.

On the other hand, the liberal cannot identify with Communism either, because he is convinced that Communist discipline is imposed for its own sake. He thinks of *Nineteen Eighty-Four* as a picture of Communist future. He has forgotten the unfulfilled prophecies of other anti-utopian novels of the nineteen-twenties, which pictured the *industrial system* (whether capitalist or Communist) as culminating in a physical hell, where men smeared with grime spent all of their waking hours amid monstrous noisy machines. This hell was supposed to have come in the nineteen-sixties, that is, right now. Instead, we see industrial plants becoming more and more like model hospitals, the work week cut in half, automation, and the problem of what to do with leisure. Extrapolations come easy, and they are always sure to make a dramatic impression; but they are most often misleading.

Still the liberal will persist in extrapolating as he does.

So we do not address our main appeal to him. We address it to the new proletariat in the newly awakened "underdeveloped" countries, the proletariat who has no commitment to the bourgeois image. Those people have seen the entrepreneur primarily in his rapacious role, primarily as an outsider, not as the American worker had seen him often as one of his own number, often as a useful, dedicated citizen. There is no reason why people who had had no stake in capitalism should not simply skip the capitalist stage of social organization. Has not the American North skipped the feudal phase? And is the North not better off than the South, which still is not over its plantation system and the social pathology derived from slavery? The colonial people can profit from our example. They can avoid our mistakes. They can identify with us, because we had not been the colonial masters of their fathers, and there is no stain of racism on us. As those people emerge as independent nations, they will shortly adopt the socialist mode of economic organization. This is not yet Communism, but it *leads* to Communism—a social system which takes care of the individual's material needs and thereby frees the individual to occupy himself with matters other than the struggle for existence.

Now this is what we mean when we speak confidently about the ultimate victory of Communism. The words are admittedly often ill-chosen and provide fuel for anti-Communist propaganda. It is easy to picture the victory of Communism in terms of a ubiquitous secret police, a humdrum monotony of a single party line, bureaucracy, and atrocious architecture. These are as incidental to the early decades of Communism as the "dark satanic mills," prostitution, and munitions cartels were incidental to the first century of industrialism.

By a victory of Communism we mean a supplanting of old images of man's role in society by a new image, which is actually more in accord with the Christian view than the old image. The wide disparity between Communist and Christian attitudes, which many hold to be diametrically opposed, will appear to historians as a disparity of means rather than of ends. The Christian message is beamed at man's inner life. The carriers of that message think that the image can be modified directly. The Communists do not think this is possible. They maintain that the image is an outgrowth of social arrangements and that social arrangements are an outgrowth of the way the productive process is organized. Therefore, the Communists wish to manipulate the latter in order to bring about changes in the former.

The Westerner is understandably concerned with what this impending victory of Communism will mean to himself and to his world. This depends on the extent to which he will be able to realize the relentless character of large-scale historical processes. Western man is not the first, nor the only one to be concerned with the prospect of dissolution of his world. It will be recalled that Western man has himself destroyed many self-contained worlds, and he has justified the process by much the same arguments that the Communists are using today. He says that he has brought civilization to the primitive peoples. He has brought Christianity. Now, it seems, the Western man's own way of life is being threatened. How is he to meet the threat?

The most widespread view, I might say the *official* view in the West, primarily in the United States, is to picture the danger as a threat of military conquest. Such situations having been coped with before, sometimes successfully, the way of meeting the supposed danger is prescribed by tradition: one arms oneself, and one adopts a military posture; one makes counterthreats.

The futility of these gestures is apparent to enlightened public opinion, even in the West. Weapons of destruction being what they have become, the "way of life" dear to the Westerner cannot possibly be preserved by military defense. Therefore, the usual justification of the military posture is made in terms of its deterrent potential. But even if one grants the deterrent effect, the "way of life" is still threatened, and the nonmilitary threat is recognized. You speak of economic penetration, of a war of propaganda aimed at the uncommitted, etc.

Well, what *can* you do about these matters? Attack us with nuclear weapons to stop us from competing in the world markets or from propagating our ideas? This would destroy you. And if you don't? If you keep your senses and realize the folly of such a "defense," what then can you do? There is only one thing left: accept our challenge. You too can compete for trade and for the souls of men. Do you think this course is self-defeating? In other words, do you admit that if the principle of free competition on which some of you say your whole civilization is based is allowed to operate on the world scale, then you would *certainly* lose? Do you foresee a checkmate in five moves? Then our case rests.

Of course, there is another source of misgivings about competing with us besides the fear of losing in a fair game. The predominant image associated with Communist leadership in the mind of Western man is that of treachery. Western man does not attribute to the Communists any motivations except those of crude self-interest. In particular, "generosity" and "fairness" are thought to be confined to the liberal outlook as values. I admit that the utterances of the Communists themselves have often supported this suspicion. But "toughness" was not invented by the Communists. Review the history of the

Western world and see what a common thing ruthlessness has been in human affairs. Who will care to enumerate instances of Spanish, British, or French ruthlessness? Who has forgotten the German *Schrecklichkeit?* How have the Japanese behaved in their brief career of Western-type empire building? What would the West do if the British had to be ostracized for what they did 100 years ago in Tasmania, the French for what they did only a few years ago in Indo-China? Do you refuse to deal with the Germans?

Why do you think that the Russians or the Chinese are so different from the British and the Germans? Yes, ruthlessness is a fact in international affairs in this early stage in the history of civilization, when the world has just begun to grope for unity. Ruthlessness is not to be ignored; but the consideration of ruthlessness as a factor to be reckoned with need not paralyze good sense; it need not degenerate into panic and provoke an irreparable act of self-destruction.

You have no choice but to compete with us. We are confident of winning, yes. But behind this confidence is an awakening recognition that human history is not the simple sequence of phases that Marx made it out to be, that social revolutions are not simply matters of seizing telephone exchanges, that bad things like usurpation of power can happen in a socialist state.[95] We may shout with even greater intensity about the superiority of our way of life to hide from ourselves some sobering revelations; but is this not what you are doing too?

Look at us, and look at you! Are we not becoming more alike? Look back one century. Are the differences between a "monarchy" and a "republic" as glaring today as they were then, when it looked that the most important political issue was between a "monarchical" and a "republican" form of government? How many of your school children know which of the European countries are republics and which are monarchies? And who cares? Whether the European countries call themselves republics or monarchies does not distinguish between their social organization. Most European monarchies today have *essentially* a republican form of government, even though their constitutions invest the monarch with formal authority.

A similar thing can happen as the socialist forms of organization evolve. In some societies, the transition will be punctuated by upheavals and trumpeted by slogans. In others, it will take place *de facto* and possibly not *de jure*. But the end result will be the same.

Now you may make the transition to Communism as painless as the inevitable transition to democratic government was made in the Scandinavian countries; or you may choose to make it painful, as the destruction of monarchy has been in France, where it took three revolutions and a disastrous war to complete the job. Or you may do the utmost folly and bring the world down in ruins about you, as you resist what is bound to happen. But you cannot avert the evolution of your society any more than we can arrest the evolution of ours.

The inevitable change in social organization is bound to change the image of man in society so that the new organization will not appear coercive, as it must appear in the transitional stage. We view the emergence of the new image as the emancipation of man. Freedom is the recognition of necessity.

THE CASE FOR INDIVIDUALISM

AS SO MANY TIMES BEFORE, the antagonists are rival brothers, like Jacob and Esau, like Rome and Carthage, Moslem and Christian.

Collectivism and individualism have both grown from the same roots. The West claims Christianity for its own and maintains that Christianity nurtures the individualist point of view, because it is concerned with the individual soul. But Christianity becomes meaningless, robbed of its communal aspect. We think of Roman law as the first explicit formulation of Right in the abstract: not as privileges granted by potentates nor as taboos backed by divine authority, but as civil rights, derived from the concept of citizenship. It is maintained that the concept of citizenship is one of the foundations of the inviolable rights of the individual. But does not the citizenship idea, as embodied in Roman law, also underlie the impersonal but all-powerful state?

I believe that commitments to collectivism and to individualism are complementary rather than antagonistic commitments. But they are pictured in the propaganda of both sides as incompatible outlooks. Therefore, in debating the issue, we must understand each separately. We must learn both languages.

In the minds of men, the commitment to self and the commitment to a collective have been split, and the alignment of power which commands men's loyalty on both sides perpetuates the split. We must begin by imagining what it must be like to be totally committed to the one or to the other. According to the rules of debate, I must present the side of collective commitment first.

A work of art is a good reflection of a commitment, and the best form of art to serve as a meeting ground of men's commitments is tragedy. There we see ourselves as we would be if we were entirely committed, but at the same time we can be spectators. A tragedy is an invention which enables man to see himself totally committed. One that will serve us well in the present debate is *He Who Must Die* (film), for it will be understood both by the dedicated collectivist and by the dedicated individualist.

The tragedy was conceived and made in the West, but it is more like a product of Russia. I mean the sort of work in which the hero is a collective, a "folk," people who live, suffer, and die together, and who find meaning in existence only through the communality of their collective experience. In short, one of the themes of *He Who Must Die* is the classical theme of the Communist revolutionary outlook.

There are two "folks." One is a relatively comfortable village in Asia Minor, living "in peace" with the Turkish masters. The other is a dispossessed population of another village who had joined Greek guerillas and had suffered the common fate of minorities of undependable loyalty.

The dispossessed, far gone in starvation, come to the prosperous village and beg to be taken in. They are brutally rejected by the local priest. In the meantime, the village is preparing for its traditional Passion Play. The drama unfolds as the villagers who are assigned their parts in the Passion Play appear to live out these parts. The film becomes a translation of the Passion into the language of our century and, incidentally, a revelation of the fountainhead from which Communism derives its moral support. Such support must exist, because no movement can endure without it, and we see that the idea of Communism does endure. It endures not because of its theory: it is a mediocre theory; not because the Communists have discovered the "correct" interpretation of history: it is a questionable interpretation, not much worse and not much better than other sweeping interpretations that have been attempted. Communism does not endure because of its military might. In the first fifteen years of its existence, the Soviet Union was weak by any military standards. The idea of Communism endures, because it derives its moral support from an idea which appeals to men deprived of hope. *Most* men on this planet have been deprived of hope during the time that the idea of Communism was spreading, something that we in the West tend to forget.

To the slaves of the Roman Empire, Christianity gave hope of everlasting life and made faith in salvation the condition for salvation. This faith demanded an abrogation of personal appetite; it demanded total surrender to the will of God. The faith offered by the Communists is somewhat of the same sort. If you all act and feel as one man, people are told, if you surrender totally to the will of the mass and act together against the common enemy, you will achieve salvation. The promise is made in terms of earthly blessings: high living standards, etc. But these are trappings, just as the promises of afterlife are trappings of Christianity. I doubt whether men would keep sacrificing everything just to increase steel production so as to insure consumers' goods to future generations. To the destitute, those future riches are not a tangible reward any more than the Christian heaven. No, Communism, like primitive Christianity, in spite of its emphasis on the future, offers real salvation, here and now, not in eternity, nor after seven five-year plans.

The salvation offered by both is the realization that human existence has a meaning and that meaning is present even at the moment of death: for the Christian a denial of death; for the Communist a merging with the mass moved by a single purpose.

In *He Who Must Die,* it is shown how the moral power derived from Christian faith becomes transformed into an equally invincible moral power which is Communist in spirit. At first, the destitute are resigned to die of starvation before the eyes of the prosperous villagers. But after "Apostle John" (of the play), taking the commandment of the New Testament literally, has turned his property over to the destitute, and after this transaction has been pronounced invalid by the local priest (the guardian of the established order), the paupers are led by the "Jesus" of the Passion Play to take possession of what they believe to be theirs. The village priest sees to it that they are met with bullets. But now that they have found leadership, the dispossessed are able to capture the provision stores and prepare with ancient shotguns, pickaxes, and scythes to repel the assault by the forces of law and order. "Jesus" is captured, turned over to the village priest by the Turkish magistrate (to whom the whole business is extremely distasteful), and is killed. He dies on the floor of the church in a posture of crucifixion. His last words are to the village prostitute, to whom he turns over the leadership of his faithful.

"I am going to die," he says, "but don't tell them. Tell them I will rejoin them."

Thus is the primitive Christian message blended with the primitive Communist one. I repeat, primitive, because the elaborate mystiques subsequently grafted on both messages have made the germinal ideas unrecognizable in what passes both for Christianity and for Communism today.

Both the pious Christian and the pious Communist may, of course, be embarrassed by this union: the Communist because he has become conditioned to shrink away from the *symbols* of religion (just like the proverbial devil); the Christian because he might feel that Christianity has been abandoned by the paupers' priest as soon as he reached for the gun to lead his people against the police. (Ordinarily, only regular soldiering is deemed compatible with a Christian's duty.)

I will not argue the theological point. Perhaps the dispossessed ceased to be Christians when they refused to watch their children starve within sight of well-equipped food stores. But they acted as they *had* to act, and in this realization that *there is only one thing to do,* they found their salvation, the meaning of existence.

Now I believe I have stated the position from which the dedicated Communist sees the world about him, the state of mind which appears to him as salvation appears to the Christian. It is the state of mind in which it is possible to move in only one direction. The primeval event which leads to this state of mind, the triggering mechanism of the Communist's total commitment, is the revolt of the destitute against the wielders of power and the hoarders of wealth.

It is this primitive, obvious, frequent event, not the elaborate "social science" that captures the Communist's commitment, just as the primitive direct feeling of love for the "other" captures the dedicated Christian, not the elaborate theology. There, I think, is the answer to the riddle which must puzzle every intellectually honest Marxist. Why have Communist ideas taken the most firm root in the lands of unurbanized masses, instead of in industrially developed countries, as was predicted by the theory? Is it not because the primitive triggering event, the revolt of the masses, had the most direct, obvious meaning in the primitive countries?

Let the Russian look at the moral roots of Russian Communism, as it was first embraced by the masses of people. Let him ask whether the success of Russian Communism was rooted more deeply in dialectics or in the fact that the Russified vulgarization of the French word *bourgeois* has in Russian an almost obscene sound?

In the minds of the destitute, capitalism was not a social arrangement but an attitude. An entrepreneur, even if he was a small trader, was one who *looked out for himself*. Nothing is harder for the American to understand than the Russian peasant's contempt for the trader. Consider: with us the trader, say the owner of the village store, is often the kindly neighbor, the solid citizen, possibly shrewd in trading, but upright and, above all, independent (a virtue in America). Like the blacksmith across the square, the trader holds his head high and enjoys the respect of his fellow citizens, because "he owes not any man."

There was no analogue to this character in the primitive Russian community. The merchant (more typically, the tavern keeper) was the village *kulak,* one who lived *on* the people, not with them. To preach the gospel of self-reliance and free enterprise to the Russian village folk would have been as futile as to preach it to a group of people adrift in a lifeboat.

Typically, the ideal of free enterprise appears ludicrous or pernicious to a collective struggling for survival. An entrepreneur attempting to do business on a battlefield—selling steel helmets or antibiotics, for example—would not command admiration or enjoy affection, no matter how badly these articles were needed. Once we understand this, we understand why innocent and harmless grocers and peddlers were shot by the thousands in Russia during the civil war. Not only were these people innocent of any crime (as we understand crime) but they were badly needed. Take the salt merchants, people who risked their lives to travel hundreds of miles on roofs of boxcars over bandit-infested steppes to get salt from the Sea of Azov to bring it to the cities. After trade and transport had broken down, this was the only source of salt supply in Russia. When these *mieshochniki* ("bag toters") were caught they were shot as "speculators." Thousands of businessmen and professional men were shot, although the majority of them with a minimum of encouragement would have contributed their talents and experience even in a completely socialist economy. But the wrath of the destitute descended upon them. Their dangerousness or usefulness was not the issue. Their outlook was the issue. Any man who was motivated by private gain (who could think how to *escape* the common fate instead of sharing it) was a social outcast and an enemy.

The ethical basis of the Communist's commitment is the condition of life where people are bound together emotionally through an awareness of *common fate,* where to try to escape it means to desert. My opponent has dismissed the primitive communities, the "exotic" cultures studied by the anthropologists as exceptions to the general theme of social evolution, as "pockets" left outside the torrent of progress. In doing so, he has by-passed the very bases of strength for his point of view. For Communism is an attempt to recapture the communal ethic and to transplant it into an industrial society. The question before us, therefore, is whether such a transplant will "take," whether it is possible for a member of an industrial society to *think* as well as act communally. For we must make the distinction between thinking communally and acting communally. On this distinction my entire case will rest.

To begin with, let us admit that communal acting is certainly normal in any industrial society. Even capitalist enterprises are gigantic co-operative units in the sense of co-ordinated and disciplined acts of their participants. My opponent has himself pointed out that the capitalist state has the capacity for organizing communal effort on a national scale in times of crisis, for example in a war. But in peacetime too it is not altogether true that the economies of capitalist states are in a constant state of chaos.

Admittedly, much competition is wasteful; admittedly overproduction is a chronic ailment of the profit system; perhaps too much productive effort is diverted into channels which contribute little to welfare. But the work does get done. Goods are produced and distributed. People's needs are satisfied to a degree, certainly no less than elsewhere. Children are raised and provided with some opportunities for taking their place in the world of work and self-fulfillment. There are some opportunities, not confined to the privileged few, for creative and imaginative activity. The ingredients of what both you and we understand by a good life are present. The only question is whether they are present to the degree warranted by what is possible under the present availability of resources and technological potential. The answer is almost certainly "No." There is a great deal of waste. But it is an open question whether the waste inherent in the competitive profit system of production is greater or less than the waste inherent in bureaucratic practices, in overcentralization, in *covert* competition between state controlled enterprises, and in all the other by-products of state socialism in the present stage.

At any rate, the relative efficiency of private and state enterprise is not the issue. As a matter of fact, not even private versus state enterprise is the central issue in our debate. For even if the economy of a "capitalist" state were predominantly under social control, my opponent would still maintain that the "social revolution" had not yet taken place and is still inevitable.

This is so, because the issue is not communal acting but communal *thinking*. It is on this issue that the basic divergence of our views occurs.

The most important tenet in the Communist position is that every free-enterprise society, even those with considerable state or co-operatively controlled sectors of economy, exhibit a class stratification, which can be erased only by a social revolution. The social revolution is typically envisaged, or has been until recently, as following the Russian example, with its inevitable violence, a dictatorship of a monolithic party, etc. Gradual transition to collective ownership or economic arrangements making for *de facto* collective ownership without *de jure* recognition (a frequent circumvention of economic orthodoxy in the United States) have been typically contemptuously dismissed as reformist or opportunist. Always class structure rather than specific economic arrangements has been the *principal* issue, as the Communists saw it. Let us therefore look at class structures at the opposite poles, the United States, the most capitalist of the capitalist states, and the U.S.S.R., the farthest advanced (according to its proponents) on the road to Communism. Let us not look at the class structures derived from formal definitions or from constitutional provisions but at class structures actually discernible, that is, discernible to the hypothetical outsider, who is studying the actual social behavior of people. What would he find?

Beginning with the behavior of people in an industrial enterprise (for that is where the Communists would tell him to begin, and we would agree), our observer would find little difference between the operation of an American and a Russian factory. He would find in both the same meticulous division of labor, the same lines of authority, somewhat stricter, I suspect, in the U.S.S.R. But we shall not pursue quantitative distinctions which tend to accentuate the differences between the positions of workers and of managers in the U.S.S.R., differences which when observed in non-Communist societies are attributed by Communists to the class structure of those societies. We shall, as I say, forego the exploration of this "paradox" and assume that the distinction between management and labor *in the work process* is about the same in the U.S.S.R. as in the U.S.A.

The inevitable conclusion is that differentials of rewards, authority, and status are by-products of the division of labor. Characteristically, those engaged in organizational tasks, whose job is the co-ordination of activities of *people,* command larger rewards (of remuneration, authority, and status) than those who are engaged in manipulating inert matter. Moreover, these differentials are characteristic of the present stage of *industrial* society rather than specifically of its capitalist or socialist variants.

Furthermore, we note that the amount of the differential is inversely related to the level of production. It is greatest in the primitive stages of the industrial system and least in the most advanced stage, quite contrary to the trend predicted by Marxist theory. The differential was tremendous in the early years of industrialization in the U.S.S.R., even among the workers. In 1946 the compensation of the Russian skilled worker was as much as eleven times that of the unskilled.[96] At that time the corresponding differential in the United States was by about a factor of 2. (I understand that the ratio has since decreased in the U.S.S.R., but I note that the ratio of a professor's salary is still eight times that of a skilled worker, compared with about twice in the United States.) The differential between the remuneration of the lowest paid worker and a top executive in a large American enterprise is by a factor of 30, and I suspect Russian enterprises will show about the same figure.

The less tangible symptoms of class differentiation, such as social status, are as much in evidence in the U.S.S.R. as in the U.S. Although the orders of the social hierarchies are not quite the same, the rank order correlation is still high. By and large, those who *direct* (people or ideas or operations) occupy a higher status than those who carry the directives out.

The usual protestations about the different *bases* of differentiation in the U.S. and the U.S.S.R. are not much help. It is maintained that class differentiation under capitalism is made on the basis of ownership alone. A careful examination of facts fails to corroborate this contention. Here class differentiation is made very largely on the basis of the role played in the productive process (with exceptions, of course, derived from tradition, regional peculiarities, etc., which are not important), that is, exactly as in the U.S.S.R. The extent of class mobility is also quite comparable in the two societies.

In short, the class structures, as observed in actual behavior and in actual relations between the members of a society, are about the same in the two societies which are said to be at the opposite poles of capitalism and socialism. We note further that the class distinctions in these two societies are less sharp than in many other societies, particularly the older ones, where the heritage of many centuries of severe social stratification continues. One might conclude, therefore, that it is the *advanced* industrial economy, characteristic of the newer rapidly changing societies, rather than either capitalism or socialism which is conducive to a progressive obliteration of class lines. In fact, the progress made in this respect during the forty years of existence of the Soviet state and in the corresponding years in the United States is about the same.

The immediate future of both the United States and the U.S.S.R., given unimpeded peaceful development, is the welfare state—an easily attainable goal in both countries. We admit that much more economic planning than presently exists in the United States will be required to reach this goal; but it is not at all evident that it will be necessary to change the very basis of economic organization to attain it, much less to engineer a "social revolution" along the traditional lines of power seizure and civil war. I note that even my opponent has expressed scepticism about the feasibility of the last alternative.

We maintain now that in order to attain the goals of the welfare state in the U.S.S.R., the discipline now imposed on the Soviet citizen, particularly with regard to his attitudes, must be relaxed. The ideal of communal thinking (as distinguished from communal acting) cannot be imposed by decree or even by Pavlovian training. If such thinking is to emerge, it must emerge as a by-product of the economic and social arrangements. In so arguing, I am freely drawing upon what I believe to be the strongest feature of Marxist philosophy, namely that attitudes are outgrowths of social arrangements rather than vice versa. The Communists should practice what they preach. They should concentrate on creating the conditions conducive to the attitudes of a socialist society instead of declaring what the attitudes of the citizens should be.

However, I do not believe that communal thinking, as it is presently envisaged by the Communists, will ever emerge even in the socialist society. With this contention I come to the very basic issue, the crux of the case for individualism. It is true that the freedom of the individual to *act* can be only within restraints imposed by society. For these restraints are inescapable. But the freedom of the individual to think and to feel—that freedom can be absolute. The case for individualism rests on the assumptions that this latter freedom *should* be absolute and that it does not conflict with any restraints which it may be necessary to impose on the *acts* of the individual in society. On the contrary, the freedom of conscience is conducive to a wise choice of such restraints.

With regard to the restraints on acts, the individualist position has little to say. Different situations require different constraints. Some situations (like wars, disaster, etc.) require very severe constraints. The constraints may very well be on economic activities of individuals. Certainly no one in the United States protests against restraints which prohibit private individuals to print money or to organize armies or to practice medicine without a license. Restraints characteristic of a socialist state in which private enterprise is kept out of certain economic activities are entirely consistent with individualism.[97] The important feature about restraints on acts is that there is little question when such restraints are violated, that is, when a law is broken. Laws are agreements. In general, a complex society requires more agreements and rules than a simple one, and man in an increasingly complex society has no choice but to agree to the rules which his society lays down.

But constraints on attitudes are something else. It is in principle impossible to know directly what a man's attitudes are. An attitude can be only inferred. Therefore, social constraints on attitudes cannot be enforced unless recourse is taken to conclusions based on suspicions. The more determined is the effort to impose attitudes, the more sensitive must be the instruments for detecting attitudes. Suspicion (you call it "vigilance") becomes an indispensable adjunct to authority. Outbursts of paranoid denunciations and blood baths have become a distinguishing feature of authoritarian societies.

This is what happened in your effort to impose communal thinking on the population. You used the image of communal thinking which was known to you, the primitive thinking of an armed citizenry fighting a civil war. *That* was the thinking you were determined to preserve in postrevolutionary years, when your people were faced with an entirely new set of problems, problems of reconstruction, education, planning, industrialization, and, above all, the problem of assuming a role as a nation in the world community, the problem which you thought you could avoid (as we had thought) and found you could not (as we did).

You say there is inherently nothing bad in discipline. That is so. But neither is there inherently anything good in it. Discipline is a means to an end. It becomes senseless (therefore bad) when it becomes an end in itself. The discipline to which the members of a symphony orchestra or a ballet submit does not extend beyond the performance. What makes discipline bearable is its limited scope. We cheerfully give instantaneous obedience to the traffic policeman and think nothing of it, because his authority is specific and circumscribed. When this authority extends beyond the time and place in which it is supposed to function, it becomes tyranny.

To summarize so far, the issue between collectivism and individualism is first of all not the degree but the appropriateness of the restraints imposed on the individual; second, whether the restraints are imposed on overt acts or on attitudes. The individualist maintains that every restraint imposed on the individual must be justified by specific circumstances, must be enforced *impersonally* in terms of objectively identifiable, publicly stated criteria, and must be confined to overt acts. Communal acting is consistent with individualism; communal thinking, at least in the way it is envisaged by the Communists, is not.

I shall now take up the argument concerning the deterministic development of society, which was central in my opponent's thesis. The argument is defensible along its main lines in that a case for a lineal development of human society can be made. There *is* progress, and it is identified with increasing spheres of co-operative effort. The conclusion that co-operative economic arrangements must eventually supplant competing ones is also defensible, especially with regard to those sectors of the economy where unquestionable and standardizable necessities are produced. Socialism, then, to the extent that it becomes or is felt to be necessary, is seen from this point of view as a social by-product of economic development. This is as far as I will go along with my opponent's thesis. Our divergence begins here and concerns mainly two issues. First, the "amount of socialism," that is, the size of the economic sector to be moved from private control and/or competition to public or co-operative control—this we hold to be determinable by circumstances, not by principle. We do not believe that socialism is *itself* a moral issue. A socialist form of economy is one of many possible forms and has its advantages and disadvantages. There are social moral issues and social ideals, but economic arrangements and the legal status of property rights should be instrumental to implementing such goals, not social ideals in themselves.

Social ideals, I agree with my opponent, have to do with the relations between a man and his society and between men in society. But there is much more to these relationships than specifications about who owns what.[98] The social ideal which I defend is one in which man acts collectively but thinks individually, and I maintain that there is no contradiction there.

I freely admit that individualism is to a great extent an outgrowth of the bourgeois outlook. But it is a mistake to think this attitude obsolete for that reason. It may be no longer applicable to certain sectors of human activity, for example, to activities requiring large concerted efforts, but this does not mean that it is not applicable *anywhere*. Not everything which we inherit becomes obsolete. Progress can be and often is cumulative. Indeed the one sector of human history where progress is most clearly demonstrable, namely science, is primarily a cumulative process. Specific scientific theories become obsolete and are supplanted; but the method is cumulative: careful, systematic observation, once it has been added to the ways in which man seeks to know the world, has remained as a perpetual heritage. So has controlled experiment; so has syllogistic deduction and mathematical deduction and statistical inference; so has the postulational method of theory construction. All these have been contributions of different outlooks, but they have not been discarded just because the outlooks in which these ideas were incubated may no longer enjoy hegemony.

So it is with individualism. There is no denying that the individualist outlook with its emphasis on freedom of conscience and civil rights was tightly associated with the entrepreneur economy, which developed into the capitalist system. But even if the capitalist system passes or evolves into other forms, one cannot conclude that *all* of its by-products must disappear. Otherwise, one should argue that science and cities should also disappear, since these too developed in the period of capital accumulation.

Now I shall say why I think that individualism will out-live both the capitalist system and the present image of communal thinking, which the Communists take to be inherent in collectivism. First, I believe that the rejection of individualism and the emphasis of communal thinking as an ethical principle is most appropriate in the condition of poverty and danger. As long as the populations of Communist states lived in poverty and as long as they felt a constant danger that their chosen path was in perpetual jeopardy, the insistence on communal thinking was understandable, even though the hegemony of such thinking means a rejection of the most valuable heritage of the bourgeois age—freedom of individual conscience. But poverty must disappear. It will disappear with increasing industrialization *whatever* the social arrangements: these can influence only the rate of its disappearance and what price will be paid for the eradication of poverty.[99] As poverty disappears, the self-awareness of the individual must come to the forefront of human consciousness, since such self-awareness is a product of prosperity and security (call them bourgeois social ideals, if you must). We already have evidence of this phenomenon in the Soviet Union.

Second and most important, individualism must be re-established in Communist countries, because this attitude goes with the scientific way of thinking. Those who accept science as a way of life (and the Communists say they do) must also accept individualism as an ethical principle. This brings me to the fundamental question: to what extent *is* science accepted as a way of life in the major societies of our day?

Science is the common heritage in both our societies, and both societies are unquestionably adapted to utilizing the

power which science confers on man over his environment—
but only to a limited extent. The limitations on both sides
stem from commitments to dogma, the antithesis of the
scientific attitude. Dogma is that portion of one's outlook
which is immune to modification.

It will be futile for me to maintain that you as Communists are bound more rigidly by dogma than we, although
it appears that way to us. Rather than try to measure the un-
measurable, I maintain from the start that both our societies
are impeded by dogmatic attitudes from developing their full
potentials. The difference is that you recognize dogma explicitly and call it Marxism (or dialectical materialism in the
natural science sphere), while we deny that our fetishes (like
"liberty") are symptoms of dogma. The effects are similar.
In the name of liberty we dare not undertake measures to
safeguard minimum standards of economic security and
health, which we can well afford. In the name of the "only
correct philosophy" you have failed to extend the realm of
scientific investigation to the nature of man and society, which
you had unequaled opportunity to do.

I believe that taking refuge in dogma is a fear reaction.
The irrational fear of planning, so conspicuous in the United
States, stems from a dread of *overt* restraints on the activities
of the individual.[100] As so often happens, an overpowering
fear incapacitates one in dealing with real dangers. In our
pathological avoidance of overt restraints, we have succumbed
to innumerable covert ones and have drifted into a drabness
of conformity.

Your irrational fear stems from the dread of "idealism."
You see "idealism" in any intellectual position which, however
remotely, admits the perceptual or the cognitive structure of
an individual in the start of a theoretical investigation. You
keep fighting the intellectual battle of the nineteenth century,
the battle against the hegemony of religious dogma, an issue

which has since lost all significance in the intellectual sphere.

The sacredness of dialectical materialist dogma has laid your science open to infiltration by unscrupulous charlatans, who, like charlatans and demagogues everywhere hide behind whatever gods are worshipped and behind the flag. Thus, the disgrace of our "Monkey Trial" in Tennessee was duplicated in the U.S.S.R. twenty years later in the infamous Lysenko affair. The obscurantist blasts against the "idealism" of "Mendelist-Morganist-Weismannist" genetics could be translated verbatim into fundamentalist anti-evolution tirades with just the proper substitution of words without disturbing the sense of the diatribes (110, 82, 138).

The witch hunts in the years of our McCarthy eclipse are well matched by the outbursts of intellectual lynching of the type the Russians call *razgrom*.[101] Again, quantitative differences are not the issue here. If such comparisons were made, I think it would be clear that the damage to Soviet science by Soviet McCarthys was the more serious in extent and in depth. The silly purification rites, initiated by Lysenko and his clique in biological science, brought demoralization to practically all sectors of Soviet science, even to such disciplines as symbolic logic and statistics.[102]

Modern developments such as cybernetics and mathematical economics had been taboo subjects for many years in the U.S.S.R., the former because in an atmosphere of fear everything foreign is suspect; the latter, because any inkling of findings which could be construed at variance with Marxist economic dogma had to be avoided at all costs. Philosophical foundations underlying the physics of the twentieth century were viciously attacked, because Lenin fifty years ago saw in them a threat to dialectical materialist dogma (57).

Since the *results* of relativity theory and of quantum mechanics had to be accepted (you cannot argue with the way inanimate matter behaves—matter does not understand philosophy), these results had to be explained by prodigious circumlocutions in order to avoid the impression of relying on operational definitions of physical variables.[103]

In the psychological realm, certain directions had to be proscribed a priori, for example, those associated with depth psychology, again out of fear that they bore the seeds of anti-Marxist heresy.

Scientists in the United States were largely spared such ignominies, but hardly because of greater scruples of our own self-appointed guardians of orthodoxy. Rather the content of science was largely ignored, because the intellectual aspect of science is not good newspaper copy in the United States. Personalities of the entertainment world, which are good copy, fared much worse.

In spite of obvious differences in emphasis and perhaps in the extent of these phenomena in the two societies which represent the opposite ideological poles, I must call attention to the similar character of the persecutions of the intellect. The propelling compulsion is in both cases the fear of subversion.

Now from the point of view of the guardians of orthodoxy, this fear of the intellect, especially the fear of science, is entirely justified. For science, when one stops to think of it, is by its very nature subversive: it has subverted every social order in which its practice was tolerated. This is so, because every social order rests on fictions, and its stability is insured only so long as the fictions remain sacrosanct.

Thus, we come to the determinist view of history from the other, the individualist end. It is true, as the Marxists say, that every social order has carried within it the seeds of its own destruction. It does not appear that any of the social orders of today are exceptions to this rule. Specifically, the collapse of the authoritarian structure of Communist ideology is insured by the very science which Communist society must nourish in order to insure its economic and military strength.

The Communist state is a mass state (as is the bourgeois democratic state), that is, it requires the active participation of the mass of citizens in public affairs. No matter that this participation must be along approved lines only; it is nevertheless participation and requires that the mass be informed. No matter that in the political sphere the information is carefully sifted and tailored. The habit of being informed persists. And along with the spoon-fed political information, technical information must also be given, and technical information cannot be divorced from general principles and theory. These, in turn, cannot be divorced from philosophical questions, and the very insistence on the "one correct philosophy" makes obvious the existence of other philosophies. The inquiring mind (which technical training will nurture regardless of the intentions of the guardians) must eventually seek out other philosophies, or create them, and when it finds them, it will "try them on." When that happens, communal thinking will disappear, and there will be no going back.

If science is to prevail, individualism will prevail, because individualism is the attitude which is in harmony with the scientific age.

Now the proponent of collectivism has suggested to us a graceful way of dealing with the inevitable victory of that outlook. We should reciprocate and suggest how to deal with perhaps the equally inevitable victory of individualism. There is no contradiction here: collectivism may well become the dominant mode of life in the area of *action,* for that is the mode appropriate for organized effort. But we hope that individualism will become the dominant mode in the area of perception, thinking, and feeling, in interpersonal relations and in creativity. In other words, we believe that a good society may mobilize the individual's *efforts* to the extent that these are required for a common goal, but it need not put a strait jacket on the individual's thoughts and attitudes. The emergence of such a society is the "victory" we hope for.

If the Communists recognize the fruits of their own prophecy, namely that the individual, relieved from the necessity of struggle for his own survival and welfare, emerges free, they should recognize the nature of that freedom. Freedom is not something specific—to do this or to do that. All specific freedoms can be granted in conditions of slavery. There can be freedom from hunger in a penitentiary. One theology defines "freedom" as "freedom to obey the will of God" (interpreted by properly licensed practitioners). Such is the freedom to vote for an approved list of candidates or, for that matter, to choose between *two* approved lists of candidates. After sufficiently intense training, any compulsion can be made to appear as the result of free choice. Only one kind of freedom cannot be granted in this way: the nonspecific freedom to be oneself.

I know this sounds ugly to your ears, because for forty years you have denied the reality of this freedom. But you have not eradicated the yearning for it, and it is too late to ascribe this yearning to remnants of "bourgeois-idealistic subjectivism." The first generation, which grew up entirely under your guidance, is now middle aged. Look well, and you will find that this yearning is increasing. Not the yearning to grow rich at others' expense, nor the yearning to withdraw from your society (Pasternak begged to be allowed to remain!), with which you confuse the individualist outlook—no, simply the yearning to be oneself—to be left alone *sometimes* in *some* matters.

If you are prudent, you will do nothing about this yearning. If you are wise, you will encourage it. If you are shrewd, you may use this development for dramatic effect, compared with which all your technological achievements will fade into insignificance. If you really want to impress the West, create a ministry of re-examination, that is, push the brief, abortive de-Stalinization campaign of 1956–57 to its logical conclusion. Think what would happen if your knowledge-hungry people got access to controversial information and were encouraged to offer alternative evaluations of what happened in the past forty years! If socialism is a stable system, why should you, who accuse us of being afraid to compete, why should you be afraid of a market of ideas? Do you not know that all the great spurts in what you (and we) call progress came just after some unorthodox ideas or exotic impressions had penetrated into a closed system? Do you think *we* could have advanced in the last forty years (and we did, at least in the sense of more equitable distribution of wealth) if *your* ideas did not penetrate to us, if the smug orthodoxy of Babbittry had not been fundamentally subverted? If your talented and passionate people were suddenly freed from stifling orthodoxy and plunged into the heady atmosphere of intellectual freedom, imbued with the spirit of collective effort, do you doubt that you could re-enact another Renaissance?

A Renaissance in Russia would be something to behold! One does not know where to start to describe what might be. Suppose, for example, a science of man was allowed to develop unhampered by the taboos of Marxism-Leninism. The land which gave birth to both Pavlov and Dostoevski could provide a much more fertile soil for scientific depth psychology than the West, where this approach partly deserves the accusation of having become an adjunct to lucrative psychiatric practice and where intuitive and experimental methods have become so widely separated.

Think of what a well-developed social depth psychology could do to enlighten historical events which are now suppressed or glossed over with shabby rationalizations. Every thoughtful Communist knows privately that there was more to the reign of terror than Stalin's personal shortcomings. Your people and above all your leaders need to know about the effects of power intoxication, about the nature of mob sadism, about mass paranoid delusions—not to judge or to condemn your own past, but to understand it.

If you are intent on building your future on social engineering, you must understand what can go wrong with the social mechanism—something which neither Marx nor Lenin can teach you, since neither of them has faced the problems which you have faced since 1928: neither has seen a socialist economy in action.

You have assumed that you can learn these things from experience—a good assumption but not a sufficient one. Theory is also indispensable, as you well recognize, but a live theory, not a dead one. But you have allowed your theory to ossify into dogma. At a time when you need a profound understanding of both capitalist and socialist economics (better to say market-controlled and socially engineered economies), you depend on worn clichés and blind yourself to facts by clinging to moralizing distinctions between everything that is "yours" and everything that is "theirs." [104] In large areas of vital importance to you, you train your young to "think with their ears" (138, p. 10), that is, to accept verbiage as explanation.

A fresh intellectual wind would sweep away the shell in which Communist thought had become encrusted. The philosophy of collective effort would then emerge as a young philosophy instead of a senile "system" buried in dog-eared volumes, an orthodoxy guarded against "revisionism" (i.e., against growth) by priests jealous of their power.

You will almost certainly dismiss this advice of an outsider. But there have been ardent believers in your own ranks who have made the same plea. Their voices were ignored,

and they will not be heeded for some time, but they will persist, as the voices who pleaded for a more enlightened Russia
have persisted throughout the nineteenth century.

If you are afraid of losing your power, you must ask
power to do what? If you assume that discipline of effort is
incompatible with the freedom of intellect and conscience,
why not put that assumption to a test? The bars need not
come down at once. If you are afraid that even a gradual
relaxation will get out of control, as the czarist regime per-
sistently believed, there is something basically wrong with your
system: it must be unstable, as the social physicist would say,
as was the system that preceded it. If so, the need for re-
examination is even more urgent.

You have always ascribed to yourselves the role of mid-
wives of history. Now you are offered a second magnificent
chance to play the part: anticipate the inevitable; be prophets
in action.

CONCLUDING REMARKS

IT SEEMS TO ME that no single framework of thought is adequate for dealing with such a complex class of phenomena as human conflict. But an acquaintance with several frameworks may serve to bring our ignorance to our attention. Awareness of ignorance is a step forward in the quest for understanding. Thus, although none of the approaches here presented is adequate, each can serve as a reminder of what has been left out in the others.

In the study of conflict, the psychology of hatred would seem to be the most directly relevant field. Lacking competence, I could not discuss this area and so could not name Part I "The Blindness of Aggression," as I was initially tempted to do, when I was planning to write this book. Instead I had to content myself with describing the existing models of conflict which are devoid of rational goals. I suspect that these models, crude as they are, come closest to the dynamics of fights.

I do not believe, of course, that a pair of differential equations (or a dozen) can explain an arms race or the outbreak of war fever. But the approach of the social physicist should remind the political historian and the social moralist that there *may* be social forces operating which are as blind and as powerful as the atmospheric factors which determine the weather. It is not enough to talk about such forces. They ought to be sought out and studied by whatever tools are available.

It is naïve to suppose that the strategies of diplomacy can be cast into a two-person game. But the ramifications of game theory bring to light the purely logical difficulties of dealing with strategy from a supposedly rational point of view.

A clash of ideologies can hardly be *the* underlying basis of large-scale social and international conflicts. But it *may* play an important part and so overshadow strategic considerations as well as bias the operation of the "blind" forces. Therefore, the roots and the role of ideology should be understood.

Before ideas come to fruition, they must germinate. The most important direct consequence of an idea is that it gives rise to more ideas. I suspect that the most important result of a systematic and many-sided study of conflict would be the changes which such a study could effect in ourselves, the conscious and unconscious, the willing and unwilling participants in conflicts. Thus, the rewards to be realistically hoped for are the indirect ones, as was the case with the sons who were told to dig for buried treasure in the vineyard. They found no treasure, but they improved the soil.

NOTES

1. This anecdote and the complete Capablanca-Marshall game appear in (16, pp. 118–19).
2. "The real cause [of the Peloponnesian War] I consider to be the one which was formally kept out of sight. The growth of the power of Athens, and the alarm which this inspired in Lacedaemon, made war inevitable." (118, p. 15.)
3. "The armaments were only the symptoms of the conflict of ambitions and ideals of those nationalist forces, which created the war. The war was brought about because Serbia, Italy, Rumania passionately desired the incorporation in their States of territories which at that time belonged to the Austrian Empire."—From the remarks of Mr. L. S. Amery, M.P., on July 20, 1936, in the House of Commons, quoted in (94).
4. To assume that influences act independently and can be added is to assume a great deal. Such actions are observed in physics (e.g., collinear forces, masses, amounts of heat, electric charge). Because the phenomena associated with these effects are particularly simple, they have been intensively studied and now constitute much of what is called exact science. However, most causal relations in chemistry and biology are not independent and not additive. We have even less reason to suppose that causal relations in the world of human behavior (if such exist) are additive.
5. A differential equation establishes a mathematical relation among variables and their rates of change with respect to each other. To solve such an equation means to eliminate the rates of change so that only the mathematical relations among the variables themselves remain. As a simple example, the equation $dy/dt = ay$ says that the rate of change of some quantity

y with respect to time is proportional to the quantity itself (as, for instance, in continuously compounded interest). The solution of this differential equation, $y = ke^{at}$, says that the quantity *y* must be an exponential function of time. The rate of change, dy/dt has been eliminated. We also say the equation has been integrated.

6. Later an interpretation will be given to negative values of *x* and *y*, so that the case where the intersection is in quadrants other than the first can also be examined.

7. To my knowledge, the earliest application of this particular mathematical method was made in the context of theoretical economics by Antoine Augustin Cournot in 1838 (20).

8. It is, however, instructive to ask what "nearly" fifty may mean. Certainly we cannot expect that in each instance exactly 50 heads will turn up in each 100 tosses. What, then, must the deviation from the expected value 50 be in order to justify an inquiry into the cause of the deviation? This question has no clear-cut answer. In general, it is impossible to inquire searchingly into the nature of causality, that is, our conception of it, without treading on shaky philosophical ground.

9. To imagine the causes of *usual* events marks a step to a higher degree of sophistication. In popular fancy, gravity was discovered as an answer to the question, "Why does an apple fall?"—an inquiry into the cause of a commonplace event. However, the answer which popular fancy ascribes to Newton, "The apple falls because of gravity," is only a pseudo-explanation: it does no more than attach a label to a presumed cause. Newton's real accomplishment was to formulate a set of assumptions from which a great many events were deduced mathematically as consequences. Among these, many were commonplace events—the fall of bodies near the surface of the earth, the motions of the moon and planets, etc. Here it was not a question of making the unexpected appear expected but of deducing many expected *but seemingly unrelated* events from the same set of assumptions, which, in virtue of their focal position as the starting points of deduction, were promoted to "causes."

10. Strictly speaking, this proposition is only a restatement of the starting assumptions under the condition that the pa-

rameters of mutual stimulation and of restraint are equal; i.e., it is still a statement of the differential equation with which the theory began. The solution of the equation (cf. note 5) would state that the growth of total expenditures is exponential (in geometric progression). This consequence can also be read off from the graph. But the proposition as stated is easier to illustrate visually: the points fall on a straight line if the armaments are plotted against the yearly increases instead of against the years.

11. The integration of equation (11) is obtained as follows. Dividing both sides by x and multiplying by dt, we obtain $dx/x = -m\ dt$. Both sides are now exact differentials and can be integrated, giving the relation between x and t: $\log_e x = -mt + K$. Here the logarithm is taken to the "natural base," $e = 2.178\ldots$, and K is an arbitrary constant. Taking anti-logarithms of both sides and noting that x must equal the initial value when $t = 0$, we obtain (12).

12. Inadvertently, one recalls Mr. Micawber's advice to Copperfield: "Annual income twenty pounds, annual expenditure nineteen nineteen six, result happiness. Annual income twenty pounds, annual expenditure twenty pounds aught and six, result misery" (24, p. 184).

13. Following other instances of usage in defining "magnitude," Richardson takes a logarithmic measure. He defines the magnitude of a "fatal quarrel" as the logarithm to the base 10 of the number of fatalities (95). Thus, the magnitude of an isolated murder is $\log_{10} 1 = 0$. Feuds and riots range in magnitude from about 1 to 3. Wars range above 3 to about 7 (the magnitude of the two world wars). Prognoses for the magnitude of a nuclear war range from 8 to 9. A fatal quarrel of magnitude slightly over 9 would wipe out the human race.

14. The literature on mathematical theories of epidemics is not as extensive as the importance of the subject and the possibility of systematic treatment would warrant. The interested reader is referred to (2), particularly to its treatment of threshold phenomena in epidemics.

15. Thus, the type of equations used in the theoretical treatment of epidemics has been used also in models of spreading excitation in neural nets (80).

16. N. Rashevsky, H. G. Landau, and others have developed interesting models, describing the propagation of imitated behavior in a population under various assumptions (88, 52).
17. Specifically, a book entitled *Germany and the Next War* (5), which appeared in 1912, was a remarkably frank expression of this point of view.
18. Recall that in another treatment (94), Richardson defines the amount of hostility in terms of armament expenditures. Here, however, he is in search of a different measure, more directly related to public opinion and more sensitive to fluctuations.
19. This hypothesis is neither necessary nor particularly realistic. It is not clear why Richardson has chosen it, unless he wished to replicate formally the arms race situation, in which mutual stimulation is central. It seems to me that self-stimulation to a high pitch of intensity is more pertinent to the etiology of war fever. The whole phenomenon could have been treated as an internal epidemic in each country, instigated by dramatic events which served to bring covert endemic hostility into consciousness, where, under the conditions of released inhibitions, it acquired an epidemic potential.
20. This point is strongly disputed in some quarters. I have heard a philosopher of science whom I respect tell the sardonic parable of a man who went about the house looking for things to fix with only a screw driver. Having tightened all the loose screws, he found some protruding nails, whereupon he fetched a file and made a groove in the cap of each nail in order to use the screw driver. The barb is well aimed; still the abuse of any method does not invalidate its legitimate use.
21. To say that the rate of increment of utility is inversely proportional to the reward, we write $du/dr = k/r$. Here u is utility, r is reward, and k the constant of proportionality. Rearranging, we have $du = k\, dr/r$, and integrating, $u = k \log_e r + A$. Here A is the constant of integration to be fixed by the initial condition.
22. The logarithmic function is slightly modified by adding one (within the parenthesis), so that utility vanishes when the reward vanishes. When nothing is produced, x and y are zero and $S_x = S_y = \log 1 = 0$.
23. The slopes of the optimal lines, given by equations (18) and

(19), are respectively $-p/q$ and $-q/p$. Since $p + q = 1$, it follows that the absolute magnitude of $-p/q$ is greater than $-q/p$ if and only if $p > q$.

24. Note first that the value of expression (26) for $p = 1$ is 0. Now take the derivative of this expression with respect to p. This is $-1/p + \beta/p^2 = (\beta/p - 1)/p$. If $p > \beta$, $\beta/p < 1$, and the derivative is always negative, i.e., the value of expression (26) increases as p decreases. But the total range of p is $(0,1)$, and we have seen that (26) is zero when p has the maximum value 1. Therefore (26) must be greater than zero when p has any value less than 1.

25. The maximum value of $-\log_e q - 1$ occurs when $q = \frac{1}{2}$, $-\log_e q = 0.693$, $-\log_e q - 1 = -0.307$.

26. We could, of course, generalize our model by endowing our two men with different reluctance coefficients. Then the conclusion would be stated in terms of the relations of these coefficients to each other and to p. The model can also be extended to more than two individuals, involving a variety of exchange networks and coalitions (30).

27. Pareto defines a function Φ, whose differential is essentially the sum of the differentials of the utility functions of the individuals who constitute the society. He calls this function (in his German article) *Gesamtnutzen* or *Totalophelimität* (77, p. 1104). What we call the social optimum is the state in which this function attains its maximum value. Of course, additivity of utilities is taken for granted in this concept, an assumption which nowadays does not enjoy much credence. In its defense it can be said that if the sum of utilities is treated as a purely theoretical construct, devoid of direct operational sense, interesting theorems can be deduced. In some situations, for example, if each individual acts so as to maximize the *Totalophelimität* purely formally, regardless of its psychological meaning, each *individual* utility will attain a value greater than that associated with the intersection of Cournot's lines. It is in this sense that the term "social optimum" deserves consideration (87).

28. N. Rashevsky has considered various implications of "egalitarian," "egotistic," "altruistic," etc., societies by examining the properties of the corresponding utility matrices, generalized to N individuals (88, Part IV).

29. The solution of the differential equation is

$$N = \frac{b\,C\,e^{bt}}{1 + q\,C\,e^{bt}}$$

Here $C = N_0/(b - qN_0)$, and N_0 is the initial population. The maximum rate of growth is attained when $N = b/2q$. The maximum level approached is b/q.

30. A mathematical solution yields the *whole* truth, whether we are interested in it or not. Solutions which are obvious but of no interest in a particular problem are called trivial.

31. See, for example, the vigorous attack on "historicism," particularly on Hegel and Marx, by K. Popper (79).

32. Definitions of probability as "degree of plausibility" or "degree of belief" are tautological and not operational. They simply suggest other names for probability. Definitions in terms of the frequency of occurrence of an event among other events are operational in principle, although they are beset with subtle technical difficulties. At any rate, the "frequency" definitions assume that the event in question is repeatable, and so they cannot be regarded as applicable to single events. Subjective probability has been defined operationally, e.g., by L. J. Savage (103). But this definition links the event in question to preferences and choices of action of some particular individual and therefore does not refer to any intrinsic property of the event.

33. A feedback in a system is an arrangement whereby the system's output (performance) becomes part of the input (i.e., is included in the stimuli impinging on the system). Positive feedback is a self-enhancing influence on the output; negative feedback is a self-restraining, hence a balancing or corrective influence.

34. For a most comprehensive list of references to works on game theory (up to 1957) see the bibliography compiled by R.D. Luce and H. Raiffa in (61).

35. A normative theory is concerned only with consequences drawn by logical inference from a set of assumptions chosen in advance. Thus, if we make the assumption that in gambling only those bets should be accepted which, if repeated many times, are expected to result in a net gain, a normative theory of gambling can prescribe for each offered bet a decision—

to accept or not to accept. An empirical or descriptive theory, on the other hand, is one which tries to account for actual events. Thus, an empirical theory of gambling would seek to establish assumptions from which *observed* gambling behavior would follow as a consequence.

36. I repeat the story as I once heard it. Being a lively one, it has probably gathered many dramatic adornments in the three centuries since the event. Braithwaite, too (12, p. 54), mentions Chevalier de Méré's losses at dice leading him to seek advice from Pascal. However, E. T. Bell (3, p. 86) states that De Méré's original problem concerned the following question: Suppose a game is won when a certain fixed number of points has been accumulated by one of the players (as in cribbage). Suppose the game is broken off before either player has the winning number of points. What is a fair division of the stakes on the basis of the points already accumulated by each player, assuming that each player makes a point with equal probability?

The reader interested in an account based on primary sources (correspondence between Pascal and Fermat) is referred to (119).

37. The argument here is exactly like that in note 21 (q.v.).

38. Literature on experimental determination of utilities, which presumably underlie decisions in risky situations, is rapidly growing. Samples are given in (21, 67, 101, 116).

39. If a variable y is related to the variable x by the relation $y = ax + b$, where a and b are constants, the process of obtaining y from x is called a linear transformation. Thus, temperature on the Fahrenheit scale is related to that on the Centigrade scale by the transformation $F = 9/5 \ C + 32$. In most of game theory, if any results are obtained in relation to a set of outcomes with associated utilities $u_1, u_2, \ldots u_n$, the same results must hold if the u_i of any player are all replaced by u_i' obtained from u_i by a linear transformation.

40. The situation resembles the one where a toss of a coin is offered to decide who pays for lunch. To accept the offer means to accept a fifty-fifty chance gamble to pay for two lunches or none; to reject the offer means to choose the certainty of paying for one lunch.

41. Sometimes the common sense conclusion is violated: a gamble is preferred to the certainty of winning the highest payoff. In such cases, if the assumption of rational behavior is to be retained, we must assign extra positive utility to the risk itself, for example, to the gain accruing to the vanity of the risk taker for accepting the risk, or the like (101).

42. However, modern decision theory has gone far beyond the calculation of odds and expected payoffs, the concerns of classical gambling theory. See, for example (117) and (103). The title of the latter monograph does not indicate the connection of statistics to its principal theme (decision theory) except to the statistician, who realizes that the theory of statistical *inference* (i.e., statistical decision) is one of the cornerstones of decision theory.

43. Note the analogy to the "stable" solutions of the several situations treated in Chapters I and IV. Stability is insured by the fact that neither party can move away from the balance point without instigating events which will worsen his position. Only a return to the balance point will restore the losses.

44. A saddle too has such a point. It is the lowest point if one moves in the saddle along the horse's back and the highest point if one moves across the horse's back. Hence also the term maximin or minimax: the maximum of the minima.

45. A complication arises if Chance too has a hand in determining some outcomes. In that case, it is assumed that the probabilities of Chance's "choices" are known. In that case, the rational player is assumed to assign *expected* utilities to each pair of strategies. The situation becomes now a new game, in which all the outcomes can be considered certain.

46. If symmetry is taken into account, then the first player has only three choices instead of nine, namely, center square, side square, and corner square. If the first player takes the center, the second has two choices, side or corner; if the first player takes corner, the second has five choices: adjacent side, nonadjacent side, corner on same side, kitty-corner, and center, and so on for the next moves.

47. Black can associate each of his 20 moves with each of White's 20 moves. This can be done in 20^{20} different ways (not 400), or about 10^{26}.

48. Perhaps it is rash to conclude that Andrei's views were Tolstoy's own at the time this novel was written, but one cannot escape the impression that Tolstoy presents Andrei's position with considerable sympathy.

49. It is possible to construct a "mind-reading machine" which will win (in the long run) playing button-button against any one who knowingly or unknowingly departs from perfectly randomized choices. If the pattern of choices is simple and regular, say R L R L R L . . . , the machine will soon "lock in" in its own choices, so as to win. If the pattern is irregular, the machine can by "studying" sufficiently long sequences of choices, detect the biases and take advantage of them. The best strategy against such a machine would be to randomize the choices completely. Then the only thing the machine could do would be to follow suit and so come out even.

    Recent, as yet unpublished experiments (personal communications from S. Kornblum and G. J. Rath) show that it is extremely difficult to produce a perfectly random sequence at will. Every one has certain characteristic biases which make his sequences depart from randomness in a fairly predictable manner.

50. It is noteworthy that the earliest (to my knowledge) published genuinely game-theoretical investigation (10) was formulated in connection with a security problem. Having essentially defined a mixed strategy (*tactique*), E. Borel raises the following question: Can Player B in a zero-sum game choose a mixed strategy in such manner that even though A finds it out, he cannot take advantage of his knowledge? The affirmative answer to this question regardless of the number of strategies available (125) is the content of von Neumann's Minimax Theorem.

51. Rationality is often assessed in terms of the extent to which actions are guided by considerations of possible consequences. The concept of rationality applied to the choice of strategy in the Prisoner's Dilemma leads to the anomalous conclusion that two "rational" players will do worse than two "irrational" ones. The recommendation of the assumption of similarity is based not so much on the conventional concept of rationality as on the notion that one must do the "proper thing." One does the

"proper thing" *regardless* of consequences and derives satisfaction from *having done* the proper thing. The proper thing can also be defined in terms of the Kantian prescription: Act in such a way that if every one acted the same way, you yourself would benefit therefrom. Note that this is not the same as the usual demands made by authorities of collectivist societies for individual sacrifices for the common good. In the latter, some vague "collective" is supposed to gain often at the expense of the individuals composing it. In situations exemplified by the Prisoner's Dilemma, the individuals *themselves* gain if they follow the Kantian prescript. We follow this ethical principle when we perform duties on the basis of a recognition that if everyone shirked this duty, we would be penalized.

52. By "classical" game theory we understand its "finished" part, namely, the theory of the two-person zero-sum game in normal form and all further developments based on the Minimax Theorem.

53. For example, the economic philosophy known as utilitarianism tacitly assumes additive utility measures, which, to make sense, must imply that utility is transferable and conservative. Only in this way can "the total amount of welfare" be given a meaning (cf. note 27).

54. In particular, the horizontal co-ordinate of P_{11} is the payoff to Luke when he plays L_1 and Matthew plays M_1; the horizontal co-ordinate of P_{12} is the payoff to Luke when he plays L_1 and Matthew plays M_2. Consider now the straight line joining P_{11} and P_{12} in Figure 13. The horizontal co-ordinate of any point on it represents the payoff to Luke when Matthew *mixes* his strategies (while Luke sticks to L_1). The greater the proportion of M_1 in Matthew's mixture, the closer the point is to P_{11} and similarly for M_2 with respect to P_{12}. Therefore, the line joining P_{11} and P_{12} can be taken to represent Luke's strategy L_1, the particular payoff upon it being determined by Matthew's mixture.

By a similar argument, we can show that the four lines joining P_{11} to P_{12}, P_{21} to P_{22}, P_{11} to P_{21}, and P_{12} to P_{22} represent the four pure strategies L_1, L_2, M_1, and M_2, respectively. The *mixed* strategies of each player are represented by other lines, and we can show mathematically that all these mixed strategy

lines are tangent to the parabola drawn through the points
$P_{21} - O - P_{22}$, shown in Figure 13.

If Luke and Matthew play their mixed strategies independently, i.e., without co-ordinating them with each other,
they can get any pair of payoffs represented by a point in the
shaded region. But if they are allowed to co-ordinate their
mixed strategies, they can get any point within the whole
quadrilateral. Since any point within the shaded region can
be improved upon by a point on the northeast boundary of
the quadrilateral, in the sense that each will get more on the
boundary, it stands to reason that Luke and Matthew can
both gain by co-ordinating their mixed strategies. The arbitration problem is to select the mixed strategies on some equity
principle and a method of co-ordinating them so as to get a
payoff point on the northeast boundary. Braithwaite uses the
orientation of the parabola to determine his equity principle.
For details see (12). We prefer an alternative but equivalent
statement of the equity criterion (see text), which is also emphasized by Luce and Raiffa (61, p. 148).

55. The line inclined 45° to the horizontal drawn through P_{11}
is represented by the equation $y = x + 1$. The equation of the
northeast boundary is $3y + 7x = 58$. Simultaneous solution of
these two equations gives $x = 5.5$; $y = 6.5$, which is the point
on the boundary half way between P_{21} and P_{12}. This point is
obtained if Luke plays every other evening while Matthew remains silent and vice versa.

56. The equation of the 45° line is now $y = x + 3$, and that of the
northeast boundary is $3y + 14x = 116$. The intersection is at
$x = 6\frac{11}{17}$; $y = 9\frac{11}{17}$, which obtains if x receives 15 out of 17
evenings. The apparent unfairness of this division is compen-
sated by the very large enjoyment Matthew gets from his two
allotted evenings. This is, of course, a consequence of comparing
interpersonal utilities.

57. These are the maximin mixed strategies of the zero-sum game.

58. In this case, the payoff matrix becomes

$$
\begin{array}{c c c}
 & M_1 & M_2 \\
L_1 & \left[\begin{array}{cc} 1, 8/5 & 7, 12/5 \\ \end{array}\right. \\
L_2 & \left. 4, 8 & 2, 4/5 \end{array}\right]
\end{array}
$$

Luke's prudential strategy is $L_1 : L_2 = 1 : 3$. His contra-prudential strategy is $L_1 : L_2 = 9 : 1$. Matthew's prudential strategy is $M_1 : M_2 = 1 : 4$; his contraprudential strategy is $M_1 : M_2 = 5 : 3$. You may verify that each gains 2.21 utiles as he passes from his prudential to his contraprudential strategy, while the other sticks to the prudential.

59. The theory of zero-sum games rests firmly on the minimax theorem and its generalizations and therefore allows a straight-forward treatment.

60. Note again that here the payoffs are supposed to be summable. This means that utilities are considered to be determined absolutely, not merely on an interval scale.

61. There are 2^N subsets of N things. But each subset determines the complementary subset. Therefore there are 2^{N-1} ways of splitting N things into two sets. For instance, there are $2^2 = 4$ ways of splitting three things, A, B, and C, namely {A, B, C} vs. {0}, where {0} is the empty subset; {A, B} vs. {C}; {A, C} vs. {B}; and {B, C} vs. {A}.

62. In mathematics, a "function" means a rule, whereby elements of one set are made to correspond respectively to elements of another. The most familiar functions assign correspondences between numbers. For example, $y = x^2$ denotes a function which assigns to every number its square. In more general contexts, the elements need not be numbers. For example, the relation "father" can be viewed as a function which assigns to every individual a unique other individual, his father. In the so-called "characteristic function" of N-person game theory, a number (the value) is assigned to each *subset* of the N players. This function was first defined by von Neumann in (125).

63. Games in which no coalition commands collectively more than the sum of the payoffs that its members command individually are called inessential games. Obviously, there are no incentives for joining a coalition in such games. We will be considering an "essential" game, where a player may stand to gain by joining a coalition.

64. Actually, this is a constant-sum game rather than a zero-sum game. It can be made zero-sum by having the majority decide how a dollar is to *change hands* among the players. The theoretical treatment of this latter game would be exactly the same.

65. In decision theory sometimes the distinction is made between risk and uncertainty. Risk is defined as a situation in which the probabilities of the possible outcomes are presumed known; in uncertainty, they are not known.

66. In this context, a player prefers imputation I_2 to I_1 if he gets more in I_2 than in I_1.

67. Periodic functions, of which the familiar sines and cosines of trigonometry are the simplest examples, underlie the whole realm of wave physics. They are of prime significance in electrodynamics, telecommunication, quantum mechanics, etc.

68. Reference to Vickrey's unpublished work is made in (61, p. 213).

69. One other way of treating coalition problems deserves attention. If the bargaining acts (offers, acceptances, rejections, promises, etc.) can be formalized, e.g., if rules can be prescribed on how, when, by whom, and to whom offers may be made, and a rule for terminating the negotiations exists, then what appears in N-person game theory as a pre-play negotiation leading to the formation of coalitions will become an N-person game in its own right, described in extensive form, i.e., as a game tree. However, *this* N-person game can have its own coalitions (coalitions formed not for playing the original game but the *bargaining* game which precedes it). Here we are faced with "infinite regress" unless at some stage coalitions are disallowed.

70. To the non-American reader: $64 was the grand prize in one of our early quiz programs. Whether in the spirit of constant striving toward greater things or as a consequence of inflation, a later program made the grand prize $64,000.

71. An interesting variation of this experiment suggests itself. Let the time when the opportunity to change one's choice is withdrawn be unknown to the players. Question: what will be the effect of the constantly threatening "freeze" on the frequency of co-operative solution?

72. There have been attempts to construct a game theory based on different conceptions which the several players have of the game. Cf. (61, p. 270) and (60).

73. One might object that Othello becomes aware of the whole business only after Iago has reported (by innuendo) Desdemona's misbehavior, and that therefore Othello can ignore the

374 | Notes to Pages 240–49

alternatives which arise when Iago does not report. We must, however, keep in mind that Othello's problem is to guess where on the game tree the subgame G starts for him. To do so, he must estimate, in view of the interests of the other players, the likelihood that *given* Iago's report, he is at a particular node. Othello must therefore reconstruct the whole game. Of course, he can make an even deeper analysis by going still further back, e.g., to Desdemona's choice of marrying him or not. Only parlor games can be supposed to start from scratch. All real life situations have histories.

74. For examples of "applied" game theory see (45) and (133). The former is serious; the latter mostly humorous, verging on the satirical. A sample excerpt will give an idea of its tone.

Two deputies in a squad car are informed of a bandit's possible movements. One of them reasons so:

"We may not need a gun tonight, but we need a pencil: this is just a two-by-two game . . . Suppose he too heads for Paxton's. Either of two things can happen. One is, we catch him, and the chance is one-half. The other is, we don't catch him—and again the chance is one-half—but there is a three-fourths chance that the doc will have a lethal touch. So the over-all probability that he will get by us but not by the doc is one-half times three-fourths, or three-eighths. Add to that the one-half chance that he doesn't get by us, and we have seven-eighths."

The other deputy objects: "I don't like this stuff. He's probably getting away while we're doodling."

The rejoinder is, "Relax. He has to figure it out too, doesn't he?"

75. The psychological literature on rote learning is immense. However, formulations of rigorous mathematical theories have not been many. For an account of early "deterministic" models (i.e., those in which only the regression line of an average learning curve is derived) see (39). The first model based on assuming specific neurological circuits and a conditioning mechanism was proposed, to my knowledge, by H. D. Landahl in 1941. For an especially interesting application of his model to an experiment with human subjects see (51). Later, refinements were introduced, based on a stochastic approach, where the distributions of response frequencies rather than average response frequency

became central. For a detailed account of this approach see (13).

76. Some provocative parallels have been drawn in recent years between organic and cultural evolution on the one hand (37) and between learning and evolution on the other (80).

77. Theories of perception have been developed to an extent second only to the theories of learning. References to experiments similar to those described here are found in (54).

78. Here we enter the realm of ideas where the Gestalt notions have been extended to whole cultures. The most provocative of these ideas relate to the role of linguistic structure in determining the world outlook or the "metaphysics" of a culture (102, 130, 131).

79. Note the slang word "game" to denote profession: the real estate game, the insurance game, etc.

80. When I first "met" Lieutenant Manion, I was struck by his resemblance to Sergeant Croft (63).

81. This aspect of personality, I understand, is often associated with the fixation of the anal stage in the psychoanalytic version of the dynamics of psycho-sexual development (26, Ch. II).

82. We have already mentioned the experiments with perception. The "functionalist" view of cultural anthropology extends the same notion to the idea that cultures too are "wholes," into which extraneous influences may or may not fit. If they fit or can be made to fit, they will be accepted, but not otherwise.

83. I believe I have presented the argument as it should be presented by a consistent Marxist. In search of material on this subject, I looked in vain for any similar argument in the writings of Marx himself (although such may exist). Instead, I found an analysis based solely on the expansion ambitions of the *South*. It was the southern system, according to Marx, that had to expand or perish; the North was on the defensive only. One cannot help wondering whether Marx's natural sympathies for the Northern cause led him to draw a sharper distinction than he does elsewhere between "free labor" (under capitalism) and slave labor (69, p. 67 ff., p. 81).

84. The psychoanalytic approach is not confined to the theory of personality. History, literature, the arts, even science are often subjected to psychoanalytic scrutiny. Examples range from an analysis of Christian theology (31) to that of chess (28).

85. Carl R. Rogers, the principal proponent of permissive psycho-

therapy, develops his theory of personality and behavior around nineteen propositions, of which we cite the two which seem most germane to this conjecture and its converse, namely, that the probability of "trying on" new images is enhanced by the removal of threat.

"XVI) Any experience which is inconsistent with the organization or structure of self may be perceived as a threat, and the more of these perceptions there are, the more rigidly the self-structure is organized to maintain itself.

"XVII) Under certain conditions, involving primarily complete absence of any threat to the self-structure, experiences which are inconsistent with it may be perceived, and examined, and the structure of self revised to assimilate and include such experiences" (98, pp. 516–17).

86. The duodecimal notation is based on powers of twelve, just as our decimal notation is based on powers of ten. Therefore in duodecimal notation "14" stands for "one dozen plus four units," which we write "16" in decimal notation.

87. Actually, whether an equation has a solution depends on what class of entities are admissible as values of the unknown. For example, the equation $x^2 - 2 = 0$ has no solution if only rational numbers are admissible, but it has two solutions if real numbers are admitted. The equation $x^2 + 2 = 0$ has no solution among the real numbers, but it has two solutions among complex numbers. Even complex numbers do not suffice to satisfy the equation $XY - YX = Z$, where Z is different from zero. But still further extensions of the number system (to hypercomplex numbers) provide a region in which solutions to such equations are found. In general, the expansion of the number concept has been largely motivated by the necessity to provide "regions of solvability" for equations, i.e., to provide regions of validity for the statement, "This equation is solvable."

88. At the university where I work there are no "no smoking" signs. Instead one reads, "Smoking permitted in offices, seminar rooms, and other designated areas." Excesses of sales zeal have made "positive thinking" vulnerable to ridicule. But this should not detract from the psychological soundness of the principle in certain contexts.

89. I have not been able to trace the source of this statement, but it

is so striking that I could not resist quoting it. At any rate the observations of Whorf (131) serve equally well as illustrations of the principle that vocabulary richness is related to the discriminations which are important in the particular culture.

90. Political activists, on the other hand, since they often use particular definitions and classifications as psychological weapons, characteristically insist that proper definitions and classifications reflect "reality." A scene in a Soviet film *Lenin in 1918* (*ca.* 1937) is a poignant illustration. A surly peasant seeks Lenin out in his Smolny Institute headquarters and asks him what the Bolsheviks intend to do for the *mujik* (peasant). Lenin quickly replies, "The *mujik* does not exist. There exist only a *bednyak* (a poor peasant), a *serednyak* (a middle peasant), and (here his index finger suddenly shoots out pointing like a pistol at the visitor) a *kulak!*"

91. "There is one difficult exercise to which we may accustom ourselves as we become increasingly culture conscious. We may train ourselves to pass judgment upon the dominant traits of our own civilization . . .

"Appraisal of our own dominant traits has so far waited till the trait in question was no longer a living issue. Religion was not objectively discussed till it was no longer the cultural trait to which our civilization was most deeply committed. Now for the first time the comparative study of religions is free to pursue any point at issue. It is not yet possible to discuss capitalism the same way, and during wartime, warfare and the problem of international relations are similarly tabu. Yet the dominant traits of our civilizations need special scrutiny" (4).

92. The protagonist is about to try to "explain away" the liberal's image of individual liberty. We have pointed out the limitations of this approach, but in this case, the protagonist cannot avoid resorting to it. The "explaining away" is an integral part of his position, which he must finally present.

93. "Here, then, repeated on the world scale, are the riches and poverty, side by side, of nineteenth-century England. And we would need the pen of a Dickens to paint the contrast between the comfortable suburban homes of a thousand Western cities and the hovels of the hungry millions I have seen from Hong Kong to Johannesburg."—Adlai Stevenson (114).

94. Here, as possibly elsewhere, the defender of the Communist

outlook is speaking sharply out of character. It is difficult to imagine a Communist expressing anything but contempt for any idea that war may have psychological as well as economic roots. My problem, however, is to make the strongest possible case for the point of view being presented. That is, if I were to advise a Communist on how to make an argument which a Western liberal might respect, I would insist that he raise the question of whether the lack of strong identification with large dramatic collective enterprise does not make war psychologically attractive (because it fills this need) to the unconscious urges of Western masses.

95. Again here are unlikely admissions by a Communist. Yet most of us would have guessed ten years ago that a de-idolization of Stalin would be utterly unthinkable within the framework of the Communist outlook.

96. Source: conversation with representatives of Soviet trade unions visiting United States in 1946.

97. Here my protagonist differs sharply from the position represented, say, by F. A. von Hayek (42). Again, as in the case of the collectivist position, my task is to present the strongest possible arguments for individualism and moreover ones which will at least be heard by the opposing side. Therefore, it becomes necessary to point out that individualism is not unavoidably linked to any feature of *laissez faire* economy. In my opinion, if it were so linked, the individualist position would be extremely difficult to defend.

98. Ownership rights are of paramount importance where socially disruptive conflicts over possession are a constant threat. Thus, ownership of narrow tracts of fertile land and of water sources often marked the borderline between life and death for primitive peoples. Accordingly, rigid (sanctified) property rights became necessary as an alternative to continual debilitating strife. Where ownership is diffuse and where rights conferred by ownership are circumscribed by complex regulations and responsibilities, it is sometimes impossible to say where the difference between "private" and "public" ownership becomes merely a matter of semantics. Thus, whether the bus service of a middle-sized American city is formally organized under public ownership or left to a private company, which is heavily

subsidized and strictly regulated, makes very little difference in the economy of the community. Yet a half century ago such issues were of the gravest concern both to the defenders and to the opponents of private enterprise.

99. The pauperization of the masses in the early decades of the Industrial Revolution and the mass starvation induced by forced collectivization of land in the U.S.S.R. (1929–33) are examples. In each case, the social dislocation and the resulting misery were ignored by the pace setters, who were blinded by their involvement with power, "progress," ideals of social organization, and other characteristically global outlooks.

100. The one genuine example of American epos is *Huckleberry Finn.* Just as Odysseus is obsessed by the single longing to return home, Huck is obsessed by a single longing to escape from people who want to run his life: his father, the well-meaning widow, the two swindlers. The linking of his fate to that of a runaway slave accentuates the theme.

101. *Razgrom:* total violent demolition. The root of this word is identical with that of *pogrom.* Politically motivated liquidations of research institutes, of intellectual currents, of literary and esthetic movements, etc., have been often described in the Russian press by this term with connotations of approval.

102. See my translation of an article from a Soviet philosophical journal, in which an attempt is made to undo some of the damage inflicted on Soviet science by the extreme xenophobia of the last years of Stalin's regime (48).

103. A volume has been devoted to critiques of the philosophical foundations of relativity theory and of quantum mechanics (27), and innumerable articles on this theme have appeared in Soviet philosophical literature. The focus of the attack is the operational definition of fundamental physical concepts. For example, the development of the theory of relativity starts with definitions of "length," "time," "interval," etc., in terms of physically demonstrable operations, with the implication that these concepts have no meaning *apart* from these operations. In quantum mechanics, the Uncertainty Principle implies that since the operations which insure the precise measurements of the position of a particle make its momentum uncertain and vice versa, it is senseless to speak about both the pre-

cise position and the precise momentum of a particle at a given instant. These views are declared by Soviet philosophers to be a reflection of idealism, i.e., the position that denies the objective reality of the world independent of observations (27, pp. 358–95). Lenin's book of fifty years ago (57) spelled out the anathema of idealism. Obsessive repetitions of his diatribes against the forerunners of modern operationalism (Mach, Avenarius, Poincaré, etc.) still pervade Soviet philosophical thought.

104. In a Soviet textbook of economics we read, for example:

"In bourgeois society, where the means of production belong to exploiters, co-operatives are a *capitalist* form of economy. In rural co-operatives dominance is wielded by the bourgeoisie, which exploits the peasant masses. In a social system where political power is in the hands of the workers and the basic means of production belong to the proletarian state, co-operatives are a *socialist* form of economy." (78, pp. 350–51. My translation; italics in original.)

Wherever labels are offered as definitive determinants of whatever is labeled, inquiry and examination of actuality is inhibited. Nowhere in the section on co-operatives do we find any trace of an economic analysis of actual, operating co-operatives, either in socialist or in capitalist countries. Such an analysis might reveal important similarities and possibly (who knows?) fundamental differences, perhaps even of the kind implied in the statement quoted. But the habit of dichotomous labeling is so ingrained in what goes for social science in the U.S.S.R. that it is apparently out of the question to ask what specifically such pronouncements refer to. Apparently, Marxism in U.S.S.R. lives only in the petrified verbiage of the *Communist Manifesto*. The painstaking labor of *Das Kapital* with its honest attempts to support a theory (whatever its merits) with masses of data, is nowhere apparent.

REFERENCES

1. Ayer, A. J. *Language, Truth, and Logic* (2d edition). New York: Dover Publications, 1950.
2. Bailey, N. T. J. *The Mathematical Theory of Epidemics*. New York: Hafner Publishing Co., 1957.
3. Bell, E. T. *Men of Mathematics*. New York: Simon and Shuster, 1937.
4. Benedict, R. *Patterns of Culture*. Boston: Houghton Mifflin & Co., 1934.
5. Bernhardi, F. von. *Germany and the Next War*. New York: Longmans, Green & Co., 1914.
6. Bernoulli, D. "Exposition of a New Theory on the Measurement of Risk." *Econometrica*, 22 (1954), pp. 23-26. [Translation by L. Sommer of "Specimen theoriae novae de mensura sortis," originally published in *Commentarii academiae scientarum imperialis Petropolitanae*, 5 (1730-31), pp. 175-92.]
7. Beverton, R. J. H., and S. J. Holt. *On the Dynamics of Exploited Fish Populations*. London: Her Majesty's Stationery Office, 1957.
8. "A Bibliography of Lewis Fry Richardson's Studies of the Causation of Wars with a View to Their Avoidance." *Conflict Resolution*, 1 (1957), pp. 305-7.
9. Borel, E. "Applications aux jeux de hasard." *Traité du calcul des probabilités et de ses applications*. Paris: Gauthier-Villar, 1938.
10. Borel, E. "Sur les systemes de formes linéaires à déterminant symétrique gauche et la théorie générale du jeu." *Comptes Rendus de l'Academie des Sciences,* January 10, 1927.
11. Boulding, K. E. *The Image: Knowledge in Life and Society*. Ann Arbor: University of Michigan Press, 1956.
12. Braithwaite, R. B. *Theory of Games as a Tool for the Moral*

Philosopher. Cambridge: Cambridge University Press, 1955.

13. Bush, R. R., and F. Mosteller. *Stochastic Models for Learning*. New York: John Wiley & Sons, 1955.

14. Carlyle, T. *On Heroes, Hero-worship, and the Heroic in History*. London and New York: Oxford University Press, 1950.

15. Chase, S. *The Tyranny of Words*. New York: Harcourt, Brace & Co., 1938.

16. Chernev, I., and F. Reinfeld. *The Fireside Book of Chess*. New York: Simon and Shuster, 1949.

17. Churchill, W. S. *Triumph and Tragedy*. Boston: Houghton Mifflin Co., 1953.

18. Coates, R. M. "The Law." *The New Yorker*, November 29, 1947.

19. Comte, A. *Social Physics*. New York: Calvin Blanchard, 1856.

20. Cournot, A. A. *Researches into the Mathematical Principles of the Theory of Wealth*. New York: The Macmillan Company, 1927. [Originally published in 1838 as *Récherches sur les principes mathématiques de la théorie des richesse*.]

21. Davidson, D., P. Suppes, and S. Siegel. *Decision Making: An Experimental Approach*. Stanford: Stanford University Press, 1957.

22. Deutsch, K. W. "Shifts in the Balance of Communication Flows; a Problem of Measurement in International Relations." *Public Opinion Quarterly*, 20 (1956), pp. 143–60.

23. Deutsch, M. "Trust and Suspicion." *Conflict Resolution*, 2 (1958), pp. 265–79.

24. Dickens, C. *The Personal History of David Copperfield*. New York: Charles Scribner's Sons, 1926.

25. Emerson, A. E. "Ecology, Evolution, and Society." *American Naturalist*, 77 (1943), pp. 97–118.

26. Erikson, E. H. *Childhood and Society*. New York: W. W. Norton & Co., 1950.

27. *Filosofskie Voprosy Sovremennoi Fiziki*. Moscow: Academy of Sciences of the U.S.S.R., 1952.

28. Fine, R. *Psychoanalytic Observations on Chess and Chess Masters*. *Psychoanalysis* (Journal of Psychoanalytic Psychology), Vol. 4, No. 3 (1956).

29. Fisher, R. A. *The Genetical Theory of Natural Selection*. Oxford: Clarendon Press, 1930.

30. Foster, C., and A. Rapoport. "Parasitism and Symbiosis in an

N-person Non-constant-sum Continuous Game." *Bulletin of Mathematical Biophysics*, 18 (1956), pp. 219–31.

31. Fromm, E. *Die Entwicklung des Christusdogmas*. Vienna: Internationaler Psychoanalytischer Verlag, 1931.

32. Fürth, R. "Physics of Social Equilibrium." *Advancement of Science* (London), 8 (1952), pp. 429–34.

33. Gause, G. F. *The Struggle for Existence*. Baltimore: The William and Wilkins Co., 1934.

34. Gause, G. F. "Verifications experimentales de la théorie mathématique de la lutte pour la vie." *Actualités scientifiques et industrielles*. Paris: Hermann et Cie., 1935.

35. Gerard, R. W. "A Biologist's View of Society." *Common Cause*, 3 (1950), p. 630. Reprinted in *General Systems*, 1 (1956), pp. 155–62.

36. Gerard, R. W. "Higher Levels of Integration." *Science*, 95 (1942), pp. 309–13.

37. Gerard, R. W., C. Kluckhohn, and A. Rapoport. "Biological and Cultural Evolution." *Behavioral Science*, 1 (1956), pp. 6–14.

38. Gerard, R. W., and A. E. Emerson. "Extrapolation from the Biological to the Social." *Science*, 101 (1945), pp. 582–85.

39. Gulliksen, H. "A Rational Equation of the Learning Curve Based on Thorndike's Law of Effect." *Journal of General Psychology*, 11 (1934), pp. 395–434.

40. Haret, S. C. *Mécanique Sociale*. Paris: Gauthier-Villars, 1910.

41. Hayakawa, S. I. *Language in Thought and Action*. New York: Harcourt, Brace & Co., 1949.

42. Hayek, F. A. von. *The Road to Serfdom*. Chicago: The University of Chicago Press, 1944.

43. Hitler, A. *Mein Kampf*. Boston: Houghton Mifflin Co., 1943.

44. Johnson, W. *People in Quandaries*. New York: Harper & Bros., 1946.

45. Kaplan, M. A. *System and Process in International Politics*. New York: John Wiley & Sons, 1957.

46. Kermack, W. O., and A. G. McKendrick. "Mathematical Theory of Epidemics." *Proceedings of the Royal Society of London*, 115 (1927), pp. 700–721.

47. Koestler, A. *Darkness at Noon*. New York: The Macmillan Company, 1952.

48. Kolman, E. "What is Cybernetics?" *Behavioral Science*, 4

(1959), pp. 132–46. [English translation with preface by A. Rapoport of an article originally published in *Voprosy Filosofii*, 1955, No. 4, pp. 148–59.]

49. Korzybski, A. *Science and Sanity* (2d edition). Lancaster, Pa.: The International Non-aristotelian Library Publishing Co., 1941.

50. Kostitzin, V. A. *Biologie Mathématique*. Paris: Libraire Armand Colin, 1937.

51. Landahl, H. D. "Studies in the Mathematical Biophysics of Discrimination and Conditioning II: Special Case: Errors, Trials, and Number of Possible Responses." *Bulletin of Mathematical Biophysics*, 3 (1941), pp. 71–77.

52. Landau, H. G. "Note on the Effect of Imitation in Social Behavior." *Bulletin of Mathematical Biophysics*, 12 (1950), pp. 221–35.

53. Landau, H. G., and A. Rapoport. "Contribution to the Mathematical Theory of Contagion and Spread of Information." *Bulletin of Mathematical Biophysics*, 15 (1953), pp. 173–83.

54. Lawrence, M. *Studies in Human Behavior*. Princeton: Princeton University Press, 1949 (mimeographed).

55. Leites, N. C., and E. Bernaut. *Ritual of Liquidation*. Glencoe, Ill.: Free Press, 1953.

56. Leites, N. C. *A Study of Bolshevism*. Glencoe, Ill.: Free Press, 1953.

57. Lenin, V. I. *Materialism and Empirio-criticism*. New York: International Publishers, 1927.

58. Lotka, A. J. *Elements of Physical Biology*. New York: Dover Publications, 1925. Reprinted in 1956 as *Elements of Mathematical Biology*.

59. Luce, R. D. "A Definition of Stability for N-person Games." *Annals of Mathematics*, 59 (1954), pp. 357–66.

60. Luce, R. D., and E. W. Adams. "The Determination of Subjective Characteristic Functions in Games with Misrepresented Pay-off Functions." *Econometrica*, 24 (1956), pp. 158–71.

61. Luce, R. D., and H. Raiffa. *Games and Decisions*. New York: John Wiley & Sons, 1957.

62. Luce, R. D., and A. A. Rogow. "A Game-theoretical Analysis of Congressional Power Distributions for a Stable Two-party System." *Behavioral Science*, 1 (1956), pp. 83–96.

63. Mailer, N. *The Naked and the Dead.* New York: New American Library, 1955.

64. Malthus, T. R. *An Essay on Population.* New York: E. P. Dutton & Co., 1914.

65. Mann, T. *The Magic Mountain.* New York: Alfred A. Knopf, 1939.

66. Mannheim, K. *Ideology and Utopia.* New York: Harcourt, Brace & Co., 1949.

67. Marschak, J. "Rational Behavior, Uncertain Prospects, and Measurable Utility." *Econometrica,* 18 (1950), pp. 111–41.

68. Marx, K. *Capital.* Chicago: Charles H. Kerr & Co., 1906.

69. Marx, K., and F. Engels. *The Civil War in the United States.* New York: International Publishers, 1940.

70. Marx, K., and F. Engels. *Manifesto of the Communist Party.* Chicago: Charles H. Kerr & Co., 1902.

71. McNeil, E. D. "Psychology and Aggression." *Conflict Resolution,* 3 (1959), pp. 195–294.

72. Meerloo, A. M. *The Rape of the Mind.* Cleveland: World Publishing Co., 1956.

73. Nash, J. F. "The Bargaining Problem." *Econometrica,* 18 (1950), pp. 155–62.

74. Nash, J. F. "Two-person Co-operative Games." *Econometrica,* 21 (1953), pp. 128–40.

75. Neyman, J., T. Park, and E. L. Scott. "Struggle for Existence. The Tribolium Model: Biological and Statistical Aspects." *Proceedings of the Third Berkeley Symposium on Mathematical Statistics and Probability.* Berkeley: University of California Press, 1955.

76. Orwell, G. *Nineteen Eighty-four.* London: Secker and Warburg, 1951.

77. Pareto, V. "Anwendungen der Mathematik auf Nationalökonomie." In *Encyklopädie der Mathematischen Wissenschaften,* Vol. 1, Part 2. Leipzig: B. G. Teubner, 1898–1904.

78. *Politicheskaya Ekonomia* (a textbook under collective authorship, issued by the Academy of Sciences of the U.S.S.R.). Moscow: Gosudarstvennoie Izdatelstvo Politicheskoi Literatury, 1954.

79. Popper, K. R. *The Open Society and Its Enemies.* Princeton: Princeton University Press, 1950.

80. Pringle, J. W. S. "On the Parallel between Learning and Evolution." *Behaviour*, 3 (1951), p. 174. Reprinted in *General Systems*, 1 (1956), pp. 90–110.

81. Raiffa, H. "Arbitration Schemes for Generalized Two-person Games" in *Contributions to the Theory of Games*, II (H. W. Kuhn and A. W. Tucker, eds.) *Annals of Mathematics Studies*, 28. Princeton: Princeton University Press, 1953.

82. Rapoport, A. "Death of Communication with Russia?" *ETC., A Review of General Semantics*, 7 (1950), pp. 83–96.

83. Rapoport, A. "Dialectical Materialism and General Semantics." *ETC., A Review of General Semantics*, 5 (1948), pp. 81–104.

84. Rapoport, A. "Mathematical Theory of Motivation Interactions of Two Individuals, I." *Bulletin of Mathematical Biophysics*, 9 (1947), pp. 17–28.

85. Rapoport, A. "Newtonian Physics and Aviation Cadets." In *Language, Meaning, and Maturity* (S. I. Hayakawa, ed.). New York: Harper & Bros., 1954.

86. Rapoport, A. *Science and the Goals of Man.* New York: Harper & Bros., 1950.

87. Rapoport, A. "Some Game-theoretical Aspects of Parasitism and Symbiosis." *Bulletin of Mathematical Biophysics*, 18 (1956), pp. 15–30.

88. Rashevsky, N. *Mathematical Biology of Social Relations.* Chicago: The University of Chicago Press, 1951.

89. Rashevsky, N. *Mathematical Biophysics* (revised edition). Chicago: The University of Chicago Press, 1948.

90. Rashevsky, N. *Mathematical Theory of Human Relations.* Bloomington, Ind.: The Principia Press, 1948.

91. Redfield, R. (ed.). *Levels of Integration in Biological and Social Systems. Biological Symposia*, 8 (1942).

92. Reichenbach, H. *The Rise of Scientific Philosophy.* Berkeley and Los Angeles: University of California Press, 1951.

93. Ricardo, D. *Principles of Political Economy and Taxation.* London: G. Bell & Sons, 1929.

94. Richardson, L. F. "Generalized Foreign Policy." *British Journal of Psychology Monographs Supplements*, 23 (1939).

95. Richardson, L. F. "Variation of the Frequency of Fatal Quarrels with Magnitude." *Journal of the American Statistical Association*, 43 (1949), pp. 523–46.

96. Richardson, L. F. "War Moods." *Psychometrika,* 13 (1948), pp. 147–74; 197–232.
97. Riesman, D. (in collaboration with R. Denney and N. Glazer). *The Lonely Crowd.* New Haven: Yale University Press, 1950.
98. Rogers, C. R. *Client-centered Therapy.* Boston: Houghton Mifflin Co., 1951.
99. Rogers, C. R. "Communication: Its Blocking and Its Facilitation." *ETC., A Review of General Semantics,* 9 (1952), pp. 83–88.
100. Rousseau, J. J. *The Social Contract.* New York: Hafner Publishing Co., 1947.
101. Royden, H. C., P. Suppes, and K. Walsh. "A Model for the Experimental Measurement of the Utility of Gambling." *Behavioral Science,* 4 (1959), pp. 11–18.
102. Sapir, E. *Language, Culture, and Personality* (L. Spier, A. I. Hallowell, and S. S. Newman, eds.). Menasha, Wis.: Sapir Memorial Publication Fund, 1941.
103. Savage, L. J. *The Foundations of Statistics.* New York: John Wiley & Sons, 1954.
104. Schelling, T. C. "Bargaining, Communication, and Limited War." *Conflict Resolution,* 1 (1957), pp. 19–36.
105. Schelling, T. C. "The Strategy of Conflict: Prospectus for a Re-orientation of Game Theory." *Conflict Resolution,* 2 (1958), pp. 203–64.
106. Seidel, L. A. "Was Malik Surprised?" *The New Yorker,* February 9, 1952.
107. Shapley, L. S. "A Value for N-person Games" in *Contributions to the Theory of Games,* II (H. W. Kuhn and A. W. Tucker, eds.) *Annals of Mathematical Studies,* 28. Princeton: Princeton University Press, 1953.
108. Shaw, G. B. *Saint Joan.* Baltimore: Penguin Books, 1951.
109. Shimbel, A. "Contribution to the Mathematical Biophysics of the Central Nervous System with Special Reference to Learning." *Bulletin of Mathematical Biophysics,* 12 (1950), pp. 241–75.
110. *The Situation in Biological Science. Proceedings of the Lenin Academy of Agricultural Sciences of the U.S.S.R.* Session July 31–August 7, 1948. Verbatim Report. Moscow: Foreign Language Publishing House, 1949.

111. Slobodkin, L. B. "Formal Properties of Animal Communities." *General Systems,* 3 (1958), pp. 93–100.
112. Spencer, H. *Principles of Sociology.* New York: D. Appleton & Co., 1910.
113. Spengler, O. *Decline of the West.* New York: Alfred A. Knopf, 1945.
114. Stevenson, A. "The Most Important Fact Today." *The Progressive,* Vol. 23, No. 7 (July, 1959).
115. Stewart, J. Q. "Demographic Gravitation: Evidence and Application." *Sociometry,* 11 (1948), pp. 31–57.
116. Suppes, P., and K. Walsh. "A Non-linear Model for the Experimental Measurement of Utility." *Behavioral Science,* 4 (1959), pp. 204–11.
117. Thrall, R. M., C. H. Coombs, and R. L. Davis (eds.). *Decision Processes.* New York: John Wiley & Sons, 1954.
118. Thucydides. *The Peloponnesian War* (Crawley translation). New York: The Modern Library, 1934.
119. Todhunter, I. *History of the Theory of Probability.* Cambridge and London: Macmillan & Co., 1865.
120. Tolstoy, L. N. *War and Peace.* Boston: Colonial Press Co., 1904.
121. Toynbee, A. *The Study of History* (abridged version). New York: Oxford University Press, 1947.
122. Traver, R. *Anatomy of a Murder.* New York: Dell Publishing Co., 1959.
123. Vinacke, W. E., and A. Arkoff. "An Experimental Study of Coalitions in the Triad." *American Sociological Review,* 22 (1957), pp. 406–15.
124. Volterra, V. *Leçons sur la théorie mathématique de la lutte pour la vie.* Paris: Gauthier-Villars, 1931.
125. Von Neumann, J. "Zur Theorie der Gesellschaftspiele." *Mathematische Annalen,* 100 (1928), pp. 295–320.
126. Von Neumann, J., and O. Morgenstern. *Theory of Games and Economic Behavior* (2d edition). Princeton: Princeton University Press, 1947.
127. Watt, K. E. F. "The Choice and Solution of Mathematical Models for Predicting and Maximizing the Yield of a Fishery." *Journal of the Fisheries Research Board of Canada,* 13 (1956), pp. 613–45.

128. Watt, K. E. F. "Studies on Population Productivity I. Three Approaches to the Optimum Yield Problem in Populations of *Tribolium confusum.*" *Ecological Monographs,* 25 (1955), pp. 269–90.

129. Whitehead, A. N. *Science and the Modern World.* New York: The Macmillan Company, 1925.

130. Whorf, B. L. *Language, Thought, and Reality.* Selected writings of Benjamin Lee Whorf (John B. Carroll, ed.). New York: John Wiley and Sons, 1956.

131. Whorf, B. L. "Science and Linguistics." *Technology Review,* 42 (1939–40), pp. 229–31.

132. Whyte, W. H., Jr. *The Organization Man.* New York: Simon and Shuster, 1956.

133. Williams, J. D. *The Compleat Strategyst.* New York: McGraw Hill, 1954.

134. Wittgenstein, L. *Tractatus Logico-philosophicus.* New York: Harcourt, Brace & Co., 1922.

135. Wright, S. "On the Roles of Directed and Random Changes in Gene Frequency in the Genetics of Populations." *Evolution,* 2 (1948), pp. 279–94.

136. Wright, S. "Evolution in Mendelian Populations." *Genetics,* 16 (1931), pp. 97–159.

137. Wright, S. "The Roles of Mutation, In-breeding, Crossbreeding, and Selection in Evolution." *Proceedings of the Sixth International Congress on Genetics,* 1932, pp. 356–66.

138. Zirkle, C. *Death of a Science in Russia.* Philadelphia: University of Pennsylvania Press, 1949.

INDEX

(Numbers marked n refer to the Notes; those marked b refer to the References)

Abel, N., 206
Abstractions, 303; levels of, 304
Additive causal relations, n4
Additivity, n27
Admissible stimuli, 289
Africa, 31
Aggression, theories of, ix
Aggressive impulses, 257
Allies, 43, 201
Alternative outcomes, 10
Ambiguity of language, 299
Amery, L. S., n3
Anal stage, n81
Anatomy of a Murder, An, 262
Andrei, Prince, 148, n48
Anthropology, 319
Anti-Communism, 313, 316
Anti-Communist(s), 284, 330
Aquinas, St. Thomas, 7
Arbitration boards, 11
Argument, 273
Aristotle, 5
Arithmetic, operations of, 206
Arithmetic of rotations, 293
Arkoff, A., 222, b123
Armament(s), 16, 17, n10; expenditures, 18, 23, 35, 37; expenditures compared with international trade, 44; limiting factors on, 17; units of, 30
Armament race(s), 29, 102; Germany vs. U.S.S.R., 44; model of, 17–19; mutual stimulation, 20, 30
Asia, 31
Assumptions of similarity, 306, n51
Assurance of understanding, 289
Astronomy, 6, 34
Athens, n2
Attitudes, 278, 283, 347–48
Austria-Hungary, 31, 36, 102
Austrian Empire, n3
Avenarius, R., n103

Balance of power, 23, 25, 211
Balance of terror, 23, 177
Balkans, 31
Bargaining, 180, 209, 218, 224, 228, 232, n69; communication in, 171–72; power, strength of communication in, 193, 210, 214; threats in, 172, 183
Basis of negotiation, 188

Battle of the Sexes, 229
Beast in the Apocalypse, 45
Beethoven, L. von, 284
Behavioral science, 85, 112
Behavior patterns, adaptive and maladaptive, 97
Belgium, 32; invaded, 56
Bell, E. T., n36, b3
Benedict, Ruth, 309, n91, b4
Bernhardi, F. von, 265 (cited), 267, 269, b5
Bernoulli, D., 118, 120–21, b6
Besuhoff, Pierre, 45
Beverton, R. J. H., xi, b7
Biological balance, 43
Biological science, 34
Bimolecular reaction, 58; model of, 100
Bluffing, 233
Bolsheviks, n90
Borel, E., b9, b10, n50
Bosnia and Herzegovina, 102
Boulding, K., xiii, b11
Bourgeoisie, 284, 320
Bourgeois, image, 330; outlook, 349; values, 350
Brainwashing, 274ff, 285
Braithwaite, R. B., xiii, 105, 182, 185, 189, 232, n36, n54, b12
Bridge, 146
Bridge on the River Kwai, The, 260
Brinkmanship, 172
Bulgaria, 31
Button-button, 157, n49

Calculated risk, 164
Callousness as by-product of involvement, 269
Capablanca, 3, n1

Capitalism, 317, 323, 330, 340, 345, n83, n91
Capitalist system, 349
Career, 320, 325
Carlyle, Thomas, 93
Carthage, 335
Cassio, 234
"Catching-up time," 40, 44
Catholic church, 5, 328
Caucuses, 211
Causality, 34, 88, 92, 109, n8; limits of, 88
Cause, 32
Celestial mechanics, 87
Central powers, 43
Chain reactions, 53
Chance, as factor in struggle for existence, 80; as player, 110, 151, 239, n45
Characteristic function, 197, n62
Charles V, 9
Checkers, 137, 146
Chemistry, 43, 58, 87, n4
Chess, 101, 103, 110, 158, 166, 304, n28; as conflict, 2ff; number of strategies in, n47; Ruy Lopez game, 3; strategies in, 138, 147
Chinese Communists, 275
Choices of action, 138ff
Christianity, 331, 335, 337
Christian(s), 314, 335; ideology, n84; Scientists, 7; view, 331
Churchill, W. S., 264(cited), 266, 268(cited), 271, b17
Citizenship, 335
City of God (Civitas dei), 6
Civil liberties, 315
Civil rights, 283, 335, 349
Civil War, 47, 313
Class, consciousness, 107, 282; mo-

bility, 344; structure, 343; struggle, 86, 319, 324, 327
Clausewitz, K. von, vii
Coalition(s), 41, 43, 195, n69; counter-, 196; experimental study of, 222; formation of, 210, 214, 232; tentative, 232
Coefficients of self-restraint, mutual restraint, 78
Coexistence of species, 81
Cold War, 95, 324
Collective effort, 269, 327, 341, 349, 356, n94
Collectivism, 313, 335
Collectivization of land in U.S.S.R., n99
Colonial empires, 31
Colonial system, 323
Commitment, 228, 258, 335
Common fate, 341
Communal, strife, 48; thinking and acting, 341
Communication, 196; as moves in game, 232; tacit, 228; taken for granted or excluded in game theory, 231; *see also* Bargaining
Communism, 5, 8, 269, 313, 316, 325, 328, 336, 341, n94–95
Communist Manifesto, n104
Communists, 275, 283, 350
Commutative law of addition, 293–94
Compelling conclusion(s), 132, 174
Compelling consequences, 22
Competing species, 76
Competitive system, 321
Comte, A., x, b19
Conditioning, 248, 274, 276; subliminal, 277

Conflict, etiology of, 11; of interest, 108, 112
Connecticut Yankee, 257
Consciousness, 269
Constituent Assembly, 283
Constant-sum, n64; *see also* Game
Constraints, 346
Controlled experiment, 33
Conversion, 273
Co-operation, 9, 36, 41, 122, 213, 322, 326; and exploitation, 60; as index of progress, 348; in Prisoner's Dilemma, 219
Co-operatives, n104
Co-operative solution, 193
Corporation, the, 325
Counterthreats, 332
Cournot, A. A., n7, b20
Cournot lines, 77
Courts, 11
Craftsmanship, 270, 272
Cribbage, n36
Critical infection density, 53
Critical mass, 53
Cultural evolution, 319, n76
Cultural exchange, 309
Cultures, 319; as wholes, n82
Cybernetics, 352

Darkness at Noon, 276
Darwin, C., 74, 259
Das Kapital, 323, n104
David Copperfield, n12
Decision theory, n65
Defense budgets, 37
Definitions, n90; agreement on, 303; nature of, 302
Degree of reality, 303
Democracy, 300, 317, 320
Desdemona, 234, n70

Determinism, xi, 86, 95; critique of, 99; of large numbers, 88; of mechanics, 90
Deterrence, 332
Deterrents, 307
Deutsch, M., 218ff, b23
Dialectical materialism, 351–52
Dickens, C. N., n93, b24
Dictatorship of the proletariat, 283
Die-hards, 211
Differential equation, n5
Dignity of man, 314
Disarmament, 28–29; rate of, 39
Discipline, 328, 345, 347, 358
Distinctions, 304
Divide-the-Dollar game, 198, n64
Dogma, 351
Dominating imputation, 202
Don Quixote, 257, 260
Dostoevski, F., 356
Dynamic systems, 85, 100

Ecological system, 82
Economic, competition, 123; interests, 281; "man," 62
Economics, 6
Education, 274
Electrodynamics, n67
Emerson, A. E., xi, b25, b38
England, 322; *see also* Great Britain
Entente, 43
Entrepreneur, 330, 340
Epidemics, 100; limiting factors of, 51; mathematical theory of, n14; psychological, 47, 49; organic, 49, 51, 57
Equilibrium, 133, 171; equilibria, 224

Equity, 167, 214, n54; game theoretical, 193; definitions of, 193
Ethical problems in game theory, 163
Ethics, vii, xii–xiii, 263
European system, instability of, 42
Executions, 48
Expectation (payoff), 151
"Expected gain" criterion, 118
"Explaining away," 274, 279–80, 284, n92
Explanation, 32
Exponential growth, 39, 75, n10
Extensive forms, n69

Fair coin, 90–91
Fascism, 328
Fatal quarrels, n13
Faust, 260
Feedback, 100, 249, n33
Ferdinand, Grand Duke of Austria, 56
Fermat, n36
Feuds, n13
Fisher, R. A., xi, b29
Forensics, 11
France, 31, 36, 43, 322, 334
Frederick the Great, 266
Freedom, 334; of conscience, 315, 349; of contract, 282; of speech, 283; of thought and feeling, 346; to obey the will of God, 355
Free enterprise, 329, 340, 346
Free will, 88, 92–93
Freud, S., 256; theory of the "subconscious," 54
Functionalism, n82
Fundamental theorem of algebra, 206
Fürth, R., x–xi, b32

Galois, E., 206

Gambles, 132, 201, 233, n40–41

Gambling, houses, 115; theory, 111

Games, constant-sum, 168, 227; co-operative, 187, 214, 228; inessential, n63; in extensive form, 141, 229; in normal form, 146, 229; non-zero-sum, 168, 173–74, 176, 195, 227, 232, 237, 308; N-person, 195, 197, 201ff, 206, 208, n69; of strategy, 108, 123, 131, 147; one-person, 111; parlor, 123; perfect information, 152; theory of, 109; value of, 134, 137; with collusion, 179–80; without communication, 215; without saddle point, 154; with saddle point, 137, 152; zero-sum, 152, 160, 167, 176, 186, 188, 195, 214, 224, 308, n50, n59, n64; *see also* Zero-sum games

Gause, G. F., xi, 80, b33–34

Gauss, K. F., 206

Genetics attacked in the U.S.S.R., 352

Genius, 93, 259, 284

Geometry, 298

Gerard, R. W., xi, b35–38

Germany, 31, 36, 55, 95, 102; rearmament of, 41, 44

Germany and the Next War, n17

Gletkin, 276

Global view, 309, n99

Good will, 21, 27, 42, 176

Gothic sculpture, 6

Graphical method, 24

Great Britain, 31, 40, 43–44, 55, 102

Great Powers, 31, 39

Greek tragedies, determinism in, 86

Grievance(s), 20, 44; terms, 36, 41

"Hang the Kaiser" movement, 57

Haret, S. C., x, b40

Hayakawa, S. I., xiv, b41

Hayek, F. A., b42

Heads and tails, 215

Hegel, 83, 86, 94, n31

"Here and now," 270

Heuristics, 166

He Who Must Die, 336

Hidden analogies, 259

Historicism, 83, n31

History, deterministic view of, 353

Hitler, A., 41, 95, 201, 265(cited), 267–68, b43

Holt, S. J., xi, b7

Holy office, 6

Hostility, amount of, 35, 55, n18

Huckleberry Finn, n100

Iago, 239, n70

Idealism, n103

Ideologies, clash of, 360

Ignition point, 53

Image, 279–80, 283, 285; clash of, 273, 280; of individual liberty, n92; of man in society, 334

Imaginary quantities, 293

Imitative behavior, 53

Imputation, 202

India, 48

Individual, freedom, 5; needs, 269

Individualism, 335, n97; economic, 68

Indochina, 333

Industrial, revolution, 322, n99; system, 329

Industrialism, 324, 341, 344, 347

Industrialization, 317, 350

Instability, 67

Instincts, 252

International politics, 102
International trade, 36
Interval scale(s), 125, 127, 181, n60
Involvement, 259, 269, n99
Irish nationalists, 56
Isolda, 257
Italy, 31, 43, n3

Jacobins, 6
Jealousy, 234
Joan of Arc, 275
Johnson, W., xiv, b44

Khrushchev, N., 271
"Know-how," 271
Koestler, A., 276, b47
Kornblum, S., n49
Kostitzin, V. A., 79, b50

Labels and referents, 304
Lacedaemon, n2
Laissez-faire, n97
Landahl, H. D., n75, b51
Landau, H. G., n16, b52–53
Language of science, 245
Languages, evolution of, 99; ambiguity of, 298
Law of Large Numbers, 91, 95, 101
Laws of Physics, 92
Learning, 248, n75
Lee, I. J., xiv
Leites, N. C., 276, b55–56
Lenin, V. I., 84, 87, 270, 282–83, 323, 352, 357, n90, n103, b57
Lenin in 1918, n90
Liberalism, 5
Liberal view, 318
Liberty, 314, 351
Lincoln, A., 313

Linear transformation, n39
Linguistic structure, n78
Little Rock, Arkansas, 50
Logic, 299
Logistic curve, 57
Lotka, A. J., xi, 79, b58
Luce, R. D., xii, 21, 209, 229, n34, n54, b59–62
Lynchings, 47, 49
Lysenko, T. D., 352

Macbeth, 260
Mach, E., n103
Magic Mountain, The, 6–8
Malik, J. A., 290
Malthus, T. R., xi, 74, b64
Manion, Lieutenant, n80
Mann, Thomas, 5, b65
Mannheim, K., 280, b66
Marburg, Conrad von, 6
Marshall, F., 2, n1
Marx, K., xi, 61, 84, 86–87, 94, 282, 323, 333, 357, n31, n83, b68, b69
Marxism, 319, 323, 344, 352, 356, n83, n104; psychoanalytic features of, 280
Marxists, 83, 283
Mass behavior, 53, 89, 94
Mass media, 51, 55
Matching pennies, 178
Mathematical, ambiguity in statements, 292; degree of specificity, 19; description, 34, 53; economics, 352; expectation, 111, 115, 165, 200; function, n61; heuristic purpose of models, 22; method, 18; models, 17; value of models, 30, 59
Mathematics, 16; as invention, 297

Maximin, 133, 135, 152, 154–55, 157, 176, 186, 197, 201, 227, 237, n44; strategy, mixed, n57

Maximization of expected utility, 162–63

McCarthy, J., 352

McNeil, E. D., ix, b71

Medea, 260

Meerloo, A. M., 275

Mental disease, 259

Mental experiments, 22

Méré, Chevalier de, 113, 114, n36

Micawber, Mr., n12

Middle Ages, 6

Military science, 11

Mind reading machine, n49

Minimax, 133; theorem, n50, n52, n59

Mobs, 50; mentality of, 51

"Monkey Trial," 352

Mood epidemics, 54, 102

Morality, 147–48, 174, 271, 283, 316, 325; of fightlike and game-like conflicts, 150

Morgenstern, O., 201, 224, b126

Moslem(s), 314, 335

Mugwumps, 211

Murder, n13; rate, 48

Mutual fear, 22, 29

Mutual stimulation, coefficient of, 36, 42

Mysticism, 5

Napoleon, 43, 45, 149

National ambitions, 22

Natural immunity, 51

Natural science, 6

Netherlands, 32

Neumann, John von, 119, 197, 201ff, 224, n50, n62, b125, b126;

minimax theorem of, 155; solution of N-person game, 201ff

Neural nets, n15

Newton, I., 87, n9

Neyman, J., xi, b75

Nineteen Eighty-Four, 277, 302, 329

NKVD, 276

Normative theory, 111, 224, 233, n35

Nuclear weapons as deterrents, 102

Numbers, problem of defining, 293

Numerology of names, 45

O'Brien, 277

Odds, 111–12

Odyssey, n100

"Omniscience," 110

One-shot play, 161

Operational definitions, 353, n103

Operationalism, n103

Opponent, 9

Optimal lines, 25, 28, 65

Organic evolution, 34, n76

Organization man, 325, 329

Orwell, G., 277, 302, b76

Othello, 234, n70

Outlook(s), xiii, 255, 278, 289

Overproduction, 341

Pacifists, 15

Parameters, 19, 21; inter- and intra-species crowding, 76; of mutual stimulation, n10; of social concern, 73

Paranoid obsession, 45

Parasite(s), 60; in miniature production exchange system, 69

Parasitism, 67, 82

Pareto, V., 71, n27, b77
Pareto point, 71, 178, 186
Park, T., xi, b75
Parlor games, 109; *see also* Games
Party discipline, 211
Pascal, B., 113
Pasternak, B., 355
Pavlov, I., 356
Payoff, 121, 132, 140; *see also* Expectation
Peace, 15
Peloponnesian War, n2
"People's Tribunals," 283
Perception, 253, 254, 255
Periodic functions, 205, n67
Persecution of the intellect, 353
Personal gain, 321
Persuasion, 273, 309
Philosophy of physical science, 85
Physical laws, determinism of, 87
Physical science, 87
Physics, 85, 108, 279, 352, n4
Poincaré, H., n103
Poker, 110, 146, 151, 233, 304
Political terror, 48
Popper, K. R., n31, b79
Portugal, 32
Power, xiii; assumption of, 333; of U. S. president, 211
Preconceived notions, 258, 279
Predator-prey system, 80, 82
Prejudice, 259
Primitive cultures, 341
Prisoner's Dilemma, 173, 175, 178, 195, 231, 239, 308, n51; experimental results, 218, 220
Private enterprise, n98
Probability, 90, 91, n32
Profit system, 341
Property rights, n98

Prudential and contraprudential, n58
Psychiatry, 256
Psychoanalysis, 279, 284, n81, n84
Psychoanalysts, 11
Psychoanalytic orientation, 282
Psychology, 268; behaviorist, 251; depth, 276, 301, 307, 353, 356; experimental, 213; Gestalt, 213, 251, n78; individual, xii; Pavlovian, 277
Psychotherapy, 268, 274, 283; nondirective, 285; permissive, 285, 286
Ptolemaic system, 6
Public opinion, 55, n18
"Pursuit of happiness," 324

Quantum mechanics, 303, 352, n67, n103
Quiz programs, n70

Racism, 330
Raiffa, H., xii, 193, 229, 232, n34, n54, b61, b81
Rashevsky, N., x, xi, n16, n28, b88, b89, b90
Rational, behavior, x, n41; gambling, 115; individual, 122, 176; opponent, 131, 163, 201; player, 226, 236, n45, n51; policies, 164; strategy, 155
Rationality, xii, 10, 107, 119, 130, 176, 179, 200, 215, 234, 237, n51; individual and group, 167; individual inadequacy of, 174; of player, 135, 137, 148
Rationalization(s), 261, 268, 284, 356
"Reasonable" precautions, 162

Recognition, 250–51
Region of validity, 287, 292, n87
Relativity theory, 352, n103
Renaissance, 6, 272
Resistance to change, 254, 259, 273, 279, 281
Restraint(s), 348, 351, n10; coefficient of, 36, 42
Revenge, 15
Ricardo, D., 62, b93
Richardson, L. F., x, xi, 14(cited), 15, 30, 35, 38(cited), 39, 42, 44, 45, 57, 58, 88, 92, 99, n13, b94, b95, b96
Riots, 47, 49, n13
Risk, 167, 201, 272, n65; attitudes toward, 233; behavior, 121; minimization of, 135; preferences between, 130; utility of, 120
Risky decisions, 213
Rivalries, 32
Rogers, C. R., xiii, 286, n85, b98, b99
Rogow, A. A., 211, b62
Roman law, 335
Rome, 335
Roth, G. J., n49
Rousseau, J. J., 62, b100
Rubashov, 276
Rumania, n3
Russia, *see* U.S.S.R.
Russian revolution, 309

Saddle point, 136, 142, 154, 187, 190, 193, 237, n44; *see also* Games
Sadism, 268, 270, 357
Saint Joan, 275
Salesmanship, 11
Sancho Panza, 257

Savage, L. J., n32, b103
Scandinavia, 334
Schelling, T. C., xiii, 215, 216, 218(cited), 227, 233, b104, b105
Scholasticism, 5
Schrecklichkeit, 333
Scientific, ethics, 123; humanism, 5; outlook, vii
Scott, E. L., xi, b75
Secularism, 5
Security, 158, 167; secrecy, n50
Selection, 300; natural, 252; of stimuli, 257
Self-defense, 15
Semantic approach, 302
Sensitivity, 259, 272
Serbia, 31, n3
Sergeant Croft, n80
Shapley, L. S., 210, b107
Shaw, G. B., 275, b108
Sherlock Holmes, 2, 259
Similarity, assumptions of, 177–78
Slavery, 330; in U.S.A., 280
Slavic nations, 31
Slobodkin, L. B., xi, b111
"Small world," 308
Social, evolution, 341; friction, 210; ideals, 348; inertia, 210; norms, 207, 225; optimum, 70, 71, n27; physics, x, xi, 85, 100, 107; psychologists, 11; revolution, 323, 333, 342, 345; science, ix; status, 344; structure, xii; values, 176, 321
Socialism, 318, 330, 342, 348, 356
Soviet Union, *see* U.S.S.R.
Spanish Civil War, 102
Speech, acquisition of, 250
Spencer, H., xii, 74, b112
Spengler, O., xi, 94, b113

Stability, 23, 67, n43; competing species, 78; instability, 100; Luce's theory of, 209; of coalition patterns, 210; of coalitions, 202; of image, 285; production and exchange system, 67

Stalin, J., 95, 201, 259, 357, n95, n102

Stalingrad, Battle of, 149

Standard scale, 182

Standards of behavior, 117

Statistical mechanics, 92

Stewart, J. Q., x, b115

Stevenson, A., n93(cited), b114

Stock market, xiii

Strategy (ies), 11, 102, 139ff, 166; concept of, 166; contraprudential, 192; co-ordination of, 214; definition of, 142; mixed, 151, 155, 158, 167, 187–88, 192; pooling of, 196; prudent, 167; prudential, 192

Strong solution of N-person game, 208

Struggle for existence, 10, 74

Subliminal advertising, 277

Subversion, fear of stability of social order, 353

Success, 320

Superstition, 33

Surplus value, theory of, 61, 324

Suspicion, 214, 257, 347

Symbiosis, 82; symbiotic system, 80

Symbolic logic, 352

Symmetry, 192; of tick-tack-toe, n46; of weights in coalition game, 223

Taboos, violations of, 33

Tasmania, 333

Technology, 17

Telecommunication, n67

Threat(s), in bargaining, 228; of force, 307; removal of, 274, 285–86; revival of, n85; to image, 286, 300; to leave coalitions, 232; to ownership rights, n98; to Western man, 331

Threshold, of nervous excitation, 53; phenomena, n14

Thucydides, n2(cited), b118

Tick-tack-toe, 10, 110, 137; number of strategies in, 146; symmetries of, 146

Tolstoy, L. N., xi, 45, 93, 148, 270, 284, n48, b120

Totalophelimität, n27

Toynbee, A., xi, 94, b121

Training, 274, 278

Triple alliance, 43

Tristan, 257

Trust, 214, 234

Turkey, 31

Uncertainty, n65; principle, 88, n103

Unconscious, 256, 279, 283; desires, 286; images, n94; selection, 258

Underdeveloped countries, 317, 330

Unforeseen circumstances, 146

United States, 47, 271, 313, 316, 322, 329, 343; attitude toward science, 353; image of, 211; tricameral legislature of, 211

U.S.S.R., 31, 36, 43, 102, 271, 283, 324, 329, 337, 339–40, 350, 352, n104; attitudes toward war in, 149; purges in, 48

Utilitarianism, n53

Utility (ies), 21, 63–64, 111, 118,

151, 164, 231, n60; additive, n53; comparison of, 182; conservative, 181, 185, n53; expected, n45; experimental determination of, n38; interpersonal comparison of, n56; maximization of, 120, 121, 131; nontransferable, 182, 186, 232; scale, 187, 213, 233, 235, 239; tautological character of, 122; transferable, n53
Utility function, 122–23, 126, 130; comparison of, 126; between different individuals, 129

Value(s), American, 309; bourgeois, 321; humanitarian, 325; liberal, 313, 332; of game, 197
Verifiability criterion, 302
Vian, Admiral, 268
Vickrey, 208, n68
Vinacke, W. E., 222, b123
Violence, 47; infectious, 48
Volterra, V., xi, 79, b124
von Neumann, John, *see* Neumann, J. von

Wallace, A. R., 74

War, vii, xiii, 15, 31, 47–48, 56, 97, 99, 123, 149, 264, 267, 272, 301, n13, n91, n94; as a fight, 150; as a game, 150; choice of waging, 93; moods, 54; vitality, 55
War and Peace, 45, 93
Wave mechanics, 240
Welfare state, 345
Western ideology, 275
Western powers, 102
Whorf, B. L., n89, b130, b131
Witch hunts, 51, 352
World image, 258–59
World outlook, 86, n78
World War I, 31, 40, 42, 55, 102; causes of, 32
World War II, 218, 267, 326; German invasion of Russia, 149
"Would-be" conclusions, 22, 29
Wright, S., xi, b135, b136, b137

Zero-sum games, mixed strategy in, 156; stability of, 137; two-person, 131, 196, 360; without saddle point, 158, 160, 163, 200; with saddle point, 131; *see also* Games